Camping in America's City & Town Parks

Discover 1,900 RV, Van and Tent Camping Areas at 1,451 Municipal Parks in 46 States

Published by:

Roundabout Publications
PO Box 569
LaCygne, KS 66040

Phone: 800-455-2207
Internet: www.RoundaboutPublications.com

Library of Congress Control Number: 2023942959

ISBN-10: 1-885464-95-9
ISBN-13: 978-1-885464-95-8

Table of Contents

Introduction

Huge portions of public lands, managed by a variety of government agencies, are available to the general public for recreational use. This book will guide you to 1,900 camping areas available at 1,451 parks operated by cities and towns in 46 states. Additional information can be found online at local websites. Please note that the camping areas accessible only by boat are not included in this guide.

Using This Guide

The guide is especially helpful when used along with Google Maps, Windows Maps, or a GPS device for locating and navigating to each camping area.

State Maps

A state map is provided to aid you in locating the camping areas. A grid overlay on each map is used when cross-referencing with each camping area.

Map Grid Chart & Alphabetical List

Following the state map is a chart showing the camping area ID number(s) located within a map grid. Following this chart is an alphabetical list of each camping area, which is especially helpful when you already know the name of an area. This list provides each location's ID number and map grid location.

Camping Area Details

Camping area details include information about each public camping area within the state. Preceding each location's name is the ID number and map grid location, which is used when referencing the state map. Listings are arranged numericaly and alphabetically by map grid coordinate.

Details for each camping area generally include the following information:

- Total number of sites or dispersed camping
- Number of RV sites
- Sites with electric hookups
- Full hookup sites, if available
- Water (central location or spigots at site)
- Showers
- RV dump station
- Toilets (flush, pit/vault, or none)
- Laundry facilities
- Camp store
- Maximum RV size limits (if any)
- Reservation information (accepted, not accepted, recommended or required)
- Generator use and hours (if limited)
- Operating season
- Camping fees charged
- Miscellaneous notes
- Length of stay limit
- Elevation in feet and meters
- Telephone number
- Nearby city or town
- GPS coordinates

The Ultimate Public Campground Project

Data for this publication is from The Ultimate Public Campground Project, which was established in 2008 to provide a consolidated and comprehensive source for public campgrounds of all types. Please note that despite our best efforts, there will always be errors to be found in the data. With over 45,000 records in our database, it is impossible to ensure that each one is always up-to-date.

Update: In 2022 The Ultimate Public Campground Project database was acquired by a GPS manufacturer. As a result, updated information for this book will no longer be available - this is the last edition.

Happy Camping!

Common Abbreviations Used

BOR	Bureau of Reclamation
CG	Campground
ORV	Off Road Vehicle
RA	Recreation Area
RP	Regional Park

Alabama

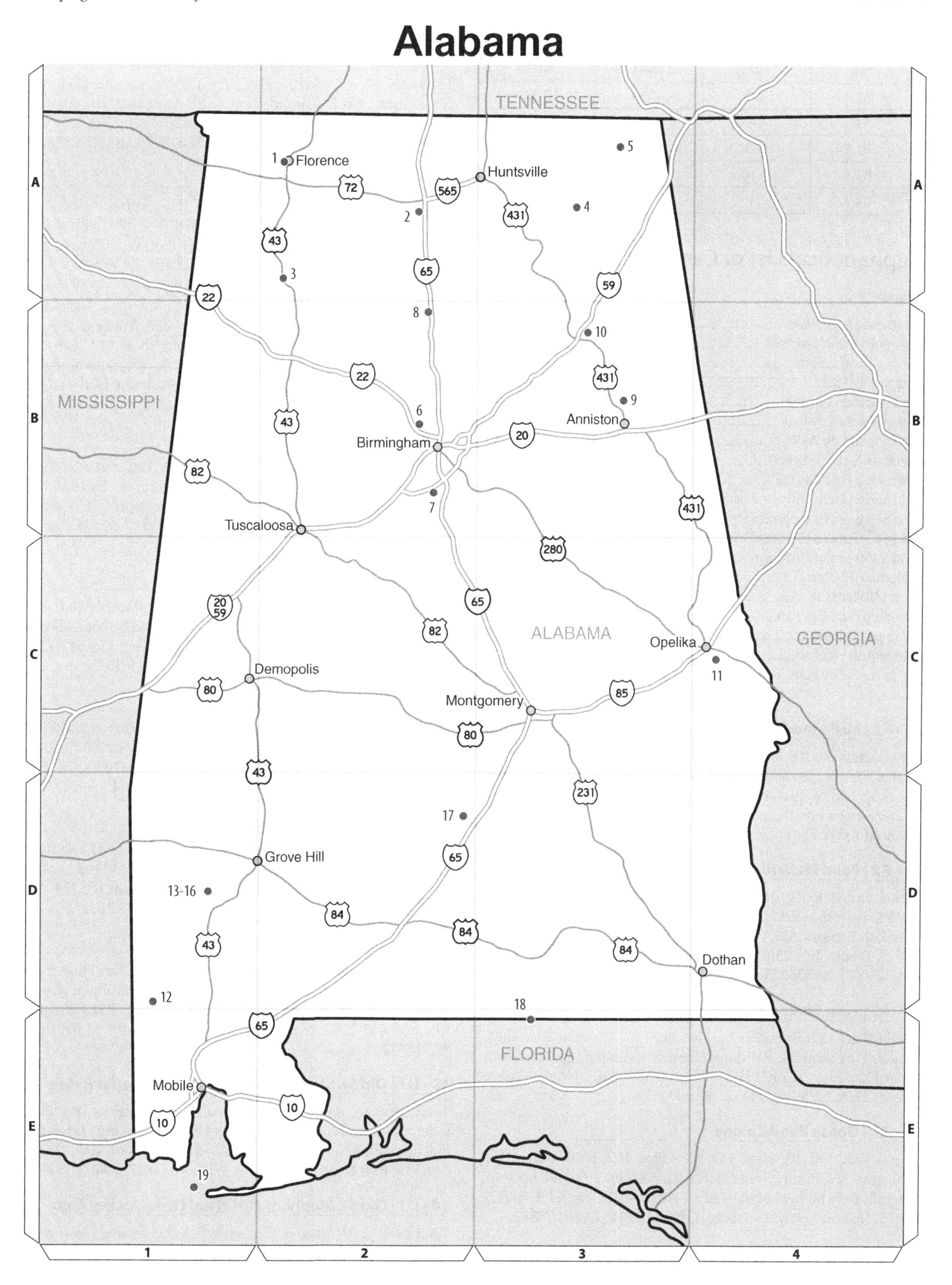
TENNESSEE
MISSISSIPPI
ALABAMA
GEORGIA
FLORIDA
Florence
Huntsville
Birmingham
Anniston
Tuscaloosa
Opelika
Demopolis
Montgomery
Grove Hill
Dothan
Mobile
1
2
3
4
5
6
7
8
9
10
11
12
13-16
17
18
19
A
B
C
D
E
72
565
431
43
65
59
22
20
82
280
20
59
85
80
231
84
10

Map	ID	Map	ID
A2	1-3	D1	12-16
A3	4-5	D2	17
B2	6-8	D3	18
B3	9-10	E1	19
C4	11		

Alphabetical List of Camping Areas

1 • A2 | McFarland City Park

Total sites: 50, RV sites: 50, Elec sites: 50, Water at site, Flush toilet, Free showers, RV dump, Tents: $14/RVs: $25, Some Full hookup, Senior discount: $5, Stay limit: 21 days, Open Mar-Nov, Reservations not accepted, Elev: 450ft/137m, Tel: 256-740-8817, Nearest town: Florence. GPS: 34.783691, -87.680908

2 • A2 | Point Mallard City CG

Total sites: 239, RV sites: 233, Elec sites: 233, Water at site, Flush toilet, Free showers, RV dump, Tents: $29/RVs: $42, 233 Full hookup, Seniors: $29, Open all year, Reservations accepted, Elev: 577ft/176m, Tel: 256-341-4826, Nearest town: Decatur. GPS: 34.575009, -86.935355

3 • A2 | Twin Forks City Park

Total sites: 137, RV sites: 74, Elec sites: 74, Water at site, Flush toilet, Free showers, RV dump, Tent & RV camping: $12, Open Mar-Oct, Elev: 826ft/252m, Tel: 205-486-4707, Nearest town: Bear Creek. GPS: 34.274452, -87.680053

4 • A3 | Goose Pond Colony

Total sites: 140, RV sites: 140, Elec sites: 109, Flush toilet, Free showers, RV dump, Tents: $18/RVs: $38-50, 109 Full hookup, Significantly higher holiday rates, Elev: 614ft/187m, Tel: 256-912-0075, Nearest town: Scottsboro. GPS: 34.593153, -86.070882

5 • A3 | Stevenson City Park

Total sites: 12, RV sites: 12, Elec sites: 12, Water at site, No toilets, No showers, No RV dump, Tent & RV camping: $10, Showers at pool, Reservations accepted, Elev: 622ft/190m, Tel: 256-437-3000, Nearest town: Stevenson. GPS: 34.856474, -85.829293

6 • B2 | Brookside Greenway

Total sites: 46, RV sites: 21, Elec sites: 21, Central water, Flush toilet, Free showers, RV dump, Tents: $10/RVs: $20, Full hookup sites, Reservations accepted, Elev: 357ft/109m, Tel: 205-674-5550, Nearest town: Brookside. GPS: 33.636528, -86.925976

7 • B2 | Hoover RV Park

Total sites: 170, RV sites: 170, Elec sites: 170, Water at site, No toilets, No showers, RV dump, No tents/RVs: $40, 170 Full hookup, Stay limit: 30 days, Open all year, Reservations accepted, Elev: 515ft/157m, Tel: 205-739-7400, Nearest town: Hoover. GPS: 33.336655, -86.847234

8 • B2 | Palomino RV Resort

Total sites: 50, RV sites: 50, Elec sites: 50, Water at site, Flush toilet, Free showers, Tents: Free/RVs: $35-45, 50 Full hookup, No generators, Open all year, Reservations accepted, Elev: 671ft/205m, Tel: 256-737-0220, Nearest town: Cullen. GPS: 34.128837, -86.876608

9 • B3 | Michael Tucker City Park

Total sites: 16, RV sites: 16, Central water, Flush toilet, Free showers, No RV dump, Tent & RV camping: $25, Open all year, Reservations required, Elev: 677ft/206m, Tel: 256-847-7349, Nearest town: Anniston. GPS: 33.737821, -85.818157

10 • B3 | Noccalula Falls City CG

Total sites: 125, RV sites: 125, Elec sites: 125, Water at site, Flush toilet, Free showers, RV dump, Tents: $20/RVs: $20-25, Also cabins, 73 Full hookup, Open all year, Elev: 686ft/209m, Tel: 256-543-7412, Nearest town: Gadsden. GPS: 34.039204, -86.023358

11 • C4 | Spring Villa Park

Total sites: 30, RV sites: 30, Elec sites: 30, Water at site, Flush toilet, Free showers, RV dump, Tent & RV camping: $35, 30 Full hookup, Open all year, Max Length: 50ft, Elev: 659ft/201m, Tel: 334-705-5552, Nearest town: Opelika. GPS: 32.585984, -85.310441

12 • D1 | Lakeview RV City Park

Total sites: 38, RV sites: 38, Elec sites: 38, Water at site, Flush toilet, Free showers, RV dump, Tent & RV camping: $28, Open all year, Reservations accepted, Elev: 233ft/71m, Tel: Info: 251-866-9647/ Res: 866-440-2267, Nearest town: Citronelle. GPS: 31.070186, -88.316547

13 • D1 | Old St. Stephens Historical Park - Cedar Ridge

Total sites: 16, RV sites: 16, Elec sites: 16, Water at site, Flush toilet, Free showers, RV dump, Tent & RV camping: $25-30, 16 Full hookup, Reservations accepted, Elev: 66ft/20m, Tel: 251-246-6790, Nearest town: St. Stephens. GPS: 31.558473, -88.031385

14 • D1 | Old St. Stephens Historical Park - Jockey Club

Total sites: 5, RV sites: 5, Elec sites: 5, Water at site, Flush toilet Free showers, RV dump, Tent & RV camping: $25-30, 5 Ful hookup, Reservations accepted, Elev: 62ft/19m, Tel: 251-246-6790, Nearest town: St. Stephens. GPS: 31.562107, -88.035355

15 • D1 | Old St. Stephens Historical Park - Lakeview

Total sites: 18, RV sites: 18, Elec sites: 18, Water at site, Flush toilet, Free showers, RV dump, Tent & RV camping: $25-30, 18 Full hookup, Reservations accepted, Elev: 122ft/37m, Tel: 251-246-6790, Nearest town: St. Stephens. GPS: 31.557751, -88.039851

16 • D1 | Old St. Stephens Historical Park - Tent Area

Total sites: 3, RV sites: 0, Central water, Flush toilet, Free showers, RV dump, Tents only: $15, Reservations accepted, Elev: 61ft/19m, Tel: 251-246-6790, Nearest town: St. Stephens. GPS: 31.559968, -88.039121

17 • D2 | Sherling Lake City Park

Total sites: 41, RV sites: 41, Elec sites: 41, Water at site, Flush toilet, Free showers, RV dump, Tent & RV camping: $30, Open all year, Elev: 558ft/170m, Tel: 334-382-3638, Nearest town: Greenville.. GPS: 31.897267, -86.673792

18 • D3 | Lake Jackson City Park

Total sites: 28, RV sites: 28, Elec sites: 28, Water at site, Flush toilet, Free showers, RV dump, Tents: $16/RVs: $31-35, 28 Full hookup, Formerly Florala SP, Senior discount Mon-Thur, Open all year, Reservations accepted, Elev: 299ft/91m, Tel: 334-858-3612, Nearest town: Florala. GPS: 30.995255, -86.317068

19 • E1 | Dauphin Island City Park

Total sites: 150, RV sites: 150, Elec sites: 150, Water at site, Flush toilet, Free showers, RV dump, Tents: $22/RVs: $36-44, 99 Full hookup, $28-$36 Sep-Feb, Stay limit: 120-180 days, Generator hours: 0700-2200, Open all year, Reservations accepted, Elev: 20ft/6m, Tel: 251-861-2742, Nearest town: Dauphin Island. GPS: 30.249822, -88.080535

Alaska

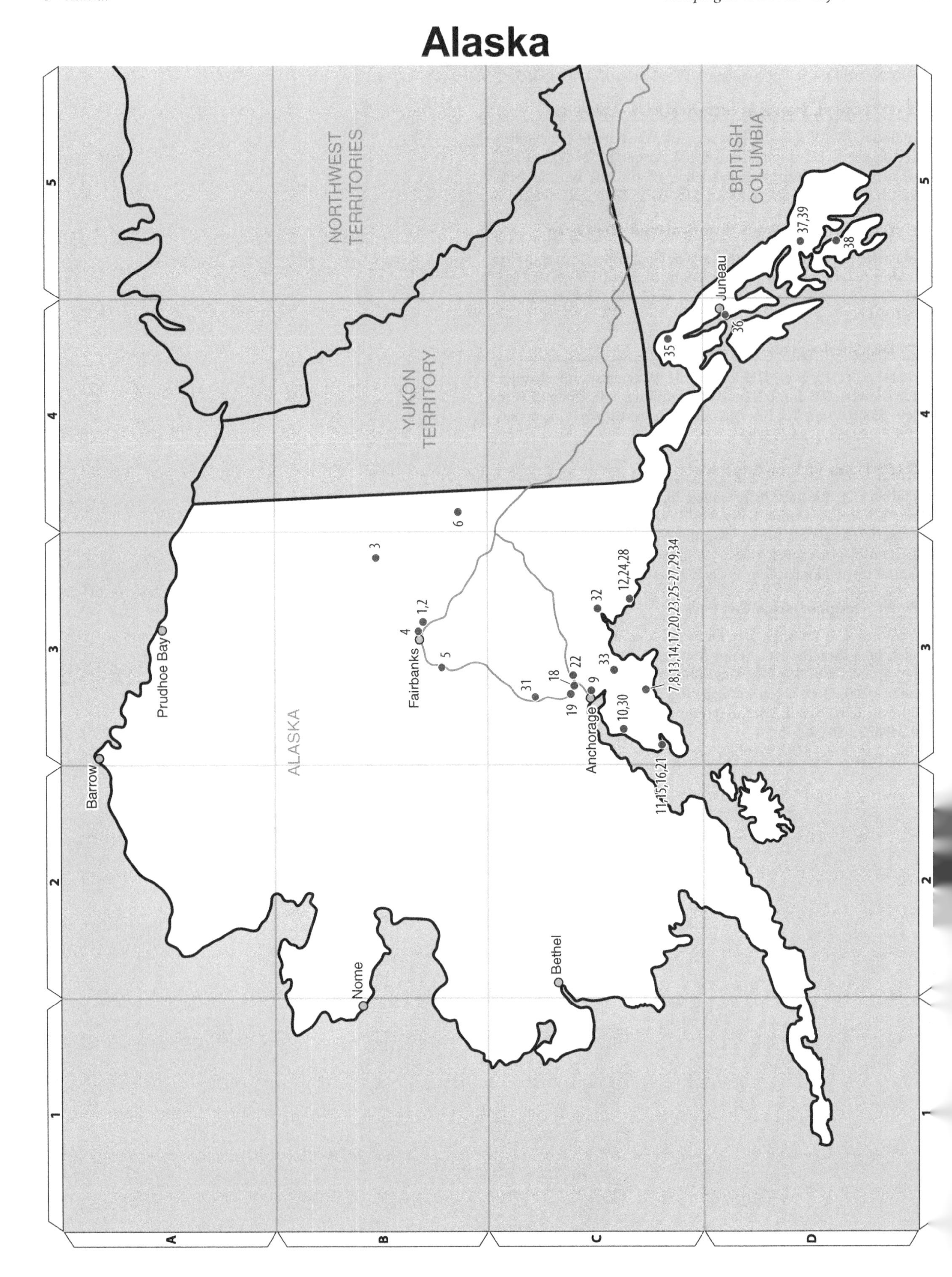
NORTHWEST TERRITORIES
YUKON TERRITORY
BRITISH COLUMBIA
ALASKA
Barrow
Prudhoe Bay
Fairbanks
Anchorage
Juneau
Nome
Bethel
1,2
3
4
5
6
7,8,13,14,17,20,23,25-27,29,34
9
10,30
11,15,16,21
12,24,28
18
19
22
31
32
33
35
36
37,39
38
A
B
C
D
1
2
3
4
5

Map	ID	Map	ID
B3	1-5	C4	35
B4	6	D4	36
C3	7-34	D5	37-39

Abbreviations for Agencies

ADFG Alaska Department of Fish and Game

Alphabetical List of Camping Areas

1 • B3 | Chena Lake RA - Lake Park

Total sites: 45, RV sites: 45, Central water, Flush toilet, Tents: $15/RVs: $20, Generator hours: 0600-2200, Open May-Sep, Reservations not accepted, Elev: 499ft/152m, Tel: 907-488-1655, Nearest town: North Pole. GPS: 64.765811, -147.223469

2 • B3 | Chena Lake RA - River Park

Total sites: 35, RV sites: 35, Central water, Flush toilet, Tents: $15/RVs: $20, Generator hours: 0600-2200, Open May-Sep, Reservations not accepted, Elev: 501ft/153m, Nearest town: North Pole. GPS: 64.793652, -147.190997

3 • B3 | Circle Municipal CG

Total sites: 5, RV sites: 5, Central water, Flush toilet, Free showers, Tent & RV camping: Free, Elev: 593ft/181m, Nearest town: Circle. GPS: 65.825319, -144.062631

4 • B3 | Pioneer Park

Total sites: 80, RV sites: 80, No tents/RVs: $12, Open May-Sep, Reservations not accepted, Elev: 443ft/135m, Nearest town: Fairbanks. GPS: 64.837583, -147.776562

5 • B3 | Riverside City Park

Total sites: 40, RV sites: 22, Elec sites: 18, Central water, Flush toilet, Free showers, RV dump, Tents: $12/RVs: $20, Elev: 525ft/160m, Tel: 907-582-2500, Nearest town: Anderson. GPS: 64.338487, -149.203005

6 • B4 | Chicken Creek RV Park

Total sites: 100, RV sites: 30, Elec sites: 30, Central water, Flush toilet, Tents: $28/RVs: $28-38, Open May-Sep, Max Length: 70ft, Reservations accepted, Elev: 1659ft/506m, Nearest town: Chicken. GPS: 64.071179, -141.934626

7 • C3 | Alice CG

Total sites: 14, RV sites: 15, No water, Vault/pit toilet, No showers, No RV dump, Tents: $20/RVs: $40, RV dump nearby $5 with rinse and potable water, Pay showers at Harbormaster, Stay limit: 14 days, Generator hours: 0700-2200, Open Apr-Sep, Reservations accepted, Elev: 8ft/2m, Tel: 907-224-4053, Nearest town: Seward. GPS: 60.112435, -149.437257

8 • C3 | Boulder CG

Total sites: 40, RV sites: 40, No water, No toilets, No showers, RV dump, Tents: $20/RVs: $40, RV dump nearby $5 with rinse and potable water, Pay showers at Harbormaster, Stay limit: 14 days, Open Apr-Sep, Max Length: 45+ft, Reservations accepted, Elev: 6ft/2m, Nearest town: Seward. GPS: 60.113085, -149.439552

9 • C3 | Centennial City CG

Total sites: 84, RV sites: 83, Elec sites: 21, Central water, Flush toilet, Free showers, RV dump, Tents: $25/RVs: $25-35, Open May-Sep, Reservations accepted, Elev: 263ft/80m, Tel: 907-343-6986, Nearest town: Anchorage. GPS: 61.228151, -149.722455

10 • C3 | Centennial City Park

Total sites: 250, RV sites: 176, Elec sites: Unk #, Central water, Vault/pit toilet, Tent & RV camping: $21, Dump Fee: $20, Reservations not accepted, Elev: 85ft/26m, Tel: 907-262-3151, Nearest town: Soldotna. GPS: 60.479188, -151.093269

11 • C3 | Fishing Hole

Total sites: 77, RV sites: 77, Central water, Flush toilet, RV dump, Tent & RV camping: $20, Stay limit: 14 days, Generator hours: 0700-2300, Reservations not accepted, Elev: 5ft/2m, Tel: 907-235-1583, Nearest town: Homer. GPS: 59.608009, -151.435087

12 • C3 | Fleming Spit (Hippy Cove) - ADFG

Dispersed sites, No water, No toilets, Tent & RV camping: Free, Reservations not accepted, Elev: 15ft/5m, Nearest town: Cordova. GPS: 60.561152, -145.743442

13 • C3 | Forest Acres CG

Total sites: 40, RV sites: 40, No water, Vault/pit toilet, Tents: $20/RVs: $40, Group tent site, Stay limit: 14 days, Generator hours: 0600-2200, Open Apr-Sep, Max Length: 40+ft, Reservations not accepted, Elev: 73ft/22m, Tel: 907-224-4053, Nearest town: Seward. GPS: 60.134369, -149.428983

14 • C3 | Harborside CG

Total sites: 30, RV sites: 30, No water, Vault/pit toilet, No tents/RVs: $40, RV dump nearby $5 with rinse and potable water, Pay showers at Harbormaster, Stay limit: 14 days, Generator hours: 0700-2200, Open Apr-Sep, Reservations accepted, Elev: 20ft/6m, Tel: 907-224-4053, Nearest town: Seward. GPS: 60.114516, -149.441245

15 • C3 | Homer Spit Tent Area 2

Total sites: 8, RV sites: 0, Central water, Flush toilet, No showers, No RV dump, Tents only: $20, Walk-to sites, Water & toilets across street, Stay limit: 14 days, Generator hours: 0700-2300, Reservations not accepted, Elev: 3ft/1m, Tel: 907-235-1583, Nearest town: Homer. GPS: 59.606075, -151.433868

16 • C3 | Hornaday Park

Total sites: 31, RV sites: 31, Central water, Vault/pit toilet, No showers, No RV dump, Tent & RV camping: $20, RV dump at Chevron station - dump/rinse water/potable water/compressed air - all free, Stay limit: 14 days, Generator hours: 0700-2300, Open May-Oct, Reservations not accepted, Elev: 373ft/114m, Tel: 907-235-1583, Nearest town: Homer. GPS: 59.651585, -151.555476

17 • C3 | Iditarod CG

Total sites: 11, RV sites: 11, Flush toilet, Pay showers, No tents/RVs: $40, Stay limit: 14 days, Generator hours: 0600-2200, Open Apr-Sep, Reservations accepted, Elev: 23ft/7m, Tel: 907-224-4053, Nearest town: Seward. GPS: 60.101277, -149.436293

18 • C3 | Lake Lucille Park

Total sites: 57, RV sites: 57, Elec sites: Unk, Central water, Vault/pit toilet, No showers, No RV dump, Tents: $10/RVs: $10-20, Stay limit: 14 days, Open May-Sep, Reservations not accepted, Elev: 337ft/103m, Tel: 907-373-9010, Nearest town: Wasilla. GPS: 61.568465, -149.478409

19 • C3 | Little Susitna River City CG

Total sites: 75, RV sites: 72, Elec sites: 72, Central water, Vault/pit toilet, RV dump, Tent & RV camping: $15, Open May-Sep, Elev: 251ft/77m, Tel: 907-355-8794, Nearest town: Houston. GPS: 61.630085, -149.797426

20 • C3 | Marathon CG

Total sites: 54, RV sites: 54, Central water, Vault/pit toilet, No showers, No RV dump, No tents/RVs: $40, RV dump nearby $5 with rinse and potable water, Pay showers at Harbormaster, Stay limit: 14 days, Generator hours: 0700-2200, Open Apr-Sep, Reservations accepted, Elev: 40ft/12m, Tel: 907-224-4053, Nearest town: Seward. GPS: 60.111341, -149.436512

21 • C3 | Mariner Park

Total sites: 34, RV sites: 34, No water, Vault/pit toilet, No showers, No RV dump, Tent & RV camping: $20, RV dump at Chevron station - dump/rinse water/potable water/compressed air - all free, Stay limit: 14 days, Generator hours: 0700-2300, Open Apr-Oct, Reservations not accepted, Elev: 3ft/1m, Tel: 907-235-1583, Nearest town: Homer. GPS: 59.632015, -151.495131

22 • C3 | Matanuska River Park

Total sites: 86, RV sites: 86, Central water, Flush toilet, Pay showers, RV dump, Tents: $20/RVs: $30, Dump fee $5, Open May-Oct, Reservations accepted, Elev: 235ft/72m, Tel: 907-861-7661, Nearest town: Palmer. GPS: 61.607555, -149.088684

23 • C3 | Obihiro (Resurrection North) CG

Total sites: 11, RV sites: 11, No water, No toilets, Tents: $20/RVs: $40, RV dump nearby with rinse and potable water, Pay showers at Harbormaster, Stay limit: 14 days, Generator hours: 0700-2200, Reservations not accepted, Elev: 7ft/2m, Nearest town: Seward. GPS: 60.108587, -149.434776

24 • C3 | Odiak Camper Park

Total sites: 30, RV sites: 30, Elec sites: 30, Central water, Flush toilet, Pay showers, RV dump, Tent & RV camping: $25, Mostly seasonal, Open May-Sep, Reservations accepted, Elev: 47ft/14m, Tel: 907-424-7282, Nearest town: Cordova. GPS: 60.536502, -145.767811

25 • C3 | Resurrection CG

Total sites: 78, RV sites: 78, Elec sites: 75, Water at site, Flush toilet, Pay showers, RV dump, Tents: $20/RVs: $55-65, RV dump nearby with rinse and potable water, Pay showers at Harbormaster, RVs Oct-Apr: $25, Stay limit: 14 days, Generator hours: 0700-2200, Reservations accepted, Elev: 15ft/5m, Tel: 907-224-4053, Nearest town: Seward. GPS: 60.106597, -149.434456

26 • C3 | Resurrection South CG

Total sites: 119, RV sites: 119, Elec sites: 25, Central water, Flush toilet, Free showers, RV dump, Tents: $20/RVs: $55-65, RV dump nearby with rinse and potable water, Pay showers at Harbormaster, Stay limit: 14 days, Generator hours: 0700-2200, Reservations not accepted, Elev: 12ft/4m, Nearest town: Seward. GPS: 60.104908, -149.434439

27 • C3 | Seward Tent Area CG

Total sites: 26, RV sites: 0, No water, Vault/pit toilet, Tents only: $20, Stay limit: 14 days, No generators, Reservations not accepted, Elev: 20ft/6m, Tel: 907-224-4053, Nearest town: Seward. GPS: 60.103837, -149.434633

28 • C3 | Shelter Cove

Total sites: 16, RV sites: 13, Central water, Flush toilet, No showers

No RV dump, Tents: $11/RVs: $11-20, Location uncertain - near ferry terminal, Stay limit: 3 days, Reservations accepted, Elev: 80ft/24m, Tel: 907-424-7282, Nearest town: Cordova. GPS: 60.555639, -145.754806

29 • C3 | Spring Creek CG

Dispersed sites, No water, Vault/pit toilet, Tents: $20/RVs: $40, Stay limit: 14 days, Generator hours: 0600-2200, Open Apr-Sep, Reservations accepted, Elev: 15ft/5m, Tel: 907-224-4053, Nearest town: Seward. GPS: 60.089171, -149.356483

30 • C3 | Swiftwater City Park

Total sites: 90, RV sites: 90, Central water, Vault/pit toilet, RV dump, Tent & RV camping: $21-26, Dump fee: $20, Reservations not accepted, Elev: 66ft/20m, Nearest town: Soldotna. GPS: 60.482308, -151.039972

31 • C3 | Talkeetna City Park

Total sites: 20, RV sites: 0, Central water, Vault/pit toilet, Tents only: $10, Elev: 348ft/106m, Nearest town: Talkeetna. GPS: 62.323281, -150.112291

32 • C3 | Valdez Glacier Dispersed

Dispersed sites, No water, No toilets, Tent & RV camping: Free, Reservations not accepted, Elev: 243ft/74m, Nearest town: Valdez. GPS: 61.148164, -146.174288

33 • C3 | Whittier Creekside City Camping

Total sites: 50, RV sites: 50, Tents: $10/RVs: $20, Open May-Oct, Max Length: 40ft, Reservations not accepted, Elev: 51ft/16m, Tel: 907-472-2670, Nearest town: Whittier. GPS: 60.771598, -148.689299

34 • C3 | Williams Park

Dispersed sites, No water, Vault/pit toilet, Tents only: $20, Stay limit: 14 days, Generator hours: 0600-2200, Open Apr-Sep, Reservations accepted, Elev: 24ft/7m, Tel: 907-224-4053, Nearest town: Seward. GPS: 60.109901, -149.436889

35 • C4 | Pullen Creek RV Park - City

Total sites: 50, RV sites: 46, Elec sites: 46, Water at site, Flush toilet, Free showers, RV dump, No tents/RVs: $40, Open May-Sep, Reservations accepted, Elev: 56ft/17m, Tel: 800-936-3731, Nearest town: Skagway. GPS: 59.451228, -135.316747

36 • D4 | Thane City CG

Dispersed sites, No water, Vault/pit toilet, Tents only: $5, Mostly occupied by homeless, Location uncertain, Open Apr-Oct, Elev: 89ft/27m, Tel: 907-586-5226, Nearest town: Juneau. GPS: 58.287007, -134.382714

37 • D5 | Shoemaker City RV Park

Total sites: 31, RV sites: 25, Elec sites: 16, Central water, Flush toilet, Free showers, RV dump, Tents: $20/RVs: $20-30, Stay limit: 5-10 days, Generator hours: 0700-2200, Reservations not accepted, Elev: 22ft/7m, Tel: 907-874-2444, Nearest town: Wrangell. GPS: 56.417868, -132.349558

38 • D5 | Thorne Bay City RV Park

Total sites: 25, RV sites: 25, Elec sites: 25, Water at site, No toilets, No showers, No tents/RVs: $25, 25 Full hookup, Showers at Harbor Facility, Stay limit: 180 days, Elev: 78ft/24m, Tel: 907-828-3380, Nearest town: Thorne Bay. GPS: 55.687023, -132.527624

39 • D5 | Wrangell City Park

Dispersed sites, No water, Vault/pit toilet, Tents only: Fee unk, Stay limit: 2 days, Reservations not accepted, Elev: 27ft/8m, Tel: 907-874-2444, Nearest town: Wrangell. GPS: 56.453844, -132.382323

Arizona

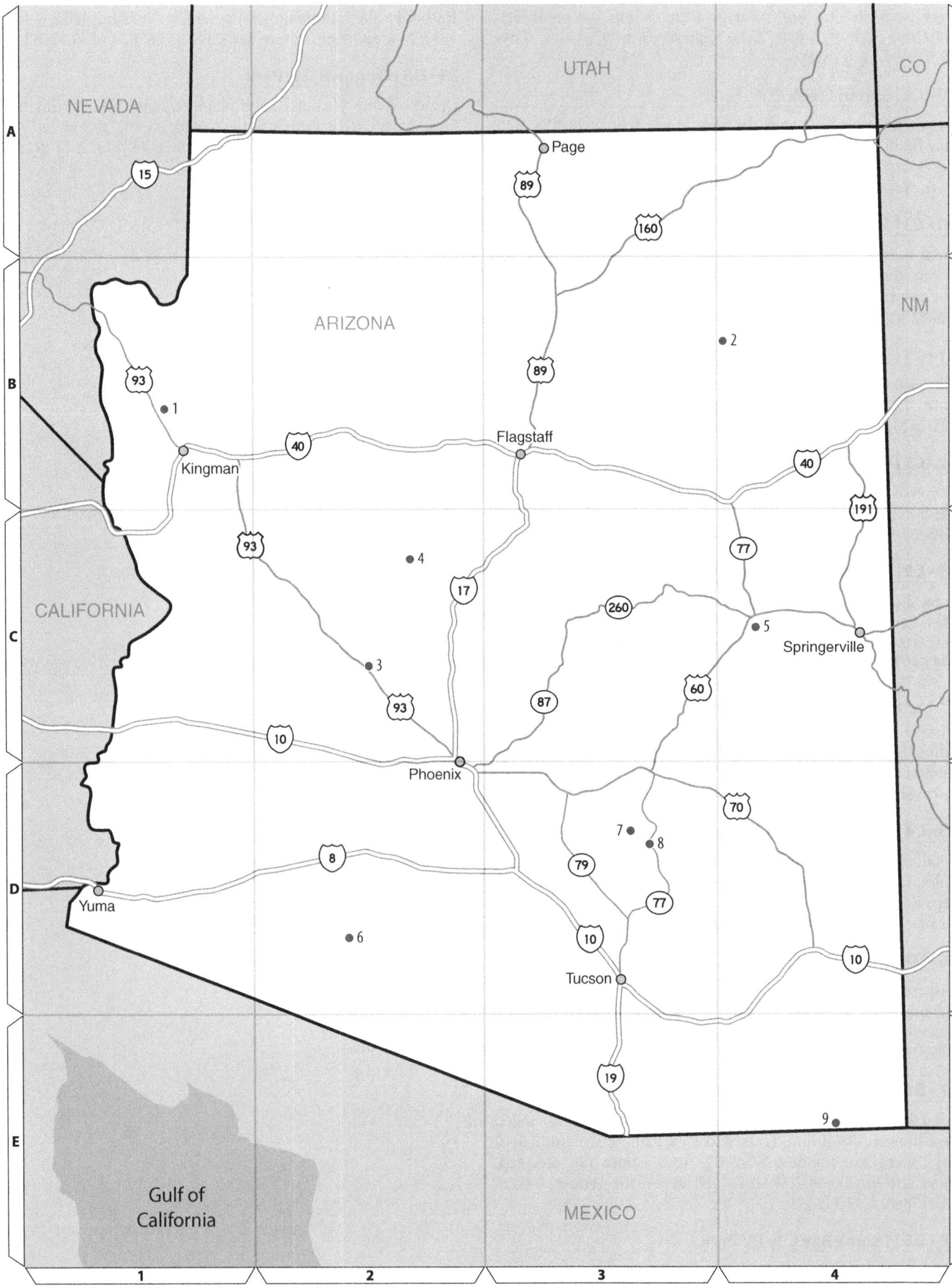

NEVADA
UTAH
CO
NM
CALIFORNIA
ARIZONA
MEXICO
Gulf of California

Page
Flagstaff
Kingman
Springerville
Phoenix
Yuma
Tucson

15
89
160
93
40
191
77
17
260
60
87
10
70
8
79
19

1
2
3
4
5
6
7
8
9

A
B
C
D
E
1
2
3
4

Map	ID	Map	ID
B1	1	D2	6
B4	2	D3	7-8
C2	3-4	E4	9
C4	5		

Alphabetical List of Camping Areas

1 • B1 | Old School Ground

Dispersed sites, No toilets, No tents/RVs: Free, Parking allowed on empty lot, Elev: 4045ft/1233m, Nearest town: Chloride. GPS: 35.413461, -114.197422

2 • B4 | Keams Canyon Community Park

Total sites: 20, RV sites: 20, Water available, Tent & RV camping: Fee unk, Elev: 6188ft/1886m, Nearest town: Keams Canyon. GPS: 35.813461, -110.204215

3 • C2 | Constellation City Park

Total sites: 35, RV sites: 35, No water, No toilets, No tents/RVs: $8, RVs must be self-contained, $12 with horse stall, RV dump at Community Center - $10, Stay limit: 7 days, Reservations not accepted, Elev: 2238ft/682m, Tel: 928-684-5451, Nearest town: Wickenburg. GPS: 33.980636, -112.711298

4 • C2 | Watson Lake City Park

Total sites: 19, RV sites: 19, Central water, Flush toilet, Free showers, No RV dump, Tent & RV camping: $20, Open only Thu-Mon nights, Open Apr-Oct, Reservations accepted, Elev: 5230ft/1594m, Tel: 928-777-1122, Nearest town: Prescott. GPS: 34.591348, -112.423225

5 • C4 | Show Low Lake City Park

Total sites: 75, RV sites: 75, Elec sites: 7, Central water, Flush toilet, Free showers, RV dump, Tents: $18/RVs: $22-30, 2 group sites, Concessionaire, Open all year, Reservations accepted, Elev: 6581ft/2006m, Tel: 888-537-7762, Nearest town: Show Low. GPS: 34.192826, -110.005989

6 • D2 | Ajo Community Golf Course

Total sites: 12, RV sites: 12, No water, No toilets, No tents/RVs: $5, Elev: 1430ft/436m, Tel: 520-387-5011, Nearest town: Ajo. GPS: 32.450839, -112.849846

7 • D3 | Kearny Lake City CG

Total sites: 12, RV sites: 12, Central water, Flush toilet, No showers, RV dump, Tent & RV camping: Free, Reservations not accepted, Elev: 1854ft/565m, Tel: 520-363-5547, Nearest town: Kearny. GPS: 33.050795, -110.897913

8 • D3 | Winkelman Flats Park

Total sites: 12, RV sites: 12, Elec sites: 12, Water at site, Flush toilet, Free showers, Tents: $20/RVs: $40, 12 Full hookup, Cold showers, Entrance fee: $10, Elev: 1939ft/591m, Tel: 520-356-7854, Nearest town: Winkelman. GPS: 32.986895, -110.766891

9 • E4 | Douglas RV Park

Total sites: 20, RV sites: 20, Elec sites: 20, Water at site, Flush toilet, Free showers, RV dump, No tents/RVs: $20-30, Open all year, Elev: 4052ft/1235m, Tel: 520-417-7339, Nearest town: Douglas. GPS: 31.375472, -109.536397

Arkansas

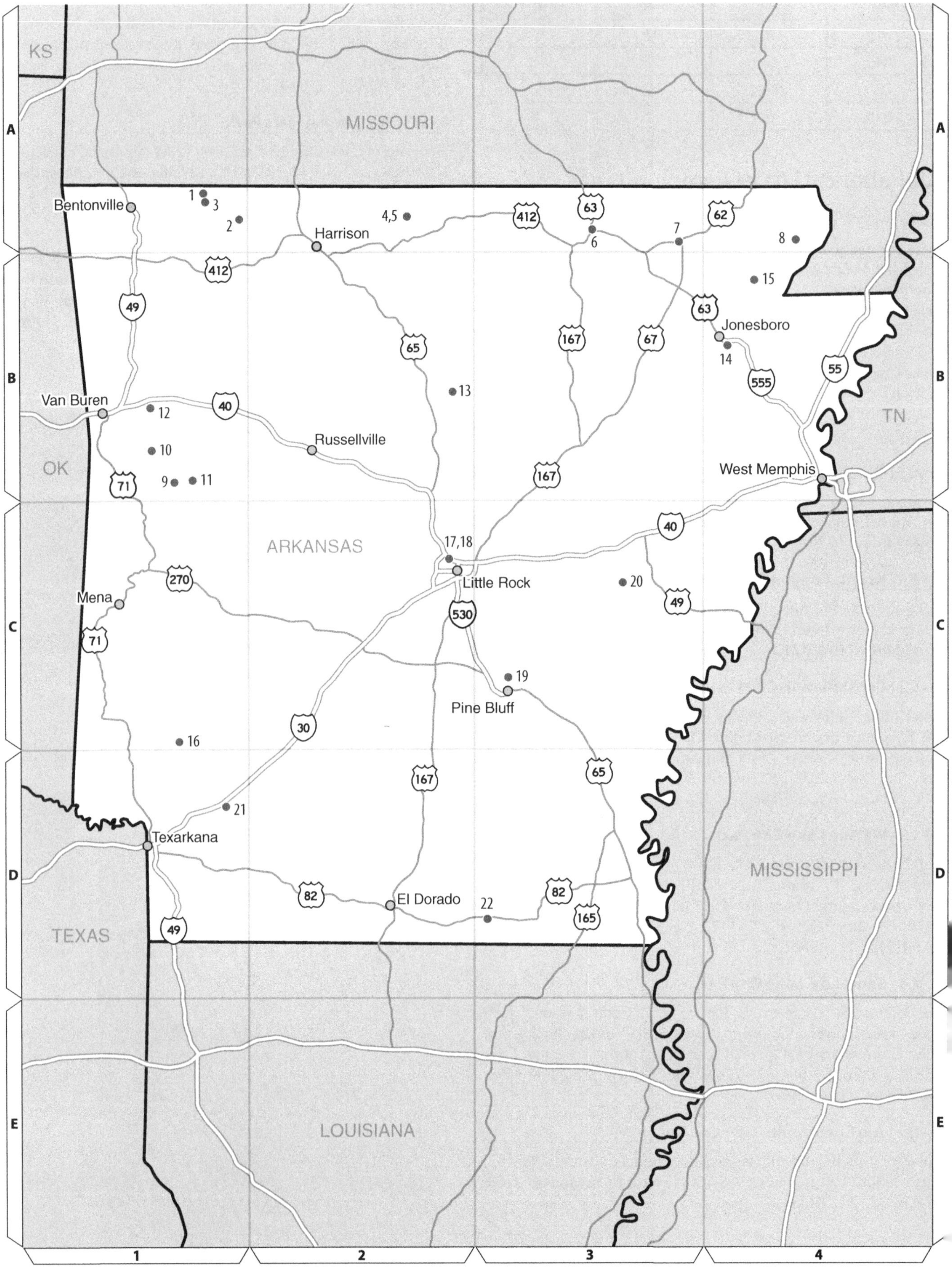

KS
MISSOURI
OK
TN
TEXAS
LOUISIANA
MISSISSIPPI
ARKANSAS
Bentonville
Harrison
Jonesboro
Van Buren
Russellville
West Memphis
Little Rock
Mena
Pine Bluff
Texarkana
El Dorado
1
2
3
4,5
6
7
8
9
10
11
12
13
14
15
16
17,18
19
20
21
22
412
63
62
49
65
167
67
555
55
40
71
270
530
30
82
165
A
B
C
D
E
1
2
3
4

Map	ID	Map	ID
A1	1-3	B4	14-15
A2	4-5	C1	16
A3	6-7	C2	17-18
A4	8	C3	19-20
B1	9-12	D1	21
B2	13	D3	22

Alphabetical List of Camping Areas

1 • A1 | Beaver Town Rec Park

Total sites: 42, RV sites: 32, Elec sites: 32, Central water, Flush toilet, Free showers, RV dump, Tents: $15/RVs: $25-35, Seniors and Veterans Discount 10%, Full hookup sites, Open Apr-Oct, Reservations accepted, Elev: 971ft/296m, Tel: 479-363-6430, Nearest town: Beaver. GPS: 36.474847, -93.770284

2 • A1 | Berryville RV Park

Total sites: 18, RV sites: 18, Elec sites: 18, Water at site, Flush toilet, Free showers, RV dump, No tents/RVs: $20, 18 Full hookup, Stay limit: 30 days, Open all year, Reservations not accepted, Elev: 1169ft/356m, Tel: 870-480-2230, Nearest town: Berryville. GPS: 36.359592, -93.564061

3 • A1 | Lake Leatherwood City Park

Total sites: 24, RV sites: 7, Elec sites: 7, Central water, Flush toilet, Free showers, RV dump, Tents: $10-15/RVs: $32, Also cabins, Open all year, Max Length: 35ft, Reservations accepted, Elev: 1056ft/322m, Tel: 479-253-7921, Nearest town: Eureka Springs. GPS: 36.434842, -93.760102

4 • A2 | Dam Site City Park

Total sites: 35, RV sites: 35, Elec sites: 35, Central water, Flush toilet, Free showers, RV dump, Tent & RV camping: $20-25, Open May-Oct, Reservations accepted, Elev: 735ft/224m, Tel: 870-405-9619, Nearest town: Bull Shoals. GPS: 36.375798, -92.573978

5 • A2 | Point Return City Park

Total sites: 21, RV sites: 21, Central water, Vault/pit toilet, RV dump, Tent & RV camping: Fee unk, Open Apr-Nov, Elev: 718ft/219m, Tel: 870-445-4775, Nearest town: Bull Shoals. GPS: 36.389991, -92.564655

6 • A3 | Hardy Camper Park

Total sites: 76, RV sites: 76, Elec sites: 76, Water at site, Flush toilet, Free showers, RV dump, Tent & RV camping: $20, Near RR, Open Mar-Oct, Elev: 361ft/110m, Tel: 870-856-2356, Nearest town: Hardy. GPS: 36.313878, -91.483033

7 • A3 | Riverfront City Park

Total sites: 10, RV sites: 10, Elec sites: 20, Central water, Flush toilet, No showers, RV dump, Tents: $10/RVs: $10-12, Sites are double w/2 elec hookups, Open all year, Reservations not accepted, Elev: 266ft/81m, Tel: 870-892-8896, Nearest town: Pocahontas. GPS: 36.254111, -90.971077

8 • A4 | Rector Memorial Park

Total sites: 3, RV sites: 3, Elec sites: 3, Central water, No toilets, No showers, RV dump, No tents/RVs: $17-27, Open all year, Elev: 279ft/85m, Tel: 870-595-3035, Nearest town: Rector. GPS: 36.257303, -90.285322

9 • B1 | Booneville Municipal Park

Total sites: 9, RV sites: 9, Elec sites: 9, Water at site, No toilets, No showers, RV dump, Tent & RV camping: $18, 9 Full hookup, Pay at police station, Seniors - $15, Open all year, Max Length: 50ft, Elev: 476ft/145m, Tel: 479-675-3508, Nearest town: Booneville. GPS: 35.139939, -93.916058

10 • B1 | Charleston Lake

Total sites: 4, RV sites: 4, Elec sites: 4, Central water, Tent & RV camping: Fee unk, Open all year, Elev: 532ft/162m, Tel: 479-965-2269, Nearest town: Charleston. GPS: 35.285533, -94.048785

11 • B1 | Magazine Municipal RV Park

Total sites: 4, RV sites: 4, Elec sites: 4, Water at site, No toilets, No showers, RV dump, Tent & RV camping: $11, Register at City Hall, Elev: 486ft/148m, Tel: 479-675-3811, Nearest town: Magazine. GPS: 35.153498, -93.806959

12 • B1 | Vine Prairie Park

Total sites: 23, RV sites: 13, Elec sites: 13, Central water, No toilets, No showers, RV dump, Tents: $10/RVs: $20, Open all year, Reservations not accepted, Elev: 426ft/130m, Tel: 479-997-8122, Nearest town: Mulberry. GPS: 35.485596, -94.062744

13 • B2 | Fairfield Bay City CG

Total sites: 57, RV sites: 33, Elec sites: 33, Water at site, Flush toilet, Free showers, RV dump, Tents: $12/RVs: $15-17, Reservations accepted, Elev: 558ft/170m, Tel: 501-884-6604, Nearest town: Fairfield Bay. GPS: 35.571050, -92.294820

14 • B4 | Craighead Forest Park

Total sites: 31, RV sites: 26, Elec sites: 26, Water at site, Flush toilet, Free showers, RV dump, Tents: $10/RVs: $20, Open all year, Max Length: 40ft, Elev: 413ft/126m, Tel: 870-933-4604, Nearest town: Jonesboro. GPS: 35.777181, -90.700094

15 • B4 | Reynolds City Park

Total sites: 11, RV sites: 11, Elec sites: 11, Water at site, Flush toilet, Free showers, RV dump, No tents/RVs: $20, Reservations not accepted, Elev: 300ft/91m, Tel: 870-239-7530, Nearest town: Paragould. GPS: 36.071922, -90.532946

16 • C1 | Nashville City Park

Total sites: 8, RV sites: 8, Elec sites: 8, Water at site, Flush toilet, No showers, RV dump, Tent & RV camping: $10-15, 1 Full hookup site, Open all year, Reservations accepted, Elev: 446ft/136m, Tel: 870-845-7405, Nearest town: Nashville. GPS: 33.946955, -93.865898

17 • C2 | Burns Park City CG

Total sites: 38, RV sites: 38, Elec sites: 38, Water at site, Flush toilet, Free showers, RV dump, Tents: $25/RVs: $20-35, 38 Full hookup, Open all year, Reservations accepted, Elev: 312ft/95m, Tel: 501-758-1424, Nearest town: North Little Rock. GPS: 34.796938, -92.313964

18 • C2 | Downtown Riverside RV Park

Total sites: 61, RV sites: 61, Elec sites: 61, Water at site, Flush toilet, Free showers, RV dump, No tents/RVs: $25-33, 61 Full hookup, Several 15% discounts, Stay limit: 14 days, Open all year, Max Length: 50ft, Reservations accepted, Elev: 262ft/80m, Tel: 501-340-5312, Nearest town: North Little Rock. GPS: 34.751628, -92.260139

19 • C3 | Pine Bluff RP - Saracen Trace RV Park

Total sites: 54, RV sites: 54, Elec sites: 54, Water at site, No toilets, No showers, RV dump, No tents/RVs: $20, Reservations not accepted, Elev: 226ft/69m, Tel: 870-534-0711, Nearest town: Pine Bluff. GPS: 34.256442, -91.984731

20 • C3 | Riverfront RV Park

Total sites: 12, RV sites: 12, Elec sites: 12, Water at site, No toilets, No showers, RV dump, Tents: $12/RVs: $20, 12 Full hookup, Open all year, Elev: 177ft/54m, Tel: 870-747-5414, Nearest town: Clarendon. GPS: 34.692661, -91.315771

21 • D1 | Fair City Park

Total sites: 220, RV sites: 220, Elec sites: 220, Water at site, Flush toilet, Free showers, RV dump, No tents/RVs: $25, 20 Full hookup for monthly renters, Open all year, Elev: 344ft/105m, Tel: 870-777-6701, Nearest town: Hope. GPS: 33.659746, -93.606104

22 • D3 | Crossett RV Park

Total sites: 119, RV sites: 119, Elec sites: 119, Water at site, Flush toilet, Free showers, RV dump, Tents: $10/RVs: $22-27, Weekly/monthly rates available, Reservations accepted, Elev: 95ft/29m, Tel: 870-364-6136, Nearest town: Crossett. GPS: 33.149959, -92.098344

California

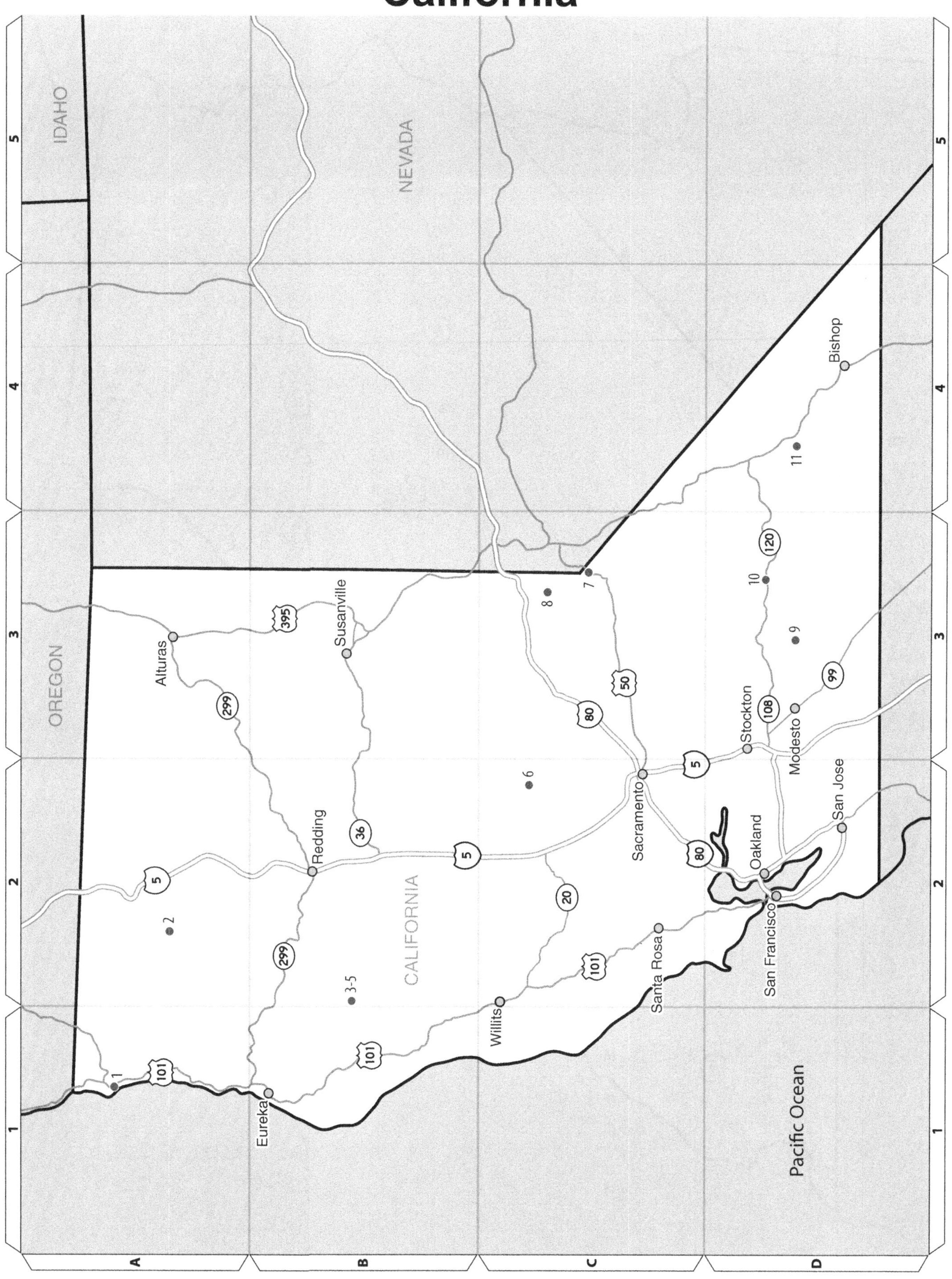
IDAHO
OREGON
NEVADA
CALIFORNIA
Pacific Ocean
Eureka
Redding
Alturas
Susanville
Willits
Santa Rosa
Sacramento
San Francisco
Oakland
San Jose
Stockton
Modesto
Bishop
5
101
299
395
36
20
80
50
108
120
99
1
2
3-5
6
7
8
9
10
11
A
B
C
D
1
2
3
4
5

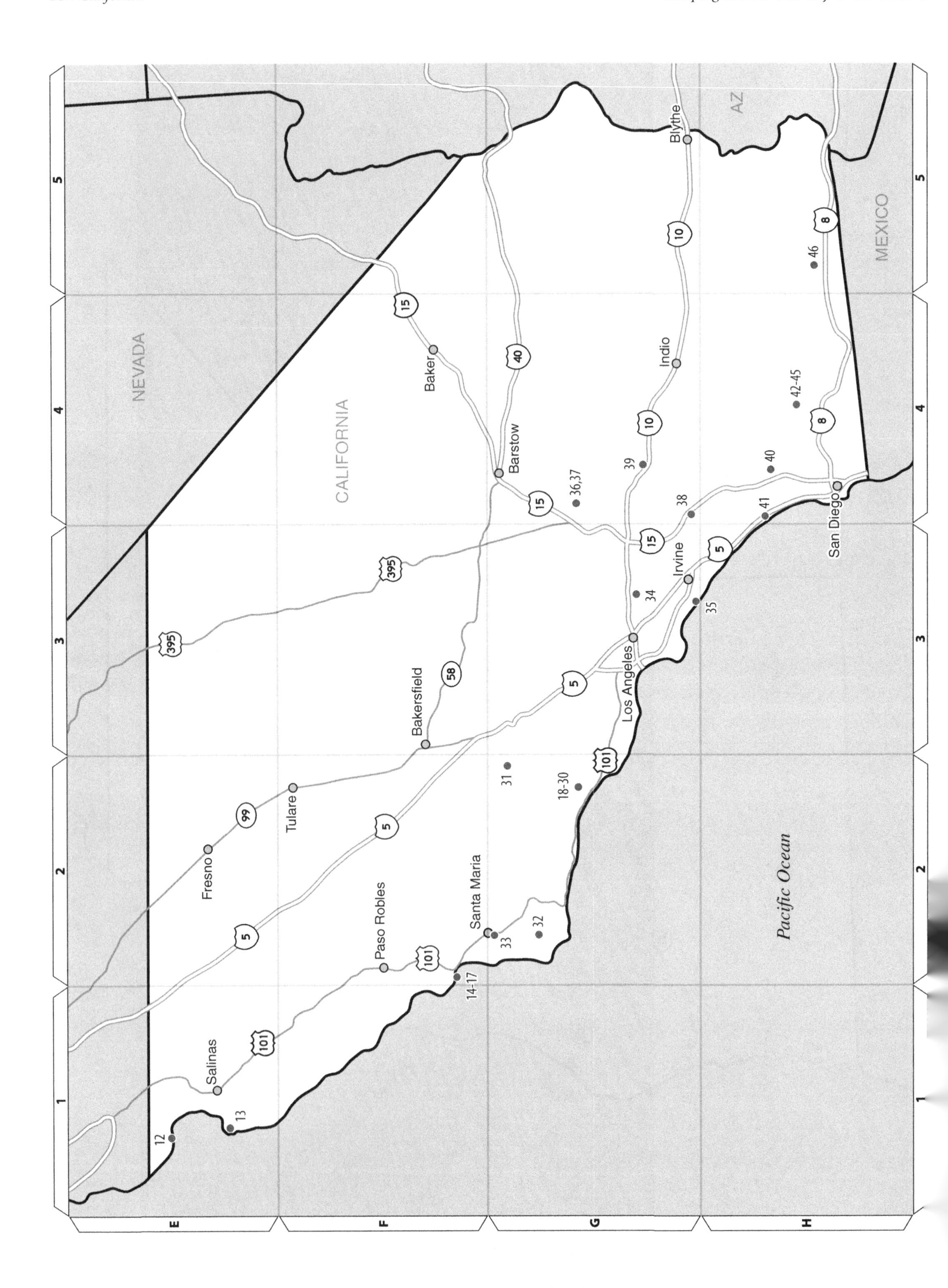
NEVADA
CALIFORNIA
AZ
MEXICO
Pacific Ocean
Salinas
Fresno
Tulare
Paso Robles
Santa Maria
Bakersfield
Baker
Barstow
Los Angeles
Irvine
Indio
Blythe
San Diego
5
99
101
395
58
15
40
10
8
12
13
14-17
18-30
31
32
33
34
35
36,37
38
39
40
41
42-45
46
1
2
3
4
E
F
G
H

Map	ID	Map	ID
A1	1	E1	12-13
A2	2	F2	14-17
B2	3-5	G2	18-33
C2	6	G3	34-39
C3	7-8	H4	40-45
D3	9-10	H5	46
D4	11		

Abbreviations for Agencies

CMWD Casitas Municipal Water District
RLCSD Ruth Lake Community Service District

Alphabetical List of Camping Areas

Name	ID	Map
Boy Scout Cove - RLCSD	3	B2
Camp High Sierra - City	11	D4
CG by The Lake City Park	7	C3
Dixon Lake City Park	40	H4
Harbor Beach	41	H4
Hesperia Lake City Park	36	G4
Hesperia Lake City Park - Equestrian	37	G4
Hobart Creek - RLCSD	4	B2
Imperial County Expo-Mid-Winter Fairgrounds	46	H5
Industry Hills Expo Center	34	G3
Johnson-Joss City Park	2	A2
La Grange ORV Park	9	D3
Lake Casitas RA - Angler - CMWD	18	G2
Lake Casitas RA - Bass - CMWD	19	G2
Lake Casitas RA - Creekside - CMWD	20	G2
Lake Casitas RA - Deer - CMWD	21	G2
Lake Casitas RA - Egret - CMWD	22	G2
Lake Casitas RA - Fox - CMWD	23	G2
Lake Casitas RA - Grebe - CMWD	24	G2
Lake Casitas RA - Hawk - CMWD	25	G2
Lake Casitas RA - Indian - CMWD	26	G2
Lake Casitas RA - Jay - CMWD	27	G2
Lake Casitas RA - Kingfisher - CMWD	28	G2
Lake Casitas RA - Mallard - CMWD	29	G2
Lake Casitas RA - Osprey - CMWD	30	G2
Lake Cuyamaca Park - Chambers - City	42	H4
Lake Cuyamaca Park - Lone Pine - City	43	H4
Lake Cuyamaca Park - South Lot - City	44	H4
Lake Cuyamaca Park - West Shore - City	45	H4
Lake Forest CG	8	C3
Launch Pointe	38	G4
Lighthouse Cove (Shoreline RV Park)	1	A1
Live Oak Riverfront Park	6	C2
Mil Potrero Park	31	G2
Noble Creek Community Park	39	G4
Port San Louis Port District - Coastal Gateway Ramp	14	F2
Port San Louis Port District - Nobi Point Turnout	15	F2
Port San Louis Port District - Overflow	16	F2
Port San Louis Port District - Woodyard Turnout	17	F2
River Park - City	32	G2
Ruth Rec CG - RLCSD	5	B2
San Jose Family Camp	10	D3
Santa Cruz Port District	12	E1
Santa Maria Fairpark	33	G2
Sunset Vista RV Park	35	G3
Veterans Memorial Park	13	E1

1 • A1 | Lighthouse Cove (Shoreline RV Park)

Total sites: 92, RV sites: 92, Elec sites: 92, Water at site, Flush toilet, Free showers, Tents: $30/RVs: $45-50, 92 Full hookup, Pet fee: $1/night, Stay limit: 30 days, Reservations accepted, Elev: 13ft/4m, Tel: 707-464-2473, Nearest town: Crescent City. GPS: 41.751811, -124.190968

2 • A2 | Johnson-Joss City Park

Dispersed sites, No water, Vault/pit toilet, Tents only: $5, $5/person, Stay limit: 3 days, Reservations accepted, Elev: 2955ft/901m, Tel: 530-467-5256, Nearest town: Etna. GPS: 41.459038, -122.898756

3 • B2 | Boy Scout Cove - RLCSD

Total sites: 27, RV sites: 27, No water, Vault/pit toilet, Tent & RV camping: $20, $2 senior discount, Reservations accepted, Elev: 2654ft/809m, Tel: Info: 707-574-6196/Res: 800-840-9545, Nearest town: Ruth. GPS: 40.314092, -123.393958

4 • B2 | Hobart Creek - RLCSD

Total sites: 18, RV sites: 18, Flush toilet, Pay showers, RV dump, Tent & RV camping: $24-26, $2 senior discount, Open May-Sep, Reservations accepted, Elev: 2740ft/835m, Tel: Info: 707-574-6196/Res: 800-840-9545, Nearest town: Mad River. GPS: 40.313265, -123.360994

5 • B2 | Ruth Rec CG - RLCSD

Total sites: 100, RV sites: 100, Central water, Flush toilet, Free showers, Tent & RV camping: $24-30, $2 senior discount, Reservations accepted, Elev: 2756ft/840m, Tel: Info: 707-574-6196/Res: 800-840-9545, Nearest town: Mad River. GPS: 40.325882, -123.392558

6 • C2 | Live Oak Riverfront Park

Total sites: 21, RV sites: 21, Water at site, Vault/pit toilet, No showers, No RV dump, Tent & RV camping: $15, Open all year, Elev: 76ft/23m, Tel: 530-822-7410, Nearest town: Live Oak. GPS: 39.274407, -121.631875

7 • C3 | CG by The Lake City Park

Total sites: 173, RV sites: 173, Elec sites: 48, Central water, Flush toilet, Pay showers, RV dump, Tents: $36/RVs: $46, Also cabins, $5 discount spring and fall, Open Apr-Oct, Reservations accepted, Elev: 6302ft/1921m, Tel: 530-542-6096, Nearest town: South Lake Tahoe. GPS: 38.943115, -119.975098

8 • C3 | Lake Forest CG

Total sites: 20, RV sites: 20, Elec sites: 20, Central water, Vault/pit toilet, No showers, No RV dump, Tent & RV camping: $20, Open May-Oct, Max Length: 20ft, Reservations not accepted, Elev: 6286ft/1916m, Tel: 530-580-6279, Nearest town: Tahoe City. GPS: 39.184097, -120.118862

9 • D3 | La Grange ORV Park

Total sites: 21, RV sites: 21, Vault/pit toilet, Tent & RV camping: $14, $3/dog, Elev: 417ft/127m, Tel: 209-525-6750, Nearest town: Modesto. GPS: 37.632881, -120.464996

10 • D3 | San Jose Family Camp

Total sites: 65, RV sites: 0, Central water, Flush toilet, Free showers, No RV dump, Tents only: $70-90, Tent-cabins on-site - no personal tents, Central dining hall, No fires/BBQ's, Open Apr-Nov, Reservations accepted, Elev: 2972ft/906m, Tel: 408-794-6523, Nearest town: Groveland. GPS: 37.828771, -120.007403

11 • D4 | Camp High Sierra - City

Total sites: 42, RV sites: 36, Elec sites: 9, Water at site, Flush toilet, Free showers, RV dump, Tent & RV camping: $35-40, Also cabins, 15 amp only, Concessionaire, Generator hours: 0600-2200, Max Length: 32ft, Reservations accepted, Elev: 8143ft/2482m, Tel: 760-934-2368, Nearest town: Mammoth Lakes. GPS: 37.638655, -118.990895

12 • E1 | Santa Cruz Port District

Total sites: 14, RV sites: 14, Elec sites: 14, Water at site, No toilets, No showers, RV dump, No tents/RVs: $52, Open all year, Max Length: 42ft, Reservations accepted, Elev: 49ft/15m, Tel: 831-475-3279, Nearest town: Santa Cruz. GPS: 36.972796, -121.998409

13 • E1 | Veterans Memorial Park

Total sites: 40, RV sites: 30, Central water, Flush toilet, Free showers, RV dump, Tents: $6/RVs: $30, $5 senior discount w/ Golden Age/Senior Pass/Access Pass, Stay limit: 3 days, Open all year, Max Length: 21ft, Elev: 344ft/105m, Tel: 831-646-3865, Nearest town: Monterey. GPS: 36.600140, -121.910510

14 • F2 | Port San Louis Port District - Coastal Gateway Ramp

Total sites: 17, RV sites: 17, Elec sites: 17, Water at site, RV dump, No tents/RVs: $85, 17 Full hookup, No fires, Reservations required, Elev: 10ft/3m, Tel: 805-903-3395, Nearest town: Port San Louis. GPS: 35.173481, -120.756136

15 • F2 | Port San Louis Port District - Nobi Point Turnout

Total sites: 2, RV sites: 2, No tents/RVs: $65, No fires, Reservations required, Elev: 10ft/3m, Tel: 805-903-3395, Nearest town: Port San Louis. GPS: 35.175704, -120.752948

16 • F2 | Port San Louis Port District - Overflow

Total sites: 22, RV sites: 22, No water, No toilets, No tents/RVs: $42, No fires, Reservations required, Elev: 10ft/3m, Tel: 805-903-3395, Nearest town: Port San Louis. GPS: 35.176266, -120.755317

17 • F2 | Port San Louis Port District - Woodyard Turnout

Total sites: 15, RV sites: 15, No tents/RVs: $65, No fires, Reservations required, Elev: 10ft/3m, Tel: 805-903-3395, Nearest town: Port San Louis. GPS: 35.175042, -120.754758

18 • G2 | Lake Casitas RA - Angler - CMWD

Total sites: 7, RV sites: 7, Elec sites: 7, Water at site, Flush toilet, Tent & RV camping: $60-66, 7 Full hookup, 2 night minimum reservation, Open all year, Reservations accepted, Elev: 594ft/181m, Tel: Info: 805-649-2233/Res:805-649-1122, Nearest town: Ojai. GPS: 34.411131, -119.338535

19 • G2 | Lake Casitas RA - Bass - CMWD

Total sites: 59, RV sites: 59, Water at site, Flush toilet, Free showers, Tent & RV camping: $38-45, 2 night minimum reservation, Open all year, Reservations accepted, Elev: 604ft/184m, Tel: Info: 805-649-2233/Res:805-649-1122, Nearest town: Ojai. GPS: 34.414011, -119.338631

20 • G2 | Lake Casitas RA - Creekside - CMWD

Total sites: 30, RV sites: 30, Central water, No RV dump, Tent & RV camping: $30-35, 2 night minimum reservation, Open all year, Reservations accepted, Elev: 604ft/184m, Tel: Info: 805-649-2233/Res:805-649-1122, Nearest town: Ojai. GPS: 34.416718, -119.339675

21 • G2 | Lake Casitas RA - Deer - CMWD

Total sites: 12, RV sites: 12, Central water, No RV dump, Tent & RV camping: $30-35, 2 night minimum reservation, Open all year, Reservations accepted, Elev: 610ft/186m, Tel: Info: 805-649-2233/Res:805-649-1122, Nearest town: Ojai. GPS: 34.417182, -119.340577

22 • G2 | Lake Casitas RA - Egret - CMWD

Total sites: 24, RV sites: 24, Water at site, No RV dump, Tent & RV camping: $38-45, 2 night minimum reservation, Open all year, Reservations accepted, Elev: 597ft/182m, Tel: Info: 805-649-2233/Res:805-649-1122, Nearest town: Ojai. GPS: 34.417059, -119.341476

23 • G2 | Lake Casitas RA - Fox - CMWD

Total sites: 46, RV sites: 40, Elec sites: 40, Water at site, RV dump, Tents: $30-35/RVs: $30-66, 32 Full hookup, 2 night minimum reservation, Open all year, Reservations accepted, Elev: 568ft/173m, Tel: Info: 805-649-2233/Res:805-649-1122, Nearest town: Ojai. GPS: 34.414101, -119.340934

24 • G2 | Lake Casitas RA - Grebe - CMWD

Total sites: 34, RV sites: 34, Central water, No RV dump, Tent & RV camping: $30-35, 2 night minimum reservation, Open all year, Reservations accepted, Elev: 610ft/186m, Tel: Info: 805-649-2233/Res:805-649-1122, Nearest town: Ojai. GPS: 34.406777, -119.348221

25 • G2 | Lake Casitas RA - Hawk - CMWD

Total sites: 32, RV sites: 32, Central water, No RV dump, Tent & RV camping: $30-35, 2 night minimum reservation, Open all year, Reservations accepted, Elev: 640ft/195m, Tel: Info: 805-649-2233/Res:805-649-1122, Nearest town: Ojai. GPS: 34.409697, -119.347553

26 • G2 | Lake Casitas RA - Indian - CMWD

Total sites: 30, RV sites: 30, Water at site, Flush toilet, Tent & RV camping: $38-45, 2 night minimum reservation, Open all year Reservations accepted, Elev: 587ft/179m, Tel: Info: 805-649-2233/Res:805-649-1122, Nearest town: Ojai. GPS: 34.408663, 119.350191

27 • G2 | Lake Casitas RA - Jay - CMWD

Total sites: 10, RV sites: 10, No water, Flush toilet, Tent & RV camping $30-35, 2 night minimum reservation, Open all year, Reservation accepted, Elev: 627ft/191m, Tel: Info: 805-649-2233/Res:805-649-1122, Nearest town: Ojai. GPS: 34.410087, -119.349168

28 • G2 | Lake Casitas RA - Kingfisher - CMWD

Total sites: 29, RV sites: 29, Central water, Vault/pit toilet, No showers, Tent & RV camping: $30-35, 2 night minimum reservation, Open all year, Reservations accepted, Elev: 728ft/222m, Tel: Info: 805-649-2233/Res:805-649-1122, Nearest town: Ojai. GPS: 34.410264, -119.353716

29 • G2 | Lake Casitas RA - Mallard - CMWD

Total sites: 48, RV sites: 48, Central water, No toilets, No showers, Tent & RV camping: $30-35, 2 night minimum reservation, Open all year, Reservations accepted, Elev: 643ft/196m, Tel: Info: 805-649-2233/Res:805-649-1122, Nearest town: Ojai. GPS: 34.408425, -119.353683

30 • G2 | Lake Casitas RA - Osprey - CMWD

Total sites: 64, RV sites: 64, Central water, Vault/pit toilet, No showers, No RV dump, Tent & RV camping: $30-35, 2 night minimum reservation, Open all year, Reservations accepted, Elev: 696ft/212m, Tel: Info: 805-649-2233/Res:805-649-1122, Nearest town: Ojai. GPS: 34.410586, -119.356299

31 • G2 | Mil Potrero Park

Total sites: 40, Tents only: Fee unk, Elev: 5682ft/1732m, Tel: 661-763-4246, Nearest town: Frazier Park. GPS: 34.853670, -119.189970

32 • G2 | River Park - City

Total sites: 35, RV sites: 35, Elec sites: 35, Water at site, Flush toilet, Pay showers, RV dump, Tent & RV camping: $30, 35 Full hookup, Open all year, Elev: 93ft/28m, Tel: 805-875-8100, Nearest town: Lompoc. GPS: 34.648371, -120.433472

33 • G2 | Santa Maria Fairpark

Total sites: 341, RV sites: 341, Elec sites: 341, Water at site, No toilets, No showers, RV dump, No tents/RVs: $45, No fires, Stay limit: 30 days, Open all year, Elev: 216ft/66m, Tel: 805-925-8824, Nearest town: Santa Maria. GPS: 34.940523, -120.440999

34 • G3 | Industry Hills Expo Center

Total sites: 19, RV sites: 19, Elec sites: 19, Water at site, RV dump, No tents/RVs: Fee unk, Open all year, Elev: 465ft/142m, Tel: 626-330-0324, Nearest town: City of Industry. GPS: 34.026448, -117.940153

35 • G3 | Sunset Vista RV Park

Total sites: 48, RV sites: 48, Elec sites: 48, Flush toilet, No showers, RV dump, No tents/RVs: $70, Water fountains, Open Oct-May, Max Length: 45ft, Reservations accepted, Elev: 39ft/12m, Tel: 714-536-5286, Nearest town: Huntington Beach. GPS: 33.654323, -117.998103

36 • G4 | Hesperia Lake City Park

Total sites: 51, RV sites: 51, Water at site, Flush toilet, Free showers, No RV dump, Tent & RV camping: $28, $2/pet - limit 2, District residents/Active Military/Veterans discount: $22, Group site: $50, Open all year, Max Length: 40ft, Reservations accepted, Elev: 2950ft/899m, Tel: 760-244-5951, Nearest town: Hesperia. GPS: 34.385958, -117.251803

37 • G4 | Hesperia Lake City Park - Equestrian

Total sites: 6, RV sites: 6, Central water, Tent & RV camping: $20, $2/pet - limit 2, Open all year, Reservations not accepted, Elev: 2928ft/892m, Tel: 760-244-5951, Nearest town: Hesperia. GPS: 34.388094, -117.248304

38 • G4 | Launch Pointe

Total sites: 151, RV sites: 123, Elec sites: 123, Central water, Flush toilet, Free showers, RV dump, No tents/RVs: $55-65, Concessionaire, Open all year, Max Length: 45ft, Elev: 1268ft/386m, Tel: 951-471-1212, Nearest town: Lake Elsinore. GPS: 33.674974, -117.372806

39 • G4 | Noble Creek Community Park

Total sites: 49, RV sites: 49, Elec sites: 21, Water at site, Flush toilet, No tents/RVs: $20-35, 12 Full hookup, Stay limit: 14 days, Generator hours: Sunrise-2200, Reservations accepted, Elev: 2580ft/786m, Tel: 951-845-9555, Nearest town: Beaumont. GPS: 33.950593, -116.988296

40 • H4 | Dixon Lake City Park

Total sites: 47, RV sites: 39, Elec sites: 10, Water at site, Flush toilet, Free showers, RV dump, Tents: $30/RVs: $50, 10 Full hookup, Pet fee: $1 each, 16 Nov-1 Mar: $18-$28, 10 Full hookup sites, Stay limit: 14 days, Open all year, Reservations accepted, Elev: 1063ft/324m, Tel: 760-741-3328, Nearest town: Escondito. GPS: 33.158014, -117.047587

41 • H4 | Harbor Beach

Dispersed sites, Central water, Flush toilet, Free showers, No RV dump, No tents/RVs: $30-35, Awnings/slide-outs prohibited, No fires, Reservations not accepted, Elev: 0ft/0m, Tel: 760-435-4500, Nearest town: Oceanside. GPS: 33.207013, -117.395204

42 • H4 | Lake Cuyamaca Park - Chambers - City

Total sites: 17, RV sites: 17, Elec sites: 17, Water at site, Flush toilet, Free showers, Tent & RV camping: $35, Also cabins, No open-flame fires, Stay limit: 14 days, Elev: 4665ft/1422m, Tel: 760-765-0515, Nearest town: Julian. GPS: 32.990581, -116.578864

43 • H4 | Lake Cuyamaca Park - Lone Pine - City

Total sites: 15, RV sites: 8, Elec sites: 8, Water at site, Vault/pit toilet, Tents: $25/RVs: $35, No open-flame fires, Stay limit: 14 days, Elev: 4665ft/1422m, Tel: 760-765-0515, Nearest town: Julian. GPS: 32.991006, -116.584535

44 • H4 | Lake Cuyamaca Park - South Lot - City

Dispersed sites, No water, Flush toilet, No showers, No RV dump, No tents/RVs: $25, Must be self-contained, Parking lot, No open-flame fires, Stay limit: 14 days, Reservations not accepted, Elev: 4657ft/1419m, Tel: 760-765-0515, Nearest town: Julian. GPS: 32.985564, -116.582204

45 • H4 | Lake Cuyamaca Park - West Shore - City

Total sites: 23, RV sites: 15, Central water, Flush toilet, No showers, No RV dump, Tent & RV camping: $25, RVs must be self-contained, No open-flame fires, Stay limit: 14 days, Open all year, Elev: 4650ft/1417m, Tel: 760-765-0515, Nearest town: Julian. GPS: 32.987775, -116.584118

46 • H5 | Imperial County Expo-Mid-Winter Fairgrounds

Total sites: 80, RV sites: 80, Elec sites: 80, Water at site, Flush toilet, Free showers, RV dump, No tents/RVs: $15-20, Elev: -59ft/-18m, Tel: 760-355-1181, Nearest town: Imperial. GPS: 32.835528, -115.566319

Colorado

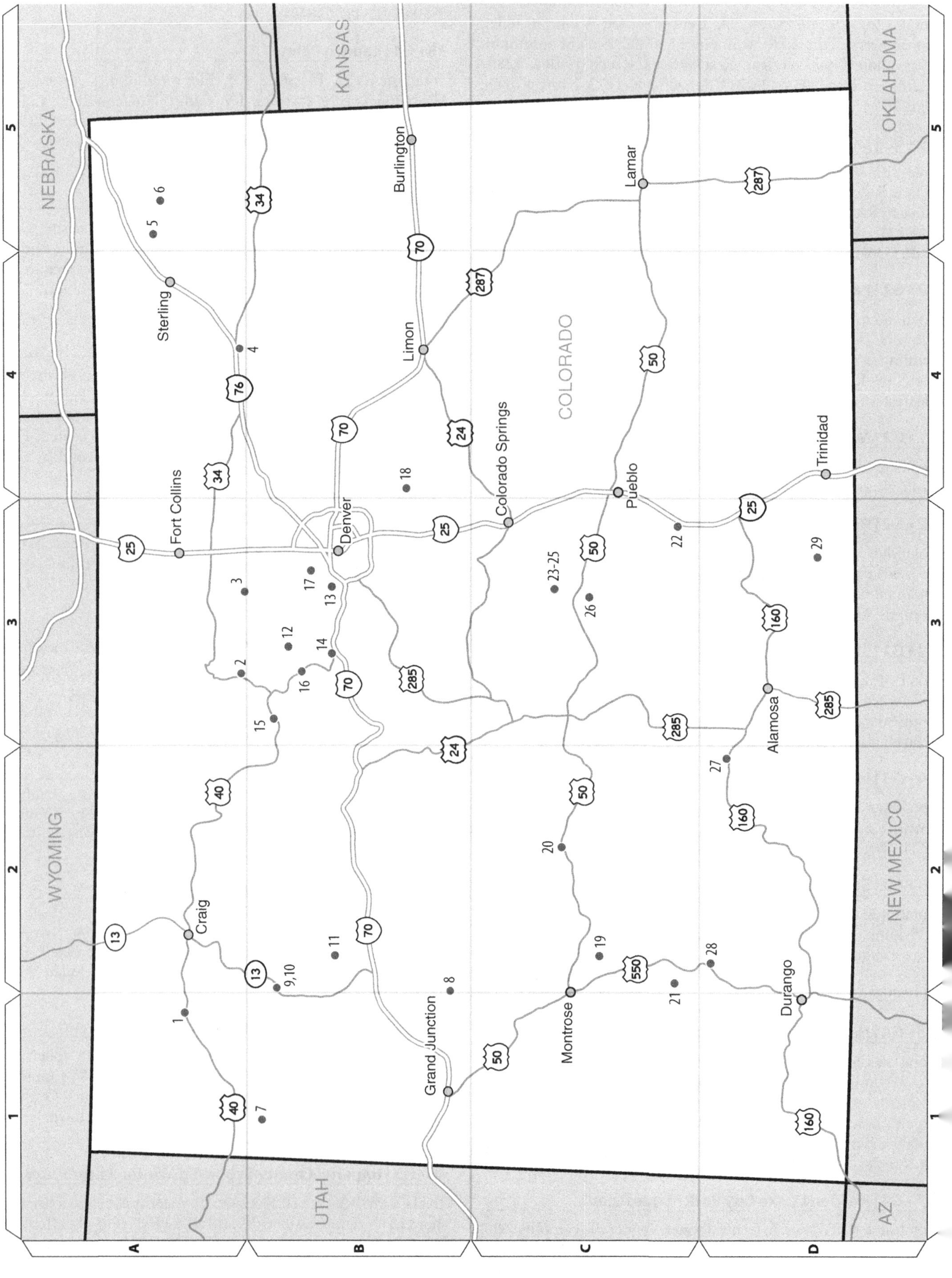

NEBRASKA
KANSAS
OKLAHOMA
WYOMING
UTAH
NEW MEXICO
AZ
COLORADO
Sterling
Burlington
Lamar
Limon
Fort Collins
Denver
Colorado Springs
Pueblo
Trinidad
Alamosa
Craig
Grand Junction
Montrose
Durango
25
34
70
76
287
50
24
285
40
13
160
550

Map	ID	Map	ID
A1	1	B3	12-17
A3	2-3	B4	18
A4	4	C2	19-21
A5	5-6	C3	22-26
B1	7	D2	27-28
B2	8-11	D3	29

Alphabetical List of Camping Areas

1 • A1 | Maybell City Park

Total sites: 30, RV sites: 30, Elec sites: 30, Central water, Flush toilet, Pay showers, RV dump, Tents: $15/RVs: $20, Dump fee: $5, Reservations not accepted, Elev: 5932ft/1808m, Nearest town: Maybell. GPS: 40.517446, -108.086411

2 • A3 | Grand Lake City Parking

Dispersed sites, No water, No toilets, No tents/RVs: Free, Parking lot, Open May-Sep, Elev: 8425ft/2568m, Tel: 970 627-3435, Nearest town: Grand Lake. GPS: 40.251744, -105.816619

3 • A3 | LaVern M. Johnson Park

Total sites: 33, RV sites: 16, Elec sites: 16, Water at site, Flush toilet, Free showers, RV dump, Tents: $15-25/RVs: $45-50, 16 Full hookup, No tents mid-Oct to mid-Apr, Open Apr-Oct, Reservations accepted, Elev: 5404ft/1647m, Tel: 303-823-6150, Nearest town: Lyons. GPS: 40.223286, -105.274037

4 • A4 | Brush Memorial City Park

Total sites: 60, RV sites: 12, Elec sites: 12, Water at site, Flush toilet, Pay showers, RV dump, Tent & RV camping: $20, First night free, Restrooms closed in winter, Open all year, Elev: 4242ft/1293m, Tel: 970-842-5001, Nearest town: Brush. GPS: 40.249122, -103.623454

5 • A5 | Fleming RV Park

Dispersed sites, No water, No toilets, No tents/RVs: Free, Just a place to park, Elev: 4239ft/1292m, Tel: 970-265-2591, Nearest town: Fleming. GPS: 40.680725, -102.845423

6 • A5 | Harvester Park

Total sites: 20, RV sites: 20, Elec sites: 20, Water at site, No toilets, No showers, RV dump, No tents/RVs: $20, Open all year, Reservations not accepted, Elev: 4053ft/1235m, Nearest town: Haxtun. GPS: 40.638819, -102.632944

7 • B1 | Rangely Camper Park

Total sites: 26, RV sites: 26, Elec sites: 7, Water available, Flush toilet, Free showers, RV dump, Tents: $15/RVs: $20, Reservations not accepted, Elev: 5233ft/1595m, Tel: 970-675-8211, Nearest town: Rangely. GPS: 40.089308, -108.789401

8 • B2 | Bonham Lake City Park

Total sites: 11, RV sites: 11, Central water, Vault/pit toilet, No showers, No RV dump, Tent & RV camping: $6, More sites further along FSR 259, Stay limit: 14 days, Reservations not accepted, Elev: 9875ft/3010m, Tel: 903-583-7555, Nearest town: Bonham. GPS: 39.103509, -107.899154

9 • B2 | Circle Park

Total sites: 9, RV sites: 0, Central water, Flush toilet, Tents only: $10, Stay limit: 7 days, Generator hours: 0700-2100, Elev: 6227ft/1898m, Nearest town: Meeker. GPS: 40.034217, -107.911578

10 • B2 | Meeker Town Park

Total sites: 9, RV sites: 9, Elec sites: 4, Central water, No toilets, No showers, No RV dump, Tent & RV camping: $20, Stay limit: 7 days, Generator hours: 0600-2200, Elev: 6243ft/1903m, Tel: 970-878-5344, Nearest town: Meeker. GPS: 40.035713, -107.910247

11 • B2 | Rifle Mountain Park

Total sites: 30, RV sites: 0, Vault/pit toilet, Tents only: $15, Reservations not accepted, Elev: 7221ft/2201m, Nearest town: Rifle. GPS: 39.726923, -107.689043

12 • B3 | Buckingham CG - City

Total sites: 10, RV sites: 0, No water, Vault/pit toilet, Tents only: Free, No ground fires, River water available, Open May-Sep, Elev: 10167ft/3099m, Tel: 303-441-3440, Nearest town: Boulder. GPS: 39.994496, -105.634342

13 • B3 | Clear Creek RV Park

Total sites: 36, RV sites: 33, Elec sites: 33, Water at site, Flush toilet, Free showers, RV dump, Tents: $32/RVs: $48-65, 22 Full hookup, Stay limit: 14 days, Open all year, Reservations accepted, Elev:

5682ft/1732m, Tel: 303-278-1437, Nearest town: Golden. GPS: 39.754336, -105.228478

14 • B3 | Empire City RV Parking

Dispersed sites, Central water, No toilets, No showers, No RV dump, No tents/RVs: Free, Elev: 8576ft/2614m, Tel: 303-569-2978, Nearest town: Emprire. GPS: 39.756677, -105.682627

15 • B3 | Pioneer Park

Total sites: 20, RV sites: 20, Central water, Vault/pit toilet, No showers, No RV dump, Tent & RV camping: Free, Near RR, Elev: 7678ft/2340m, Tel: 970-725-6200, Nearest town: Hot Sulphur Springs. GPS: 40.074270, -106.108160

16 • B3 | Sitzmark CG

Total sites: 8, RV sites: 2, Central water, Vault/pit toilet, No showers, No RV dump, Tent & RV camping: $16, Reservations not accepted, Elev: 8720ft/2658m, Tel: 970-726-4118, Nearest town: Winter Park. GPS: 39.928303, -105.787875

17 • B3 | Standley Lake RP

Total sites: 88, RV sites: 63, No water, Flush toilet, No RV dump, Tent & RV camping: $22, Outdoor showers, RV dump at wastewater treatment facility: 13150 Huron St, $7 daily entrance fee, Open May-Sep, Reservations accepted, Elev: 5541ft/1689m, Tel: 303-425-1097, Nearest town: Westminster. GPS: 39.874934, -105.126562

18 • B4 | Casey Jones Park

Total sites: 25, RV sites: 25, Elec sites: 25, Water at site, No toilets, No showers, RV dump, Tents: $10/RVs: $30, Open all year, Elev: 6572ft/2003m, Tel: 303-646-2346, Nearest town: Elizabeth. GPS: 39.363611, -104.584454

19 • C2 | Buckhorn Lakes Dispersed

Dispersed sites, No water, Tents only: Free, 4x4 recommended, Reservations not accepted, Elev: 9800ft/2987m, Nearest town: Montrose. GPS: 38.334466, -107.649865

20 • C2 | Palisades Senior RV Park

Total sites: 59, RV sites: 59, Elec sites: 59, Water at site, Flush toilet, Free showers, RV dump, No tents/RVs: $45, Open May-Sep, Reservations accepted, Elev: 7710ft/2350m, Tel: 970-641-4951, Nearest town: Gunnison. GPS: 38.547099, -106.946481

21 • C2 | Telluride Town Park

Total sites: 33, RV sites: 28, Central water, Flush toilet, Pay showers, No RV dump, Tents: $19/RVs: $33, Walk-to sites, Seniors 59+: $14/$20, Stay limit: 7 days, Generator hours: 0800-2200, Open May-Oct, Max Length: 30ft, Reservations not accepted, Elev: 8770ft/2673m, Tel: 970-728-2173, Nearest town: Telluride. GPS: 37.935094, -107.806461

22 • C3 | Greenhorn Meadows Park

Total sites: 30, RV sites: 15, Central water, Flush toilet, Free showers, RV dump, Tents: $20/RVs: $30, Open all year, Reservations accepted, Elev: 5938ft/1810m, Tel: 719-821-7062, Nearest town: Colorado City. GPS: 37.936248, -104.845857

23 • C3 | Red Canyon Park - Site 3

Dispersed sites, No water, Vault/pit toilet, Tent & RV camping: Free, 72-hour limit, Elev: 6455ft/1967m, Tel: 719-269-9028, Nearest town: Canon City. GPS: 38.592487, -105.253526

24 • C3 | Red Canyon Park - Sites 1-2

Dispersed sites, No water, Vault/pit toilet, Tent & RV camping: Free, 72-hour limit, Elev: 6236ft/1901m, Tel: 719-269-9028, Nearest town: Canon City. GPS: 38.585925, -105.248665

25 • C3 | Red Canyon Park - Sites 4-5

Dispersed sites, No water, Vault/pit toilet, Tent & RV camping: Free, 72-hour limit, Elev: 6435ft/1961m, Tel: 719-269-9028, Nearest town: Canon City. GPS: 38.591336, -105.254842

26 • C3 | Temple Canyon Park

Dispersed sites, No water, No toilets, Tent & RV camping: Free, Stay limit: 3 days, Elev: 6096ft/1858m, Tel: 719-269-9028, Nearest town: Canon City. GPS: 38.406851, -105.311406

27 • D2 | Del Norte Town Park

Total sites: 5, RV sites: 5, Central water, Flush toilet, RV dump, No tents/RVs: Free, Permission required to use water, Stay limit: 1 day, Elev: 7889ft/2405m, Tel: 719-657-3400, Nearest town: Del Norte. GPS: 37.684076, -106.352264

28 • D2 | Molas Lake Public Park - City

Total sites: 50, RV sites: 50, Central water, Flush toilet, Pay showers, No RV dump, Tents: $12-18/RVs: $15-45, Elev: 10541ft/3213m, Tel: 970-759-2218, Nearest town: Silverton. GPS: 37.749999, -107.681091

29 • D3 | Monument Lake Park

Total sites: 42, Water at site, Flush toilet, Free showers, RV dump, Tents: $30/RVs: $40-45, Also cabins, Concession, Full hookup sites, Open May-Oct, Max Length: 50ft, Reservations accepted, Elev: 8589ft/2618m, Tel: 719-886-8226, Nearest town: Stonewall. GPS: 37.206519, -105.047179

Florida

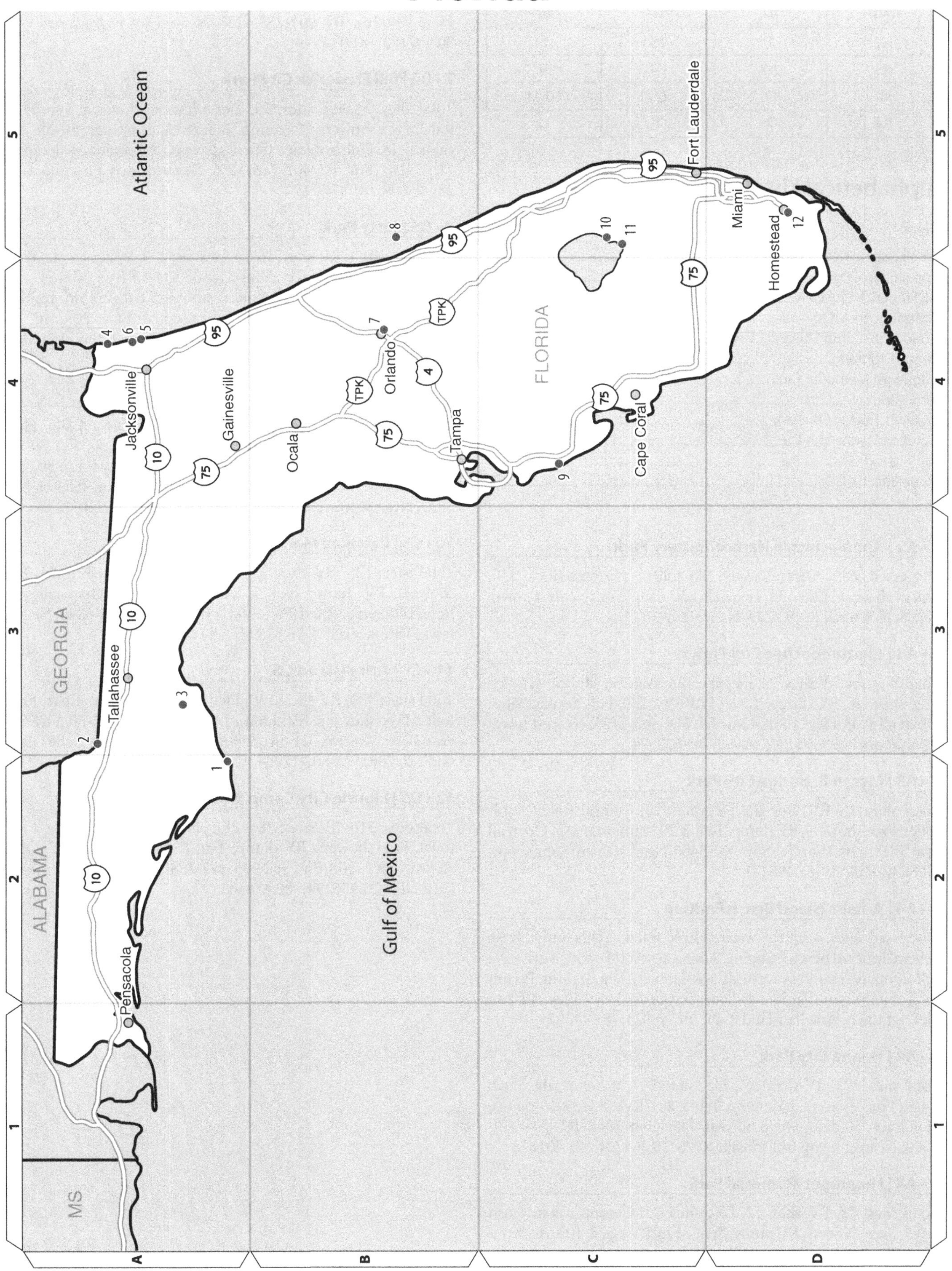

Atlantic Ocean
Gulf of Mexico
FLORIDA
GEORGIA
ALABAMA
MS
Jacksonville
Gainesville
Ocala
Orlando
Tampa
Cape Coral
Fort Lauderdale
Miami
Homestead
Tallahassee
Pensacola
95
75
10
4
TPK
1
2
3
4
5
6
7
8
9
10
11
12
A
B
C
D

Map	ID	Map	ID
A2	1	B5	8
A3	2-3	C4	9
A4	4-6	C5	10-11
B4	7	D5	12

Alphabetical List of Camping Areas

1 • A2 | Appalachicola Harbor/Battery Park

Dispersed sites, Central water, No toilets, No tents/RVs: $30, Open all year, Elev: 3ft/1m, Tel: 850-653-7274, Nearest town: Apalachicola. GPS: 29.722970, -84.980910

2 • A3 | Chattahoochee City Park

Total sites: 34, RV sites: 24, Elec sites: 24, Water at site, Flush toilet, Free showers, RV dump, Tents: $10/RVs: $30, Full hookup sites, Open all year, Elev: 138ft/42m, Tel: 850-663-2123, Nearest town: Chattahoochee. GPS: 30.700992, -84.852874

3 • A3 | Myron B. Hodge City Park

Total sites: 26, RV sites: 26, Elec sites: 26, Central water, Flush toilet, Free showers, RV dump, Tent & RV camping: $15, Open all year, Elev: 49ft/15m, Tel: 850-962-5486, Nearest town: Sopchoppy. GPS: 30.050641, -84.498731

4 • A4 | Amelia Island Beach Parking

Dispersed sites, Central water, Flush toilet, Tents only: Free, Several miles of beach camping, Access at several point, Must have self-contained sanitary waste disposal units, 24-hour limit, Permit required for non-county residents, Stay limit: 1 day, Elev: 4ft/1m, Nearest town: Amelia Island. GPS: 30.598921, -81.442879

5 • A4 | Hanna City Park

Total sites: 293, RV sites: 267, Elec sites: 267, Water at site, Flush toilet, Free showers, RV dump, Tents: $21/RVs: $34, Also cabins, Stay limit: 30 days, Open all year, Elev: 33ft/10m, Tel: 904-249-4700, Nearest town: Jacksonville. GPS: 30.364201, -81.401678

6 • A4 | Huguenot Memorial Park

Total sites: 72, RV sites: 72, Elec sites: 72, Central water, Flush toilet, Free showers, RV dump, Tents: $23/RVs: $27, 10% discount for active military/senior citizens, Pet fee: $5.35 per pet/stay/limit 3, Open all year, Max Length: 45ft, Reservations accepted, Elev: 10ft/3m, Tel: 904-255-4255, Nearest town: Mayport. GPS: 30.407173, -81.414009

7 • B4 | Bill Frederick City Park

Total sites: 36, RV sites: 36, Elec sites: 36, Water at site, Flush toilet, Free showers, RV dump, Tent & RV camping: $20-25, Also cabins, 14 Full hookup, Open all year, Reservations accepted, Elev: 92ft/28m, Tel: 407-246-4486, Nearest town: Orlando. GPS: 28.503009, -81.477095

8 • B5 | Jetty Park

Total sites: 184, RV sites: 167, Elec sites: 120, Water at site, Flush toilet, Free showers, RV dump, Tents: $34-43/RVs: $46-64, Also cabins, 90 Full hookup, Lower summer and county-resident rates, Open all year, Reservations accepted, Elev: 20ft/6m, Tel: 321-783-7111, Nearest town: Cape Canaveral. GPS: 28.406545, -80.594596

9 • C4 | Turtle Beach CG

Total sites: 39, RV sites: 39, Elec sites: 39, Water at site, Flush toilet, Free showers, RV dump, Tent & RV camping: $60, 39 Full hookup, No pets, May-Jul: $50/Aug-Oct: $42, Stay limit: 30 days, Open all year, Reservations accepted, Elev: 13ft/4m, Tel: 941-349-3839, Nearest town: Sarasota. GPS: 27.220076, -82.516602

10 • C5 | Pahokee Marina and CG

Total sites: 125, RV sites: 125, Elec sites: 125, Flush toilet, Free showers, RV dump, Tent & RV camping: $35, Open all year, Reservations accepted, Elev: 36ft/11m, Tel: 561-714-5848, Nearest town: Pahokee. GPS: 26.823975, -80.668457

11 • C5 | Torry Island CG

Total sites: 380, RV sites: 380, Elec sites: 380, Water at site, Flush toilet, Free showers, RV dump, Tents: $17/RVs: $24-30, Open all year, Elev: 30ft/9m, Tel: 561-996-6322, Nearest town: Belle Glade. GPS: 26.706112, -80.717054

12 • D5 | Florida City Camp Site and RV Park

Total sites: 310, RV sites: 280, Elec sites: 280, Water at site, Flush toilet, Free showers, RV dump, Tent & RV camping: $35, Open all year, Elev: 16ft/5m, Tel: 305-248-7889, Nearest town: Florida City. GPS: 25.456294, -80.478403

Georgia

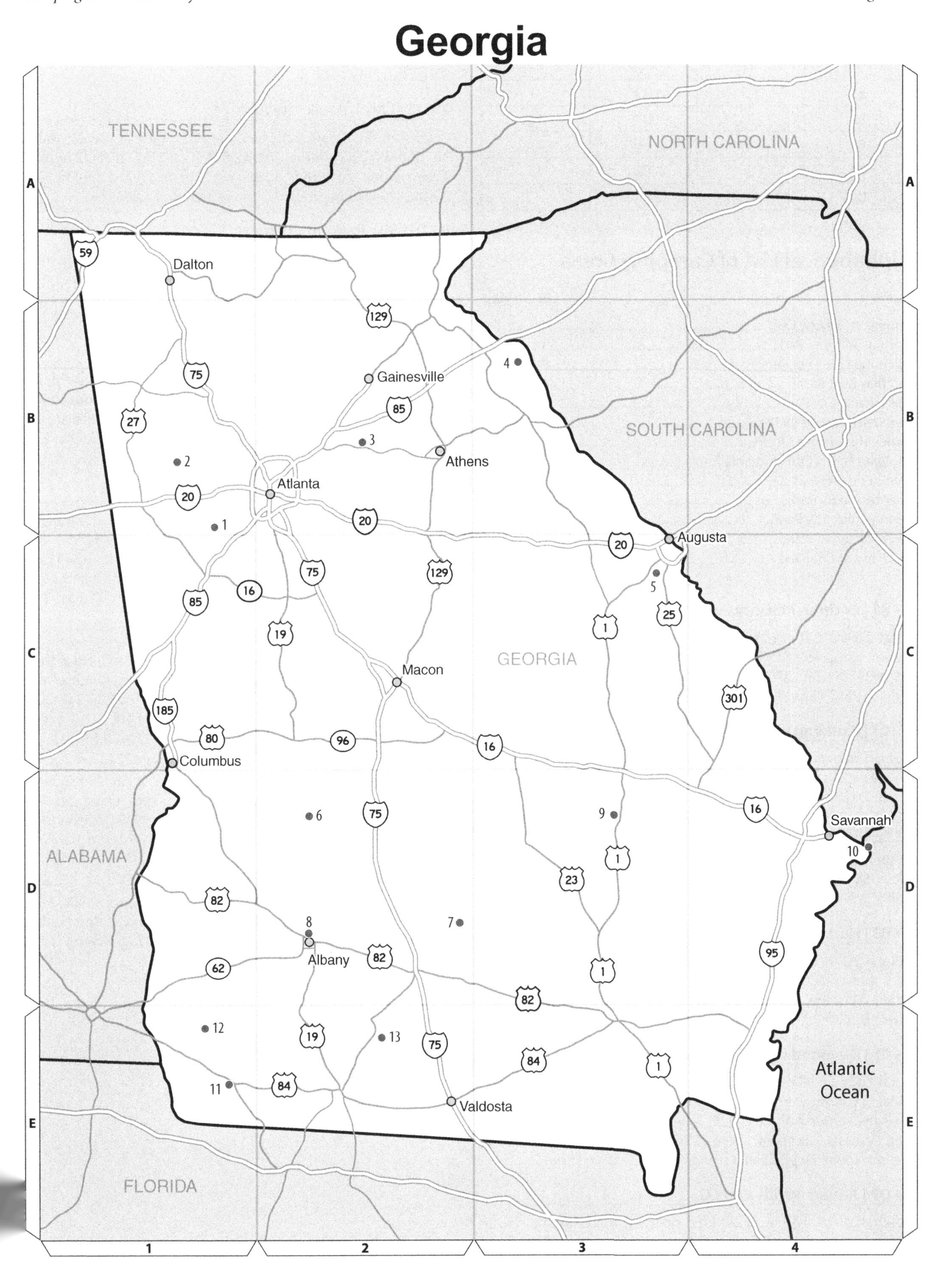
TENNESSEE
NORTH CAROLINA
SOUTH CAROLINA
GEORGIA
ALABAMA
FLORIDA
Atlantic Ocean
Dalton
Gainesville
Athens
Atlanta
Augusta
Macon
Columbus
Savannah
Albany
Valdosta
A
B
C
D
E
1
2
3
4
59
129
75
27
85
20
16
19
25
1
185
80
96
301
23
82
62
95
84
1
2
3
4
5
6
7
8
9
10
11
12
13

Map	ID	Map	ID
B1	1-2	D3	9
B2	3	D4	10
B3	4	E1	11-12
C3	5	E2	13
D2	6-8		

Alphabetical List of Camping Areas

1 • B1 | Cochran Mill City Park

Total sites: 10, RV sites: 0, Vault/pit toilet, Tents only: $20, $5/person camp fee, $15 entrance fee, Reservations required, Elev: 837ft/255m, Tel: 770-463-8881, Nearest town: Chattahoochee Hills. GPS: 33.571959, -84.714502

2 • B1 | Paulding Forest City of Atlanta Tract

Dispersed sites, No water, No toilets, Tents only: Free, Reservations not accepted, Elev: 1194ft/364m, Tel: 706-265-3707, Nearest town: Dawsonville. GPS: 33.890402, -84.941234

3 • B2 | James Shackleford City Park

Dispersed sites, No water, Vault/pit toilet, Tents only: Fee unk, Elev: 887ft/270m, Tel: 770-963-4002, Nearest town: Auburn. GPS: 33.988439, -83.844564

4 • B3 | Hartwell Lakeside RV Park

Total sites: 78, RV sites: 62, Elec sites: 62, Water at site, Flush toilet, Free showers, RV dump, Tents: $25/RVs: $39-45, Concessionaire, Open Mar-Sep, Elev: 732ft/223m, Tel: 706-213-2045, Nearest town: Hartwell. GPS: 34.377686, -82.913574

5 • C3 | Diamond Lakes Regional Park

Total sites: 26, RV sites: 26, Elec sites: 26, Water at site, Flush toilet, Free showers, RV dump, Tents: $15/RVs: $30, 26 Full hookup, Seniors/military: $25, New in 2018, Stay limit: 30 days, Reservations accepted, Elev: 226ft/69m, Tel: 706-826-1370, Nearest town: Hephzibah. GPS: 33.351196, -82.095174

6 • D2 | Andersonville City CG

Total sites: 25, RV sites: 25, Elec sites: 25, Water at site, Flush toilet, Free showers, RV dump, Tent & RV camping: $25, Elev: 415ft/126m, Tel: 229-924-2558, Nearest town: Anderson. GPS: 32.195801, -84.142334

7 • D2 | Ellis T. Paulk City Park

Total sites: 60, RV sites: 25, Elec sites: 25, Water at site, No toilets, No showers, RV dump, Tents: $10/RVs: $30, 25 Full hookup, Reservations required, Elev: 299ft/91m, Tel: 229-426-5050, Nearest town: Fitzgerald. GPS: 31.684299, -83.264946

8 • D2 | The Parks at Chehaw

Total sites: 62, RV sites: 44, Elec sites: 62, Water at site, Flush toilet, Free showers, RV dump, Tents: $18/RVs: $20-28, Seniors: $8, Open all year, Reservations accepted, Elev: 233ft/71m, Tel: 229-430-5275, Nearest town: Albany. GPS: 31.617440, -84.137780

9 • D3 | Sweet Onion RV Park

Total sites: 12, RV sites: 12, Elec sites: 12, Water at site, RV dump, No tents/RVs: $20, 12 Full hookup sites, Generator hours: 0800-2200, Open all year, Max Length: 80ft, Reservations not accepted, Elev: 265ft/81m, Tel: 912-537-7661, Nearest town: Vidalia. GPS: 32.200517, -82.371609

10 • D4 | Rivers End City Park

Total sites: 106, RV sites: 94, Elec sites: 94, Water at site, Flush toilet, Free showers, RV dump, Tents: $32-59/RVs: $47-99, Also cabins, 94 Full hookup, Check Low-Mid-High-Peak season rates, Open all year, Reservations accepted, Elev: 26ft/8m, Tel: 912-786-5518, Nearest town: Tybee Island. GPS: 32.022314, -80.851595

11 • E1 | Earl May Boat Basin

Total sites: 10, RV sites: 10, Elec sites: 10, Water at site, Flush toilet, Free showers, RV dump, Tent & RV camping: $14, Open all year, Reservations not accepted, Elev: 134ft/41m, Tel: 229-248-2010, Nearest town: Albany. GPS: 30.900574, -84.594114

12 • E1 | Spring Creek City Park

Total sites: 7, RV sites: 7, Elec sites: 7, Water at site, No showers, RV dump, No tents/RVs: $15, Full hookup sites, Dump fee: $10, Open all year, Elev: 161ft/49m, Tel: 229-758-9929, Nearest town: Colquitt. GPS: 31.171531, -84.741736

13 • E2 | Spencefield RV Park

Total sites: 100, RV sites: 100, Elec sites: 100, Water at site, Flush toilet, Free showers, No tents/RVs: $30, Open all year, Reservations accepted, Elev: 289ft/88m, Tel: 229-890-5425, Nearest town: Moultrie. GPS: 31.131188, -83.712383

Idaho

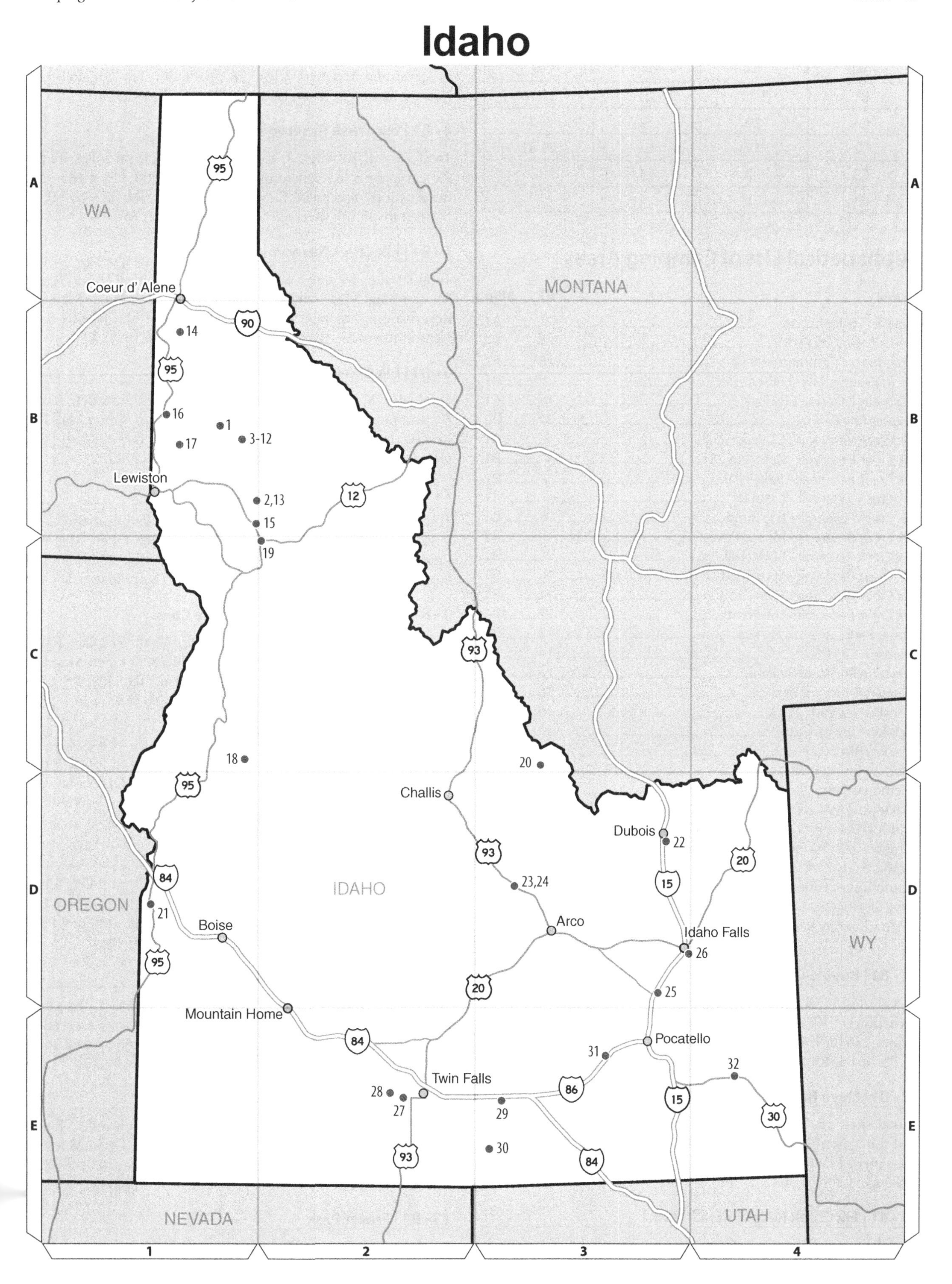

WA
MONTANA
OREGON
IDAHO
NEVADA
UTAH
WY
Coeur d' Alene
Lewiston
Boise
Mountain Home
Twin Falls
Challis
Arco
Dubois
Idaho Falls
Pocatello
95
90
12
93
84
20
15
86
30
14
16
1
3-12
17
2,13
15
19
18
20
21
22
23,24
25
26
27
28
29
30
31
32
A
B
C
D
E
1
2
3
4

Map	ID	Map	ID
B1	1-17	D3	22-26
C1	18	E2	27-28
C2	19	E3	29-31
C3	20	E4	32
D1	21		

Alphabetical List of Camping Areas

1 • B1 | Boville City Park

Total sites: 12, RV sites: 12, Elec sites: 12, Water at site, No toilets, No showers, RV dump, No tents/RVs: $20, Reservations accepted, Elev: 2868ft/874m, Tel: 208-826-3603, Nearest town: Boville. GPS: 46.856130, -116.393302

2 • B1 | Deyo Reservoir West - City

Total sites: 15, RV sites: 15, Elec sites: 15, Water at site, Vault/pit toilet, Tent & RV camping: $18, Open all year, Reservations accepted, Elev: 3050ft/930m, Tel: 208-435-4406, Nearest town: Weippe. GPS: 46.368262, -116.011173

3 • B1 | Elk Creek Reservoir - CT Park

Total sites: 4, RV sites: 4, Central water, Vault/pit toilet, Tent & RV camping: $16, Generator hours: 0700-2200, Open May-Oct, Reservations accepted, Elev: 2835ft/864m, Tel: 208-669-0528, Nearest town: Elk River. GPS: 46.773551, -116.175341

4 • B1 | Elk Creek Reservoir - Dam Site

Total sites: 1, RV sites: 1, Central water, Vault/pit toilet, Tent & RV camping: $16, Generator hours: 0700-2200, Open May-Oct, Reservations accepted, Elev: 2818ft/859m, Tel: 208-669-0528, Nearest town: Elk River. GPS: 46.767615, -116.167674

5 • B1 | Elk Creek Reservoir - Jarvey Park

Total sites: 6, RV sites: 6, Central water, Vault/pit toilet, Tent & RV camping: $16, Generator hours: 0700-2200, Open May-Oct, Reservations accepted, Elev: 2856ft/871m, Tel: 208-669-0528, Nearest town: Elk River. GPS: 46.776762, -116.169413

6 • B1 | Elk Creek Reservoir - Lakeside

Total sites: 5, RV sites: 5, Central water, Vault/pit toilet, Tent & RV camping: $16, Generator hours: 0700-2200, Open May-Oct, Reservations accepted, Elev: 2835ft/864m, Tel: 208-669-0528, Nearest town: Elk River. GPS: 46.775031, -116.172311

7 • B1 | Elk Creek Reservoir - Log Pond

Total sites: 5, RV sites: 5, Central water, Vault/pit toilet, No tents/RVs: $25, Generator hours: 0700-2200, Open May-Oct, Reservations accepted, Elev: 2827ft/862m, Tel: 208-669-0528, Nearest town: Elk River. GPS: 46.783339, -116.174686

8 • B1 | Elk Creek Reservoir - Moose Cove

Total sites: 11, RV sites: 11, Central water, Vault/pit toilet, Tent & RV camping: $16, Generator hours: 0700-2200, Open May-Oct, Reservations accepted, Elev: 2856ft/871m, Tel: 208-669-0528, Nearest town: Elk River. GPS: 46.771868, -116.168171

9 • B1 | Elk Creek Reservoir - RD Merrill

Total sites: 15, RV sites: 15, Central water, Vault/pit toilet, Tent & RV camping: $16, Generator hours: 0700-2200, Open May-Oct, Reservations accepted, Elev: 2835ft/864m, Tel: 208-669-0528, Nearest town: Elk River. GPS: 46.772518, -116.175231

10 • B1 | Elk Creek Reservoir - Spur Road

Total sites: 17, RV sites: 17, Central water, Vault/pit toilet, Tent & RV camping: $16, Generator hours: 0700-2200, Open May-Oct, Reservations accepted, Elev: 2888ft/880m, Tel: 208-669-0528, Nearest town: Elk River. GPS: 46.770155, -116.174851

11 • B1 | Elk Creek Reservoir - Swim Dock

Total sites: 1, RV sites: 0, Central water, Vault/pit toilet, Tents only: $16, Generator hours: 0700-2200, Open May-Oct, Reservations accepted, Elev: 2844ft/867m, Tel: 208-669-0528, Nearest town: Elk River. GPS: 46.769554, -116.172899

12 • B1 | Elk Creek Reservoir - The Point

Total sites: 6, RV sites: 6, Central water, Vault/pit toilet, Tent & RV camping: $16, Generator hours: 0700-2200, Open May-Oct Reservations accepted, Elev: 2842ft/866m, Tel: 208-669-0528 Nearest town: Elk River. GPS: 46.772174, -116.171612

13 • B1 | Fraser Park

Total sites: 5, RV sites: 5, Central water, Flush toilet, Tent & RV camping: Fee unk, Elev: 3092ft/942m, Nearest town: Weippe. GPS: 46.388193, -116.046903

14 • B1 | Harrison City CG

Total sites: 30, RV sites: 19, Elec sites: 19, Water at site, Flush toilet, Free showers, RV dump, Tents: $16/RVs: $37-45, 19 Full hookup, Open May-Oct, Reservations accepted, Elev: 2165ft/660m, Tel: 208-689-3212, Nearest town: Harrison. GPS: 47.453393, -116.787575

15 • B1 | Kamiah Riverfront Park

Total sites: 4, RV sites: 4, Central water, Flush toilet, No showers, No tents/RVs: $5, 48-hour limit, Max Length: 40ft, Reservations not accepted, Elev: 1168ft/356m, Tel: 208-935-2672, Nearest town: Kamiah. GPS: 46.229696, -116.018128

16 • B1 | Scenic 6 City Park

Total sites: 22, RV sites: 22, Elec sites: 22, Water at site, Flush toilet, Free showers, RV dump, Tents: $10/RVs: $30, Also cabins, 22 Full hookup, Open all year, Reservations accepted, Elev: 2579ft/786m, Tel: 208-582-2069, Nearest town: Potltch. GPS: 46.919894, -116.894112

17 • B1 | Troy City RV CG

Total sites: 9, RV sites: 9, Elec sites: 9, Water at site, No toilets, No showers, RV dump, No tents/RVs: $25, Stay limit: 15 days, Open Apr-Nov, Max Length: 70ft, Reservations accepted, Elev: 2463ft/751m, Tel: 208-835-2741, Nearest town: Troy. GPS: 46.731759, -116.765292

18 • C1 | Donnelly Lakeside City Park

Total sites: 16, RV sites: 16, Vault/pit toilet, Tent & RV camping: $10, Max Length: 24ft, Reservations not accepted, Elev: 4872ft/1485m, Tel: 208-325-8859, Nearest town: Donnelly. GPS: 44.726208, -116.092794

19 • C2 | Kooskia City Park

Total sites: 3, RV sites: 3, Elec sites: 3, Water at site, No toilets, No showers, No RV dump, Tent & RV camping: Fee unk, Unconfirmed, Reservations not accepted, Elev: 1266ft/386m, Nearest town: Kooskia. GPS: 46.135373, -115.980815

20 • C3 | Leadore City Park

Total sites: 8, RV sites: 5, Flush toilet, Pay showers, Tent & RV camping: $5, Open all year, Elev: 5948ft/1813m, Nearest town: Leadore. GPS: 44.686719, -113.368234

21 • D1 | Old Fort Boise Park

Total sites: 12, RV sites: 9, Elec sites: 9, Water at site, Flush toilet, Free showers, RV dump, Tents: $10/RVs: $15, 9 Full hookup, Open May-Oct, Max Length: 34ft, Reservations accepted, Elev: 2264ft/690m, Tel: 208-722-5138, Nearest town: Parma. GPS: 43.781014, -116.933599

22 • D3 | Dubois City Park

Total sites: 4, RV sites: 4, Central water, Flush toilet, No tents/RVs: Free, Reservations not accepted, Elev: 5157ft/1572m, Nearest town: Dubois. GPS: 44.177127, -112.234147

23 • D3 | Mackay River Park

Total sites: 39, RV sites: 39, Elec sites: 39, Water at site, Flush toilet, Free showers, RV dump, Tent & RV camping: $25, 39 Full hookup, Open May-Sep, Max Length: 30ft, Elev: 5909ft/1801m, Tel: 208-588-2296, Nearest town: Mackay. GPS: 43.910439, -113.620035

24 • D3 | Mackay Tourist Park

Total sites: 40, RV sites: 40, Central water, Flush toilet, Tent & RV camping: Free, 2 nights free, Reservations ($30 flat rate for up to 10 days) available if paying, Stay limit: 10 days, Generator hours: 0800-2200, Reservations accepted, Elev: 5904ft/1800m, Tel: 208-588-2274, Nearest town: Mackay. GPS: 43.911468, -113.621556

25 • D3 | Memorial Park

Total sites: 18, RV sites: 18, Elec sites: 18, Water at site, Flush toilet, No showers, No RV dump, Tent & RV camping: $20, Parking lot at airport, Free dump station at fire department, Stay limit: 14 days, Open Apr-Oct, Reservations accepted, Elev: 4492ft/1369m, Tel: 208-786-8600, Nearest town: Blackfoot. GPS: 43.206962, -112.345631

26 • D3 | South Tourist Park

Total sites: 24, RV sites: 18, No toilets, RV dump, Tent & RV camping: $15, Stay limit: 14 days, Open May-Oct, Max Length: 40ft, Reservations not accepted, Elev: 4685ft/1428m, Tel: 208-612-8580, Nearest town: Idaho Falls. GPS: 43.472457, -112.055558

27 • E2 | Cedar Draw City Park

Total sites: 10, RV sites: 10, Elec sites: 4, Central water, Vault/pit toilet, Tents: $8/RVs: $12, Reservations not accepted, Elev: 3759ft/1146m, Tel: 208-326-5001, Nearest town: Filer. GPS: 42.566287, -114.627264

28 • E2 | Chamber of Commerce RV Park

Total sites: 4, RV sites: 4, Elec sites: 4, Water at site, RV dump, No tents/RVs: $25, Stay limit: 3 days, Elev: 3826ft/1166m, Tel: 208-543-6682, Nearest town: Buhl. GPS: 42.593815, -114.747865

29 • E3 | Heyburn Riverside RV Park

Total sites: 29, RV sites: 29, Elec sites: 29, Water at site, Flush toilet, Free showers, RV dump, Tents: $20/RVs: $28, 29 Full hookup, Seniors: $2 dscount, Open Mar-Nov, Reservations accepted, Elev: 4173ft/1272m, Tel: 208-431-2977, Nearest town: Heyburn. GPS: 42.546303, -113.758642

30 • E3 | OakleyCity RV Park

Total sites: 17, RV sites: 11, Elec sites: 11, Water at site, Flush toilet, Pay showers, RV dump, Tents: $7/RVs: $15, Full hookup sites, Open May-Sep, Reservations accepted, Elev: 4583ft/1397m, Tel: 208-862-3313, Nearest town: Oakley. GPS: 42.237711, -113.882028

31 • E3 | Willow Bay City RA

Total sites: 90, RV sites: 70, Elec sites: 70, Water at site, Flush toilet, Free showers, RV dump, Tents: $20/RVs: $45, Full hookup sites, Open all year, Max Length: 50ft, Elev: 4380ft/1335m, Tel: 208-226-2688, Nearest town: American Falls. GPS: 42.805815, -112.834189

32 • E4 | Oregon Trail City Park

Dispersed sites, No water, Vault/pit toilet, Tent & RV camping: Free, Reservations not accepted, Elev: 5735ft/1748m, Tel: 208-547-4964, Nearest town: Soda Springs. GPS: 42.657539, -111.653491

Illinois

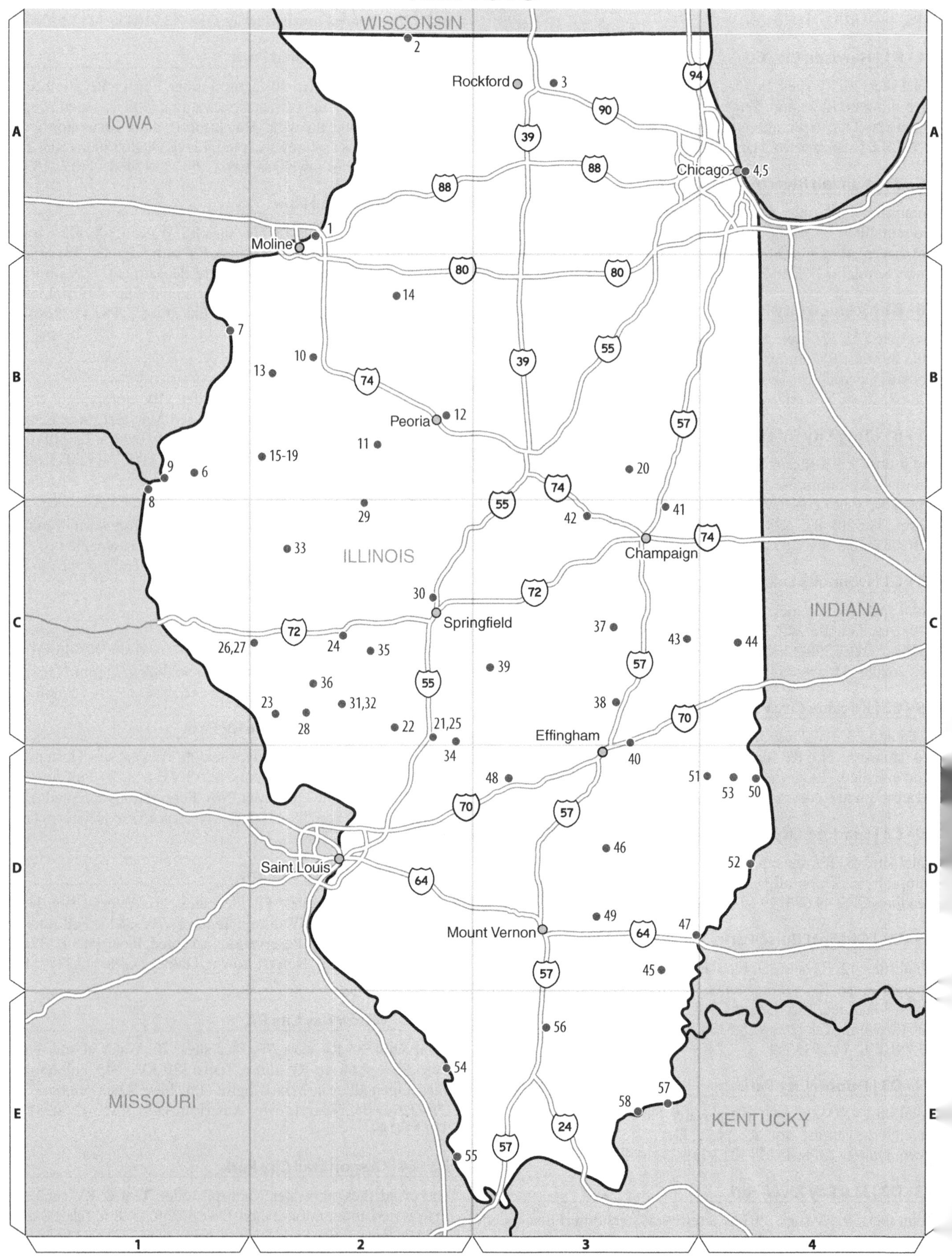
WISCONSIN
IOWA
ILLINOIS
INDIANA
MISSOURI
KENTUCKY
Rockford
Chicago
Moline
Peoria
Champaign
Springfield
Effingham
Saint Louis
Mount Vernon
A
B
C
D
E
1
2
3
4
1
2
3
4,5
6
7
8
9
10
11
12
13
14
15-19
20
21,25
22
23
24
26,27
28
29
30
31,32
33
34
35
36
37
38
39
40
41
42
43
44
45
46
47
48
49
50
51
52
53
54
55
56
57
58
94
90
39
88
80
74
55
57
72
70
64
24

Map	ID	Map	ID
A2	1-2	C3	37-43
A3	3-5	C4	44
B1	6-9	D3	45-49
B2	10-19	D4	50-53
B3	20	E2	54-55
C2	21-36	E3	56-58

Alphabetical List of Camping Areas

Name	ID	Map
Allison City CG	10	B2
Arrowhead Lake City CG	56	E3
Blake Lowry Horse Camp	21	C2
Boone County Fairgrounds	3	A3
Burrell Woods Park	45	D3
Canton Lake	11	B2
Carl Spindler City CG	12	B2
Carlinville Lake	22	C2
Cave-in-Rock Village CG	57	E3
Charley Brown City Park	46	D3
Citizens Lake Park	13	B2
Devil`s Backbone Park	54	E2
Francis City Park	14	B2
Hilltop City CG	47	D3
Illiniwek Forest Preserve	1	A2
Jaycee City Park	6	B1
Jurgens City Park	37	C3
Kampsville River Park	23	C2
Lake Jacksonville	24	C2
Lake Lou Yaeger Bicentennial CG	25	C2
Lake Mattoon CG West	38	C3
Lake Taylorville City CG	39	C3
Leaverton City Park	50	D4
McCormick Place - 18th St Lot	4	A3
McCormick Place - 31st St Lot	5	A3
Montrose City Park	40	C3
Oblong Park and Lake	51	D4
Pittsfield City Lake	26	C2
Pittsfield City Lake Primitive	27	C2
Prairie Pines City CG	41	C3
Rainey City Park	28	C2
Riverfront City Park	29	C2
Riverside CG	7	B1
Riverside City Park	52	D4
Riverside Park CG	30	C2
Riverview Campsites	58	E3
Rives Lake - Backside	31	C2
Rives Lake - Ballfield	32	C2
Robinson City Park	53	D4
Salt Creek Area 21	42	C3
Schuy-Rush City Park	33	C2
Sherwood Forest	34	C2
South City Park	20	B3
Spring Lake City Park	15	B2
Spring Lake Park - Primitive Pines 1,2	16	B2
Spring Lake Park - Trail Camp 1	17	B2
Spring Lake Park - Trail Camp 2	18	B2
Spring Lake Park - Trail Camp 3	19	B2
Thebes Landing Park	55	E2
Twin Lakes City Park	44	C4
Vandalia Lake	48	D3
Warsaw Riverfront Park	8	B1
Watertower Park	43	C3
Waverly Lake City Park	35	C2
Wayne City Park	49	D3
White Hall Reservoir - Custer Park	36	C2
Wildcat Springs Park	9	B1
Winslow Community Park	2	A2

1 • A2 | Illiniwek Forest Preserve

Total sites: 85, RV sites: 60, Elec sites: 60, Water at site, Flush toilet, Free showers, RV dump, Tents: $15/RVs: $21, County resident discount: $3-$6, Open Apr-Oct, Reservations not accepted, Elev: 574ft/175m, Tel: 309-755-7165, Nearest town: Hampton. GPS: 41.564552, -90.402725

2 • A2 | Winslow Community Park

Total sites: 9, RV sites: 9, Elec sites: 9, Water at site, No toilets, No showers, RV dump, Tents: $3/RVs: $5-6, Stay limit: 6 days, Open May-Sep, Max Length: 30ft, Reservations accepted, Elev: 777ft/237m, Tel: 815-367-2110, Nearest town: Winslow. GPS: 42.498567, -89.795002

3 • A3 | Boone County Fairgrounds

Total sites: 75, RV sites: 75, Elec sites: 75, Water at site, Flush toilet, Free showers, No RV dump, No tents/RVs: Fee unk, Elev: 784ft/239m, Tel: 815-547-6829, Nearest town: Belvidere. GPS: 42.279453, -88.851428

4 • A3 | McCormick Place - 18th St Lot

Dispersed sites, No water, No toilets, No showers, No RV dump, No tents/RVs: $22, Parking lot, Reservations accepted, Elev: 589ft/180m, Nearest town: Chicago. GPS: 41.856364, -87.614762

5 • A3 | McCormick Place - 31st St Lot

Dispersed sites, No water, No toilets, No showers, No RV dump, No tents/RVs: $22, Parking lot, Reservations accepted, Elev: 602ft/183m, Nearest town: Chicago. GPS: 41.838414, -87.609871

6 • B1 | Jaycee City Park

Total sites: 15, RV sites: 15, Elec sites: 15, Water at site, Tent & RV camping: $10, Open all year, Reservations accepted, Elev: 674ft/205m, Tel: 217-357-3625, Nearest town: Carthage. GPS: 40.425306, -91.151461

7 • B1 | Riverside CG

Total sites: 73, RV sites: 73, Elec sites: 73, Water at site, Flush toilet, Free showers, RV dump, Tents: $8/RVs: $17, Open Apr-Nov, Reservations not accepted, Elev: 561ft/171m, Tel: 309-374-9070, Nearest town: Keithsburg. GPS: 41.098287, -90.943345

8 • B1 | Warsaw Riverfront Park

Total sites: 20, RV sites: 10, Elec sites: 10, Water at site, Vault/pit toilet, No showers, RV dump, Tents: $9/RVs: $15, Pay at city hall, Near RR, RV dump behind Water Works on Main Street,

Reservations not accepted, Elev: 532ft/162m, Tel: 217-256-3214, Nearest town: Warsaw. GPS: 40.354635, -91.445805

9 • B1 | Wildcat Springs Park

Total sites: 10, RV sites: 5, Elec sites: 5, Central water, RV dump, Tents: $10/RVs: $20-25, $5 dump fee, Reservations not accepted, Elev: 571ft/174m, Tel: 217-847-3944, Nearest town: Hamilton. GPS: 40.402755, -91.346982

10 • B2 | Allison City CG

Total sites: 142, RV sites: 142, Elec sites: 101, Water at site, Flush toilet, Free showers, RV dump, Tents: $18/RVs: $35, 21 Full hookup, Open Apr-Oct, Elev: 794ft/242m, Tel: 309-344-1534, Nearest town: Galesburg. GPS: 40.984497, -90.391667

11 • B2 | Canton Lake

Total sites: 25, RV sites: 25, Elec sites: 25, Water at site, Flush toilet, Free showers, RV dump, Tents: $11-13/RVs: $15, $1 discount for Canton residents, Open Apr-Oct, Elev: 643ft/196m, Tel: 309-647-9600, Nearest town: Canton. GPS: 40.567327, -89.983777

12 • B2 | Carl Spindler City CG

Total sites: 78, RV sites: 78, Elec sites: 78, Water at site, Flush toilet, Free showers, RV dump, Tents: $15/RVs: $23-27, Some Full hookup sites, Ratesalmost double for Summer Concert Series Jun & Jul, Open Mar-Nov, Reservations accepted, Elev: 459ft/140m, Tel: 309-699-3549, Nearest town: East Peoria. GPS: 40.710765, -89.538062

13 • B2 | Citizens Lake Park

Total sites: 30, RV sites: 30, Elec sites: 30, Water at site, Flush toilet, Free showers, RV dump, Tents: $10/RVs: $19, 30 Full hookup, Near RR, Open Apr-Sep, Reservations accepted, Elev: 762ft/232m, Tel: 309-734-6924, Nearest town: Monmouth. GPS: 40.908472, -90.663635

14 • B2 | Francis City Park

Total sites: 60, RV sites: 60, Elec sites: 60, Central water, No toilets, No showers, RV dump, Tents: $10/RVs: $13, Open Mar-Oct, Reservations not accepted, Elev: 824ft/251m, Tel: 309-852-0511, Nearest town: Kewanee. GPS: 41.279594, -89.860049

15 • B2 | Spring Lake City Park

Total sites: 77, RV sites: 77, Elec sites: 77, Water at site, Flush toilet, Free showers, RV dump, Tents: $20/RVs: $20-40, Also cabins, 8 Full hookup - $35, Open Apr-Oct, Reservations accepted, Elev: 704ft/215m, Tel: 309-833-2052, Nearest town: Macomb. GPS: 40.509034, -90.715343

16 • B2 | Spring Lake Park - Primitive Pines 1,2

Total sites: 2, No water, Tents only: $20, Hike-in, Open Apr-Oct, Reservations required, Elev: 711ft/217m, Tel: 309-833-2052, Nearest town: Macomb. GPS: 40.511771, -90.708486

17 • B2 | Spring Lake Park - Trail Camp 1

Dispersed sites, Tents only: $20, Hike-in, Open Apr-Oct, Reservations required, Elev: 688ft/210m, Tel: 309-833-2052, Nearest town: Macomb. GPS: 40.507879, -90.728209

18 • B2 | Spring Lake Park - Trail Camp 2

Dispersed sites, Tents only: $20, Hike-in, Open Apr-Oct, Reservations required, Elev: 687ft/209m, Tel: 309-833-2052, Nearest town: Macomb. GPS: 40.508625, -90.730105

19 • B2 | Spring Lake Park - Trail Camp 3

Dispersed sites, Tents only: $20, Hike-in, Open Apr-Oct, Reservations required, Elev: 689ft/210m, Tel: 309-833-2052, Nearest town: Macomb. GPS: 40.510255, -90.734972

20 • B3 | South City Park

Total sites: 9, RV sites: 9, Elec sites: 9, Water at site, Flush toilet, Free showers, RV dump, Tent & RV camping: $10, Pay at police station, Stay limit: 7 days, Open Apr-Oct, Reservations not accepted, Elev: 748ft/228m, Tel: 217-784-5872, Nearest town: Gibson City. GPS: 40.457353, -88.372586

21 • C2 | Blake Lowry Horse Camp

Total sites: 25, RV sites: 25, Elec sites: 25, Water at site, Flush toilet, Free showers, No RV dump, Tents: $12/RVs: $20-25, Open Apr-Oct, Reservations accepted, Elev: 693ft/211m, Tel: 217-324-5441, Nearest town: Litchfield. GPS: 39.198044, -89.614465

22 • C2 | Carlinville Lake

Total sites: 35, RV sites: 31, Elec sites: 31, Water available, Flush toilet, Free showers, Tents: $15/RVs: $23-27, Generator hours: 0600-2200, Open Apr-Oct, Elev: 624ft/190m, Tel: 217-854-8931, Nearest town: Carlinville. GPS: 39.244397, -89.848724

23 • C2 | Kampsville River Park

Total sites: 10, RV sites: 10, Elec sites: 5, Water at site, Flush toilet, Free showers, RV dump, Tent & RV camping: Fee unk, 5 Full hookup, Elev: 430ft/131m, Tel: 618-653-4421, Nearest town: Kampsville. GPS: 39.301737, -90.609993

24 • C2 | Lake Jacksonville

Total sites: 8, RV sites: 8, Elec sites: 8, Water at site, Flush toilet, Free showers, RV dump, Tents: $12-15/RVs: $25-30, Many more seasonal sites, Discounts for local residents, Open Apr-Oct, Reservations accepted, Elev: 655ft/200m, Tel: 217-479-4646, Nearest town: Jacksonville. GPS: 39.678412, -90.192618

25 • C2 | Lake Lou Yaeger Bicentennial CG

Total sites: 60, RV sites: 44, Elec sites: 44, Water at site, Flush toilet, Free showers, RV dump, Tents: $12-17/RVs: $20-25, Open Apr-Oct, Reservations accepted, Elev: 664ft/202m, Tel: 217-324-4771, Nearest town: Litchfield. GPS: 39.194403, -89.606139

26 • C2 | Pittsfield City Lake

Total sites: 27, RV sites: 27, Elec sites: 27, Water at site, No toilets, No showers, RV dump, Tent & RV camping: $15, Water is non-potable, Elev: 633ft/193m, Tel: 217-285-4484, Nearest town: Pittsfield. GPS: 39.630728, -90.749358

27 • C2 | Pittsfield City Lake Primitive

Dispersed sites, No water, Vault/pit toilet, Tents only: $5, Elev 617ft/188m, Tel: 217-285-4484, Nearest town: Pittsfield. GPS 39.643198, -90.759578

28 • C2 | Rainey City Park

Dispersed sites, No water, No toilets, No tents/RVs: Free, No fires, Reservations not accepted, Elev: 602ft/183m, Nearest town: Carrollton. GPS: 39.306414, -90.407451

29 • C2 | Riverfront City Park

Total sites: 12, RV sites: 12, Elec sites: 12, Water at site, Flush toilet, No showers, RV dump, Tents: $10/RVs: $25, No water in winter, Reservations accepted, Elev: 452ft/138m, Tel: 309-543-6240, Nearest town: Havana. GPS: 40.303931, -90.065452

30 • C2 | Riverside Park CG

Total sites: 87, RV sites: 87, Elec sites: 75, Water at site, Flush toilet, Free showers, RV dump, Tents: $20/RVs: $25-35, 8 Full hookup, Open all year, Reservations accepted, Elev: 587ft/179m, Tel: 217-753-0630, Nearest town: Springfield. GPS: 39.857843, -89.621483

31 • C2 | Rives Lake - Backside

Total sites: 26, RV sites: 26, Elec sites: 26, Water at site, RV dump, Tents: $10-15/RVs: $10-20, Open Apr-Oct, Reservations accepted, Elev: 588ft/179m, Tel: 217-491-2739, Nearest town: Greenfield. GPS: 39.338573, -90.196261

32 • C2 | Rives Lake - Ballfield

Total sites: 64, RV sites: 64, Elec sites: 64, Water at site, RV dump, Tents: $10-15/RVs: $10-20, Open Apr-Oct, Reservations accepted, Elev: 585ft/178m, Tel: 217-491-2739, Nearest town: Greenfield. GPS: 39.342727, -90.197374

33 • C2 | Schuy-Rush City Park

Total sites: 77, RV sites: 77, Elec sites: 77, Water at site, RV dump, Tent & RV camping: $20, Open all year, Elev: 597ft/182m, Tel: 217-322-6628, Nearest town: Rushville. GPS: 40.083381, -90.552905

34 • C2 | Sherwood Forest

Total sites: 275, RV sites: 275, Elec sites: 200, Central water, Flush toilet, Free showers, RV dump, Tents: $20/RVs: $25, Also cabins, Open Apr-Oct, Elev: 636ft/194m, Tel: 217-532-5211, Nearest town: Hillsboro. GPS: 39.179462, -89.469894

35 • C2 | Waverly Lake City Park

Dispersed sites, No toilets, Tent & RV camping: Free, Stay limit: 3 days, Elev: 659ft/201m, Tel: 217-435-4611, Nearest town: Waverly. GPS: 39.600479, -90.012463

36 • C2 | White Hall Reservoir - Custer Park

Total sites: 14, RV sites: 14, Water at site, Tent & RV camping: $15, Must register at police station, Open Apr-Oct, Elev: 587ft/179m, Tel: 217-374-2135, Nearest town: White Hall. GPS: 39.447276, -90.380594

37 • C3 | Jurgens City Park

Total sites: 7, RV sites: 7, Elec sites: 7, Water at site, Flush toilet, Free showers, RV dump, Tent & RV camping: $20, Open all year, Reservations not accepted, Elev: 666ft/203m, Tel: 217-543-2294, Nearest town: Arthur. GPS: 39.711341, -88.476012

38 • C3 | Lake Mattoon CG West

Total sites: 28, RV sites: 28, Elec sites: 28, Water at site, Flush toilet, Free showers, RV dump, Tent & RV camping: Fee unk, Open Apr-Oct, Elev: 659ft/201m, Tel: 217-234-3611, Nearest town: Mattoon. GPS: 39.358927, -88.470206

39 • C3 | Lake Taylorville City CG

Total sites: 200, RV sites: 200, Elec sites: 200, Central water, Flush toilet, Free showers, RV dump, Tents: $10/RVs: $20, Generator hours: 0600-2300, Open Apr-Oct, Reservations accepted, Elev: 597ft/182m, Tel: 217-824-5606, Nearest town: Taylorville. GPS: 39.524507, -89.262066

40 • C3 | Montrose City Park

Total sites: 10, RV sites: 4, Elec sites: 4, Water at site, Flush toilet, No showers, No RV dump, Tents: $5/RVs: $15, Elev: 596ft/182m, Nearest town: Montrose. GPS: 39.172623, -88.377156

41 • C3 | Prairie Pines City CG

Total sites: 95, RV sites: 95, Elec sites: 95, Water at site, Flush toilet, Free showers, RV dump, No tents/RVs: $27, 95 Full hookup, $20 Nov-Mar - no water, Open all year, Reservations accepted, Elev: 732ft/223m, Tel: 217-893-0438, Nearest town: Rantoul. GPS: 40.284346, -88.149922

42 • C3 | Salt Creek Area 21

Total sites: 21, RV sites: 21, Vault/pit toilet, Tent & RV camping: Free, Generator hours: 0600-2200, Open Mar-Nov, Reservations not accepted, Elev: 701ft/214m, Tel: 309-928 3412, Nearest town: Farmer City. GPS: 40.235509, -88.644895

43 • C3 | Watertower Park

Total sites: 5, RV sites: 5, Elec sites: 5, No water, No toilets, No showers, No RV dump, Tent & RV camping: $10, Stay limit: 7 days, Reservations not accepted, Elev: 655ft/200m, Nearest town: Oakland. GPS: 39.660401, -88.022637

44 • C4 | Twin Lakes City Park

Total sites: 6, RV sites: 6, Elec sites: 6, Central water, Flush toilet, Free showers, RV dump, Tent & RV camping: $12, Stay limit: 14 days, Elev: 683ft/208m, Tel: 217-465-7601, Nearest town: Paris. GPS: 39.633763, -87.698211

45 • D3 | Burrell Woods Park

Total sites: 30, RV sites: 30, Elec sites: 30, Water at site, Flush toilet, Free showers, RV dump, Tent & RV camping: $20, 25 Full hookup, Showerhouse closed mid-Oct to mid-Apr, Open all year, Elev: 407ft/124m, Tel: 618-382-2693, Nearest town: Carmi.. GPS: 38.100103, -88.193942

46 • D3 | Charley Brown City Park

Total sites: 85, RV sites: 85, Elec sites: 85, Water at site, Flush toilet, Free showers, RV dump, Tents: $6/RVs: $18, Reservations not accepted, Elev: 505ft/154m, Tel: 618-662-4625, Nearest town: Flora. GPS: 38.664645, -88.537775

47 • D3 | Hilltop City CG

Total sites: 25, RV sites: 25, Elec sites: 25, Water at site, Flush toilet, Free showers, RV dump, Tent & RV camping: $22, Open Apr-Oct,

Elev: 453ft/138m, Tel: 618-375-3671, Nearest town: Grayville. GPS: 38.247855, -87.985612

48 • D3 | Vandalia Lake

Total sites: 150, RV sites: 150, Elec sites: 25?, Central water, Flush toilet, Free showers, RV dump, Tents: $7/RVs: $20, $15 for 65 and older (Mon-Thurs only), Open May-Sep, Elev: 538ft/164m, Tel: 618-283-4770, Nearest town: Vandalia. GPS: 39.008848, -89.145263

49 • D3 | Wayne City Park

Total sites: 4, RV sites: 4, Elec sites: 4, Tent & RV camping: $10, Reservations not accepted, Elev: 446ft/136m, Tel: 618-895-2241, Nearest town: Wayne City. GPS: 38.349645, -88.595885

50 • D4 | Leaverton City Park

Total sites: 30, RV sites: 30, Elec sites: 30, Water at site, Flush toilet, Free showers, RV dump, Tent & RV camping: Fee unk, Open Apr-Nov, Elev: 442ft/135m, Tel: 618-586-2147, Nearest town: Palestine. GPS: 38.996865, -87.599397

51 • D4 | Oblong Park and Lake

Total sites: 8, RV sites: 8, Elec sites: 8, Water at site, Flush toilet, Free showers, RV dump, Tent & RV camping: $10, Showerhouse closed Nov-Apr, Open all year, Reservations not accepted, Elev: 495ft/151m, Tel: 618-592-3431, Nearest town: Oblong. GPS: 39.004109, -87.898858

52 • D4 | Riverside City Park

Total sites: 9, RV sites: 9, Elec sites: 9, Central water, Vault/pit toilet, No showers, No RV dump, Tent & RV camping: Fee unk, Elev: 413ft/126m, Tel: 618-948-2335, Nearest town: St Francisville. GPS: 38.590819, -87.641306

53 • D4 | Robinson City Park

Total sites: 8, RV sites: 8, Elec sites: 8, Water at site, RV dump, Tent & RV camping: $10, Stay limit: 3 days, Elev: 538ft/164m, Tel: 618-544-3834, Nearest town: Robinson. GPS: 38.996834, -87.741596

54 • E2 | Devil`s Backbone Park

Total sites: 52, RV sites: 52, Elec sites: 52, Water at site, Flush toilet, Free showers, RV dump, Tent & RV camping: Fee unk, 16 Full hookup, Open May-Sep, Elev: 417ft/127m, Tel: 618-684-6192, Nearest town: Grand Tower. GPS: 37.639172, -89.512328

55 • E2 | Thebes Landing Park

Total sites: 25, RV sites: 25, Elec sites: 25, Water at site, No toilets, No showers, RV dump, Tent & RV camping: Fee unk, Near famus RR bridge, Open all year, Reservations accepted, Elev: 338ft/103m, Tel: 618-764-2658, Nearest town: Thebes. GPS: 37.220024, -89.462359

56 • E3 | Arrowhead Lake City CG

Total sites: 66, RV sites: 66, Elec sites: 66, Water at site, Flush toilet, Free showers, RV dump, Tent & RV camping: $18, Also cabins, No water in winter, Open all year, Elev: 456ft/139m, Tel: 618-983-3535, Nearest town: Johnston City. GPS: 37.827767, -88.910087

57 • E3 | Cave-in-Rock Village CG

Total sites: 10, RV sites: 10, Elec sites: 10, Central water, Vault/pit toilet, No showers, No RV dump, Tent & RV camping: Fee unk, Max Length: 30ft, Elev: 368ft/112m, Tel: 618-289-3238, Nearest town: Cave-in-Rock. GPS: 37.467323, -88.165865

58 • E3 | Riverview Campsites

Total sites: 12, RV sites: 12, Elec sites: 12, RV dump, Tent & RV camping: $18, Elev: 351ft/107m, Tel: 618-926-4640, Nearest town: Rosiclare. GPS: 37.418117, -88.344300

Indiana

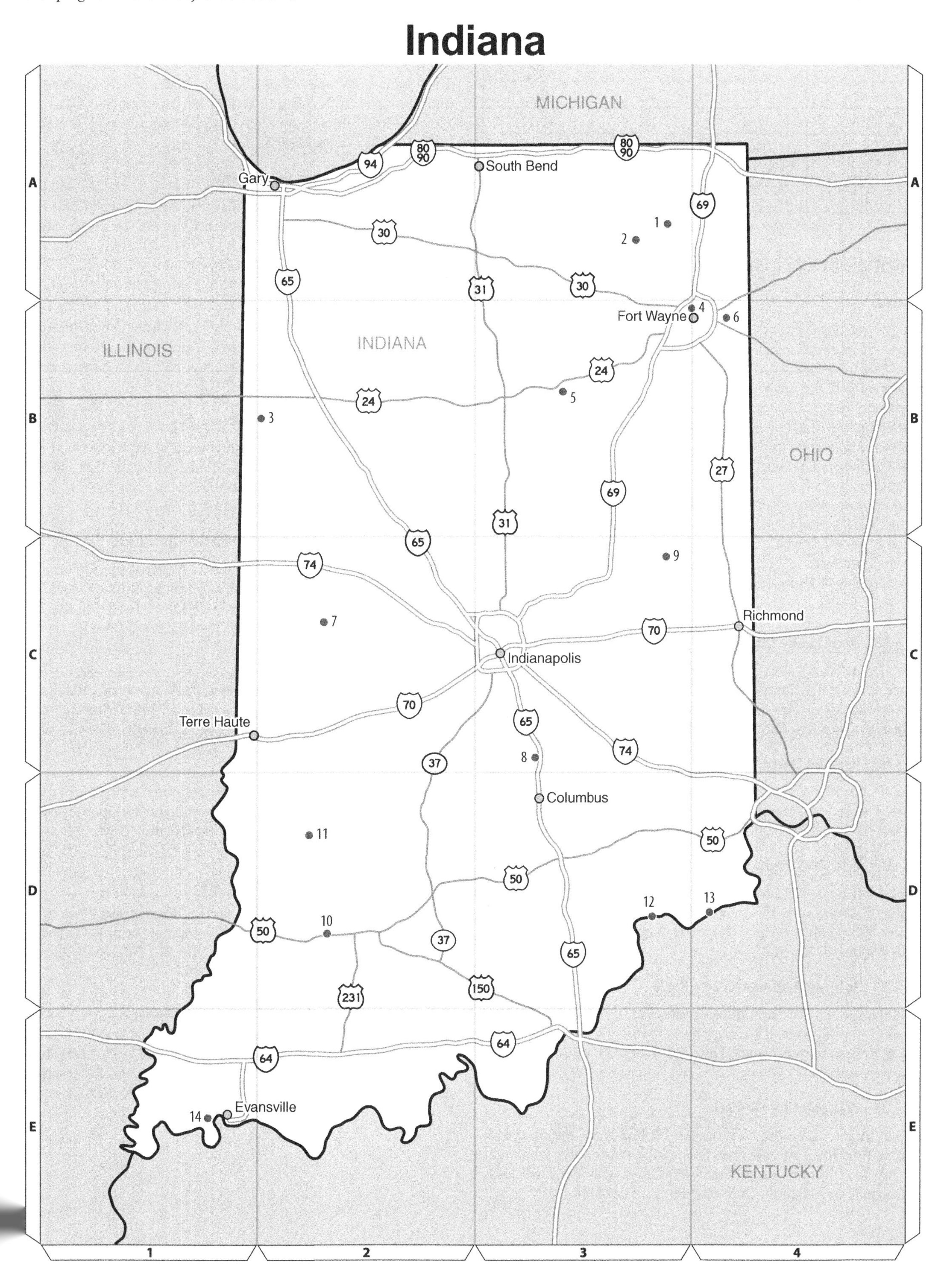
MICHIGAN
ILLINOIS
INDIANA
OHIO
KENTUCKY
South Bend
Gary
Fort Wayne
Indianapolis
Richmond
Terre Haute
Columbus
Evansville
1
2
3
4
5
6
7
8
9
10
11
12
13
14
94
80 90
69
30
65
31
24
27
74
70
37
50
150
231
64
A
B
C
D
E
1
2
3
4

Map	ID	Map	ID
A3	1-2	C3	8-9
B2	3	D2	10-11
B3	4-5	D3	12
B4	6	D4	13
C2	7	E1	14

Alphabetical List of Camping Areas

Name	ID	Map
Bixler Lake City CG	1	A3
Burdette City Park	14	E1
Earl Park Town Park	3	B2
Hidden Diamonds City Park	2	A3
Irwin City Park	8	C3
Jefferson Township Community Park	6	B4
Johnny Appleseed City Park	4	B3
Lake Waveland City Park	7	C2
Madison City Park	12	D3
Montgomery Raritan Park - Civic Club	10	D2
Paul Ogle Riverfront Park	13	D4
Prairie Creek Reservoir	9	C3
Sunset City Park	11	D2
Wabash City RV Park	5	B3

1 • A3 | Bixler Lake City CG

Total sites: 50, RV sites: 50, Elec sites: 50, Water at site, Flush toilet, Free showers, RV dump, Tents: $20/RVs: $20-25, $3 higher holiday weekends, Open Apr-Oct, Elev: 965ft/294m, Tel: 260-242-6898, Nearest town: Kendallville. GPS: 41.443871, -85.250581

2 • A3 | Hidden Diamonds City Park

Total sites: 10, RV sites: 6, Elec sites: 6, Water at site, Tents: $6/RVs: $6-14, Reservations not accepted, Elev: 925ft/282m, Tel: 260-636-2246, Nearest town: Albion. GPS: 41.386954, -85.420246

3 • B2 | Earl Park Town Park

Total sites: 30, RV sites: 30, Elec sites: 20, Water at site, Flush toilet, Free showers, RV dump, Tents: $8/RVs: $15, Open all year, Elev: 800ft/244m, Tel: 219-474-6108, Nearest town: Fowler. GPS: 40.686852, -87.416512

4 • B3 | Johnny Appleseed City Park

Total sites: 43, RV sites: 40, Elec sites: 40, Central water, Flush toilet, Free showers, RV dump, Tents: $16/RVs: $22, Open Apr-Nov, Reservations accepted, Elev: 774ft/236m, Tel: 260-427-6720, Nearest town: Fort Wayne. GPS: 41.112131, -85.120062

5 • B3 | Wabash City RV Park

Total sites: 17, RV sites: 17, Elec sites: 17, Tent & RV camping: $15, Shared electric posts, No open fires, Pay at Wastewater Treatment Plant, Stay limit: 7 days, Elev: 666ft/203m, Tel: 260-563-2941, Nearest town: Wabash. GPS: 40.790985, -85.824114

6 • B4 | Jefferson Township Community Park

Total sites: 6, RV sites: 6, Elec sites: 6, Water at site, Flush toile Free showers, No RV dump, Tent & RV camping: $20, Near RR Elev: 764ft/233m, Tel: 260-749-1360, Nearest town: New Haver GPS: 41.075137, -84.929715

7 • C2 | Lake Waveland City Park

Total sites: 53, RV sites: 53, Elec sites: 53, Water at site, Flush toile Free showers, RV dump, Tents: $16/RVs: $16-28, Reservation accepted, Elev: 768ft/234m, Tel: 765-435-2073, Nearest towr Waveland. GPS: 39.887081, -87.076723

8 • C3 | Irwin City Park

Total sites: 12, RV sites: 12, Elec sites: 12, No water, Vault/pit toile No showers, No RV dump, Tent & RV camping: $15, Reservation not accepted, Elev: 689ft/210m, Tel: 812-526-3535, Nearest towr Edinburgh. GPS: 39.360954, -85.969376

9 • C3 | Prairie Creek Reservoir

Total sites: 200, RV sites: 200, Elec sites: 200, Water at site, Flus toilet, Free showers, RV dump, Tents: $12/RVs: $24, Mostl seasonal, Open Apr-Oct, Elev: 1003ft/306m, Tel: 765-747-477 Nearest town: Muncie. GPS: 40.139502, -85.279397

10 • D2 | Montgomery Raritan Park - Civic Club

Total sites: 87, RV sites: 77, Elec sites: 77, Water at site, Flush toile Free showers, RV dump, Tent & RV camping: $20-24, Open Apr Oct, Reservations accepted, Elev: 518ft/158m, Tel: 812-486-325 Nearest town: Montgomery. GPS: 38.669220, -87.040850

11 • D2 | Sunset City Park

Total sites: 29, RV sites: 29, Elec sites: 29, Water at site, RV dump Tents: $5/RVs: $20, Open Apr-Oct, Elev: 554ft/169m, Tel: 812 798-3861, Nearest town: Linton. GPS: 39.053512, -87.142446

12 • D3 | Madison City Park

Total sites: 34, RV sites: 34, Elec sites: 34, Water at site, Flush toile Free showers, RV dump, Tent & RV camping: $25, Open Apr-Oc Elev: 479ft/146m, Tel: 812-265-8308, Nearest town: Madisor GPS: 38.732304, -85.365464

13 • D4 | Paul Ogle Riverfront Park

Total sites: 25, RV sites: 20, Elec sites: 12, Water at site, Flush toile Free showers, RV dump, Tent & RV camping: Fee unk, Generato hours: 0500-2400, Elev: 450ft/137m, Tel: 812-571-1659, Neares town: Vevay. GPS: 38.745144, -85.064402

14 • E1 | Burdette City Park

Total sites: 24, RV sites: 24, Elec sites: 24, Water at site, Flush toile Free showers, RV dump, Tent & RV camping: $27-33, Also cabin 18 Full hookup, Nov-Mar: $22-$27, Open all year, Reservation accepted, Elev: 472ft/144m, Tel: 812-435-5602, Nearest towr Evansville. GPS: 37.945384, -87.648668

Iowa

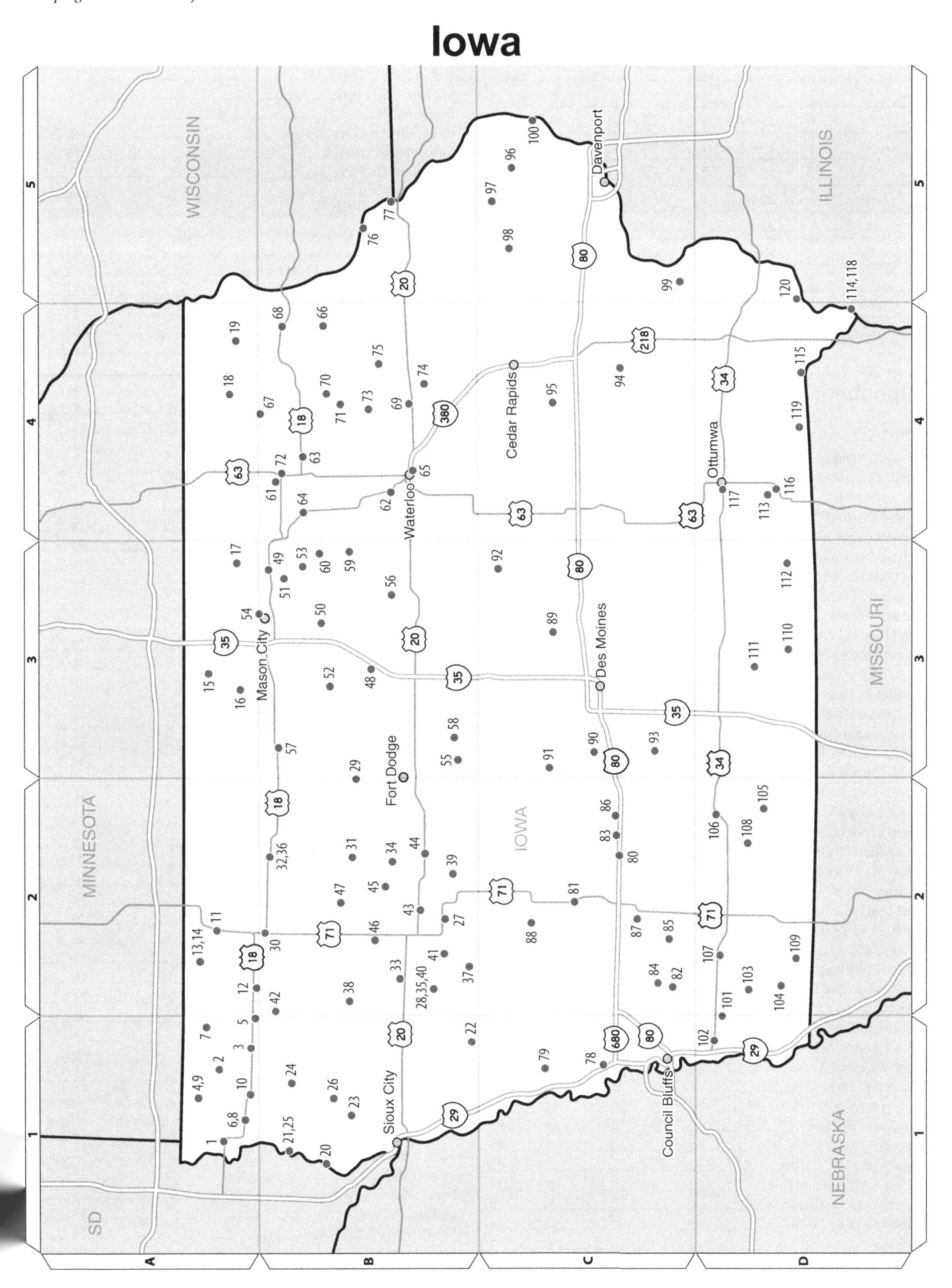
WISCONSIN
MINNESOTA
SD
NEBRASKA
MISSOURI
ILLINOIS
IOWA
Davenport
Cedar Rapids
Waterloo
Mason City
Fort Dodge
Des Moines
Ottumwa
Sioux City
Council Bluffs

Map	ID	Map	ID
A1	1-10	C2	80-88
A2	11-14	C3	89-93
A3	15-17	C4	94-95
A4	18-19	C5	96-100
B1	20-26	D1	101-102
B2	27-47	D2	103-109
B3	48-60	D3	110-112
B4	61-75	D4	113-119
B5	76-77	D5	120
C1	78-79		

Alphabetical List of Camping Areas

Name	ID	Map
Adair City Park	80	C2
Airport Lake Park	61	B4
Akron City Park	20	B1
Albert the Bull CG	81	C2
Arnolds Park City Park	11	A2
Ashton Wildwood Park	89	C3
Big Woods Lake	62	B4
Bobwhite CP	110	D3
Boehner Pond	101	D1
Brad Niewoehner Memorial Park	63	B4
Camp Crescent Park	27	B2
Carson City Park	82	C2
Casey City Park	83	C2
Cedar View Park	64	B4
Chautauqua City Park	84	C2
Cinder Path RV Park	111	D3
Cobb City Park	28	B2
Cocklin Fish Farm	85	C2
Dakota City Memorial Park	29	B2
Deep Creek CG	96	C5
Deerwood City Park	65	B4
Dows Pool Park	48	B3
Drakesville City Park	113	D4
East Leach Park	30	B2
Eastside City Park	49	B3
Elbert Park	31	B2
Elkader City Park	66	B4
Finley's Landing City Park	76	B5
Five Island City CG	32	B2
Foote City Park	1	A1
Fort Atkinson City CG	67	B4
Fort Madison City CG	120	D5
Galva City Park	33	B2
Galvin Memorial Park	50	B3
Gateway City Park	68	B4
George City CG	2	A1
George Wyatt City Park	51	B3
Glenwood Lake City Park	102	D1
Gordon Prange City Park	34	B2
Hawarden City RV Park	21	B1
Hills Park	3	A1
Horseshoe Pond	97	C5
Hubinger Landing Park	114	D4
Ida Grove City Park	35	B2
Imogene TH	103	D2
Independence City RV Park	69	B4
Indian Lake City Park	115	D4
Iowa River RV Park	52	B3
Island Park - City	4	A1
Island Park City Park	90	C3
Kalona City CG	94	C4
Kearny SP	36	B2
Kiron Living Memorial Trail Park	37	B2
Klocks Island City Park	70	B4
Koser Spring Lake Park	38	B2
Lake Fisher City CG	116	D4
Lake Mills Campsite	15	A3
Lelah Bradley City Park	112	D3
Manti City Park	104	D2
Mapleton Roadside Park	22	B1
Marble Rock City Park	53	B3
Margaret MacNider Park	54	B3
Marlin E. Fogle RA	105	D2
Maynard City Park	71	B4
McCreight City Park	98	C5
McKinley City Park	106	D2
Menlo City Park	86	C2
Merrill Community Park - Upper	23	B1
Middle Amana City Park	95	C4
Mike Macke Memorial Park	39	B2
Miller City Park	5	A1
Miller Riverview City Park	77	B5
Missouri Valley City Park	78	C1
Montgomery County Fairgrounds	107	D2
Moorehead Pioneer CP	40	B2
Neebel City Park	12	A2
New Hampton City CG	72	B4
North End City Park	99	C5
Oak Park	55	B3
Odebolt Memorial Walk RV Park	41	B2
Oelwein City Park	73	B4
Orange City Veterans Park	24	B1
Ottumwa City Park	117	D4
Pammel City Park	16	A3
Pattee City Park	91	C3
Pisgah City Park	79	C1
Prairie Bridges City Park	56	B3
Primghar City Park	42	B2
Pulpit Rock City CG	18	A4
Quasqueton Veterans Memorial Park	74	B4
Rivers Bend CG	6	A1
Riverside CG	43	B2
Riverview City Park	100	C5
Riverview Park	92	C3
Robinson City Park	7	A1
Rock Valley Municipal CG	8	A1
Rockwell City RV Park	44	B2
Schildberg RA	87	C2
Scout City Park	75	B4
Silver Lake City Park	13	A2
South City Park	57	B
South Shore City Park	14	A
Spring Park	17	A

1 • A1 | Foote City Park

Total sites: 4, RV sites: 4, Elec sites: 4, Water at site, Flush toilet, Free showers, RV dump, Tent & RV camping: Fee unk, Unconfirmed, Elev: 1476ft/450m, Tel: 712-753-4833, Nearest town: Inwood. GPS: 43.309039, -96.436373

2 • A1 | George City CG

Total sites: 11, RV sites: 11, Elec sites: 11, Central water, Flush toilet, Free showers, RV dump, Tent & RV camping: $15, Open May-Sep, Elev: 1364ft/416m, Nearest town: George. GPS: 43.339131, -95.994673

3 • A1 | Hills Park

Total sites: 26, RV sites: 26, Elec sites: 26, Water at site, Vault/pit toilet, No showers, RV dump, Tents: $10/RVs: $15, Reservations not accepted, Elev: 1398ft/426m, Tel: 712-295-7200, Nearest town: Sheldon. GPS: 43.191066, -95.852558

4 • A1 | Island Park - City

Total sites: 22, RV sites: 22, Elec sites: 22, Water at site, RV dump, Tent & RV camping: $15, Also cabins, Reservations not accepted, Elev: 1348ft/411m, Tel: 712-472-2553, Nearest town: Rock Rapids. GPS: 43.436076, -96.166238

5 • A1 | Miller City Park

Total sites: 26, RV sites: 26, Elec sites: 26, Water at site, Flush toilet, Free showers, RV dump, Tent & RV camping: $18, Elev: 1545ft/471m, Tel: 712-930-3842, Nearest town: Sanborn. GPS: 43.177406, -95.666709

6 • A1 | Rivers Bend CG

Total sites: 81, RV sites: 74, Elec sites: 74, Water at site, Flush toilet, Free showers, RV dump, Tents: $10/RVs: $17-25, 19 Full hookup, Stay limit: 14 days, Generator hours: 0800-2300, Open Apr-Oct, Elev: 1234ft/376m, Tel: 712-476-6065, Nearest town: Rock Valley. GPS: 43.214009, -96.309819

7 • A1 | Robinson City Park

Total sites: 13, RV sites: 13, Elec sites: 13, Water at site, Flush toilet, Free showers, RV dump, Tent & RV camping: $10, Reservations accepted, Elev: 1503ft/458m, Tel: 712-754-2729, Nearest town: Sibley. GPS: 43.399241, -95.736295

8 • A1 | Rock Valley Municipal CG

Total sites: 6, RV sites: 6, Elec sites: 6, No toilets, No showers, Tent & RV camping: Fee unk, Open Apr-Oct, Max Length: 50ft, Reservations not accepted, Elev: 1258ft/383m, Tel: 712-476-5707, Nearest town: Rock Valley. GPS: 43.201921, -96.291235

9 • A1 | Westside City Park

Total sites: 8, RV sites: 8, Central water, Flush toilet, Free showers, RV dump, Tent & RV camping: $15, Reservations not accepted, Elev: 1375ft/419m, Nearest town: Rock Rapids. GPS: 43.431499, -96.182701

10 • A1 | Westside City Park

Total sites: 3, RV sites: 3, Water at site, Tent & RV camping: $5, Free for 1st 3 days, Elev: 1417ft/432m, Nearest town: Hull. GPS: 43.190504, -96.141027

11 • A2 | Arnolds Park City Park

Total sites: 15, RV sites: 15, Elec sites: 15, Central water, Flush toilet, Free showers, Tents: $25/RVs: $35, Open May-Aug, Reservations not accepted, Elev: 1445ft/440m, Tel: 712-332-2341, Nearest town: Arnolds Park. GPS: 43.366686, -95.132537

12 • A2 | Neebel City Park

Total sites: 6, RV sites: 6, Elec sites: 6, Tent & RV camping: Fee unk, Reservations not accepted, Elev: 1447ft/441m, Tel: 712-928-2240, Nearest town: Hartley. GPS: 43.176225, -95.477149

13 • A2 | Silver Lake City Park

Total sites: 15, RV sites: 8, Elec sites: 8, Central water, Flush toilet, Free showers, RV dump, Tents: $10/RVs: $25, Open Apr-Oct, Reservations accepted, Elev: 1460ft/445m, Tel: 712-540-2605, Nearest town: Lake Park. GPS: 43.447560, -95.326480

14 • A2 | South Shore City Park

Total sites: 13, RV sites: 10, Elec sites: 10, Central water, No toilets, No showers, No RV dump, Tents: $10/RVs: $25, Reservations accepted, Elev: 1447ft/441m, Tel: 712-832-3588, Nearest town: Lake Park. GPS: 43.433157, -95.340761

15 • A3 | Lake Mills Campsite

Total sites: 4, RV sites: 4, Elec sites: 4, No toilets, No showers, No RV dump, Tent & RV camping: $12, Unconfirmed, Elev: 1283ft/391m, Tel: 641-592-3251, Nearest town: Lake Mills. GPS: 43.409589, -93.532514

16 • A3 | Pammel City Park

Total sites: 43, RV sites: 43, Elec sites: 43, Central water, Flush toilet, Free showers, RV dump, No tents/RVs: $15, Use entrance off East J St, Stay limit: 14 days, Open May-Oct, Reservations not accepted, Elev: 1199ft/365m, Tel: 641-585-3574, Nearest town: Forest City. GPS: 43.259212, -93.631389

17 • A3 | Spring Park

Total sites: 12, RV sites: 12, Central water, Tent & RV camping: $6, Open May-Nov, Elev: 1119ft/341m, Tel: 641-732-3709, Nearest town: Osage. GPS: 43.276636, -92.850751

18 • A4 | Pulpit Rock City CG

Total sites: 136, RV sites: 104, Elec sites: 136, Central water, Flush toilet, Free showers, RV dump, Tents: $15-18/RVs: $22-42, Weekends/holidays: $40-$42 for RVs, Open Apr-Oct, Reservations accepted, Elev: 915ft/279m, Tel: 563-382-9551, Nearest town: Decorah. GPS: 43.297692, -91.810014

19 • A4 | Waukon City Park CG

Total sites: 28, RV sites: 28, Elec sites: 28, Water at site, Flush toilet, Free showers, RV dump, Tents: $15/RVs: $20-25, Reservations accepted, Elev: 1250ft/381m, Tel: 563-568-0081, Nearest town: Waukon. GPS: 43.257660, -91.473910

20 • B1 | Akron City Park

Total sites: 17, RV sites: 17, Elec sites: 17, Central water, Flush toilet, Free showers, Tent & RV camping: $10, Open May-Oct, Reservations not accepted, Elev: 1145ft/349m, Tel: 712-568-2041, Nearest town: Akron. GPS: 42.831665, -96.556002

21 • B1 | Hawarden City RV Park

Total sites: 7, RV sites: 7, Elec sites: 7, Water at site, RV dump, No tents/RVs: $10, Full hookup sites, Reservations not accepted, Elev: 1178ft/359m, Tel: 712-551-2565, Nearest town: Hawarden. GPS: 43.002535, -96.487543

22 • B1 | Mapleton Roadside Park

Total sites: 18, RV sites: 18, Elec sites: 18, No toilets, No showers, No RV dump, Tent & RV camping: $15, Elev: 1148ft/350m, Tel: 712-881-1351, Nearest town: Mapleton. GPS: 42.169535, -95.789112

23 • B1 | Merrill Community Park - Upper

Total sites: 10, RV sites: 10, Elec sites: 10, Water at site, No toilets, No showers, No RV dump, Tent & RV camping: $20, 10 Full hookup, Elev: 1198ft/365m, Tel: 712-938-2514, Nearest town: Merrill. GPS: 42.717633, -96.255462

24 • B1 | Orange City Veterans Park

Total sites: 16, RV sites: 16, Elec sites: 16, Water at site, Flush toilet, Free showers, RV dump, Tent & RV camping: $15-20, Some Full hookup, $25-$30 during Tulip Festival, Elev: 1423ft/434m, Tel: 712-707-4885, Nearest town: Orange City. GPS: 43.001144, -96.069233

25 • B1 | Veterans Memorial Park

Total sites: 4, RV sites: 4, Elec sites: 4, Water at site, RV dump, No tents/RVs: $10, Full hookup sites, Reservations not accepted, Elev: 1177ft/359m, Tel: 712-551-2565, Nearest town: Hawarden. GPS: 43.000923, -96.487105

26 • B1 | Willow Creek City CG

Total sites: 42, RV sites: 38, Elec sites: 38, Water at site, Flush toilet, Free showers, Tents: $10/RVs: $20-25, Open Apr-Sep, Reservations accepted, Elev: 1191ft/363m, Tel: 712-540-4984, Nearest town: Le Mars. GPS: 42.803411, -96.155211

27 • B2 | Camp Crescent Park

Total sites: 167, RV sites: 167, Elec sites: 167, Water at site, Flush toilet, Free showers, RV dump, Tent & RV camping: $18-22, Also cabins, 74 Full hookup, Open Apr-Sep, Elev: 1234ft/376m, Tel: 712-657-2189, Nearest town: Lake View. GPS: 42.307274, -95.042289

28 • B2 | Cobb City Park

Total sites: 45, RV sites: 45, Elec sites: 45, Central water, Flush toilet, Free showers, RV dump, Tents: $10/RVs: $18, Operated by American Legion, Reservations not accepted, Elev: 1241ft/378m, Tel: 712-364-3739, Nearest town: Ida Grove. GPS: 42.351759, -95.473958

29 • B2 | Dakota City Memorial Park

Total sites: 15, RV sites: 13, Elec sites: 13, Water at site, Tent & RV camping: $15, Elev: 1061ft/323m, Nearest town: Dakota City. GPS: 42.723679, -94.193578

30 • B2 | East Leach Park

Total sites: 108, RV sites: 108, Elec sites: 108, Water at site, Flush toilet, Free showers, RV dump, Tents: $12/RVs: $12-15, Some Full hookup, Open Apr-Oct, Elev: 1305ft/398m, Tel: 712-580-7265, Nearest town: Spencer. GPS: 43.134727, -95.139203

31 • B2 | Elbert Park

Total sites: 6, RV sites: 6, Elec sites: 6, Water at site, No toilets, No showers, RV dump, Tents: $8/RVs: $14-17, Open Apr-Oct, Elev: 1207ft/368m, Tel: 712-335-4841, Nearest town: Pocahontas. GPS: 42.739381, -94.666281

32 • B2 | Five Island City CG

Total sites: 21, RV sites: 21, Elec sites: 21, Water at site, Flush toilet, Free showers, RV dump, Tents: $10/RVs: $25, Also cabins, 21 Full hookup, Stay limit: 14 days, Reservations not accepted, Elev: 1229ft/375m, Tel: 712-852-4030, Nearest town: Emmetsburg. GPS: 43.123864, -94.671787

33 • B2 | Galva City Park

Total sites: 3, RV sites: 3, Elec sites: 3, No toilets, No showers, No RV dump, Tent & RV camping: Fee unk, Unconfirmed, Elev: 1326ft/404m, Nearest town: Galva. GPS: 42.505520, -95.414245

34 • B2 | Gordon Prange City Park

Total sites: 6, RV sites: 6, Elec sites: 6, Water at site, Tents: $10/RVs: $18, 5 Full hookup, Pay at City Hall, Generator hours: 0700-2300, Open Apr-Oct, Reservations accepted, Elev: 1234ft/376m, Tel: 712-468-2411, Nearest town: Pomeroy. GPS: 42.551053, -94.689028

35 • B2 | Ida Grove City Park

Total sites: 6, RV sites: 3, Elec sites: 3, Central water, No toilets, No showers, RV dump, Tents: $3/RVs: $8, Reservations not accepted Elev: 1217ft/371m, Tel: 712-364-2428, Nearest town: Ida Grove GPS: 42.348024, -95.467128

36 • B2 | Kearny SP

Total sites: 26, RV sites: 16, Elec sites: 16, Central water, Flush toilet, Free showers, Tents: $10/RVs: $15, Managed by city Reservations not accepted, Elev: 1227ft/374m, Tel: 712-852-3383 Nearest town: Emmetsburg. GPS: 43.121685, -94.679813

37 • B2 | Kiron Living Memorial Trail Park

Total sites: 8, RV sites: 8, Elec sites: 8, No tents/RVs: $15

Reservations accepted, Elev: 1307ft/398m, Tel: 712-675-4700, Nearest town: Kiron. GPS: 42.192896, -95.325467

38 • B2 | Koser Spring Lake Park

Total sites: 48, RV sites: 48, Elec sites: 48, Water at site, Flush toilet, Free showers, RV dump, Tents: $12/RVs: $20, 48 Full hookup, Reservations accepted, Elev: 1188ft/362m, Tel: 712-225-2715, Nearest town: Cherokee. GPS: 42.738046, -95.556851

39 • B2 | Mike Macke Memorial Park

Total sites: 5, RV sites: 5, Elec sites: 5, Water at site, Flush toilet, Free showers, No RV dump, Tents: $5/RVs: $10, Reservations not accepted, Elev: 1119ft/341m, Tel: 712-464-3185, Nearest town: Lake City. GPS: 42.271535, -94.762249

40 • B2 | Moorehead Pioneer CP

Dispersed sites, No water, Vault/pit toilet, No showers, No RV dump, Tent & RV camping: $8, Open all year, Reservations not accepted, Elev: 1253ft/382m, Tel: 712-364-3300, Nearest town: Ida Grove. GPS: 42.357061, -95.479951

41 • B2 | Odebolt Memorial Walk RV Park

Total sites: 6, RV sites: 6, Elec sites: 6, Tent & RV camping: $8-10, No fires, Elev: 1371ft/418m, Tel: 712-668-2231, Nearest town: Odebolt. GPS: 42.307591, -95.249246

42 • B2 | Primghar City Park

Total sites: 15, RV sites: 15, Elec sites: 15, Water at site, Flush toilet, No showers, No RV dump, Tent & RV camping: $15, Open Apr-Sep, Reservations not accepted, Elev: 1496ft/456m, Tel: 712-957-2435, Nearest town: Primghar. GPS: 43.084488, -95.623777

43 • B2 | Riverside CG

Total sites: 20, RV sites: 20, Elec sites: 20, Water at site, Flush toilet, Free showers, RV dump, Tents: $8/RVs: $14, Elev: 1171ft/357m, Tel: 712-662-7593, Nearest town: Sac City. GPS: 42.419457, -94.985317

44 • B2 | Rockwell City RV Park

Total sites: 15, RV sites: 15, Elec sites: 15, Water at site, Flush toilet, Free showers, RV dump, Tent & RV camping: $15, 15 Full hookup, Elev: 1207ft/368m, Tel: 712-297-7041, Nearest town: Rockwell City. GPS: 42.400502, -94.639721

45 • B2 | Straight CP

Total sites: 14, RV sites: 14, Elec sites: 14, Water at site, Flush toilet, RV dump, Tents: $10/RVs: $15, Also cabins, Full hookup sites, Reservations not accepted, Elev: 1217ft/371m, Tel: 712-288-4466, Nearest town: Fonda. GPS: 42.579354, -94.848036

46 • B2 | Sunrise City CG

Total sites: 131, RV sites: 103, Elec sites: 103, Water at site, Flush toilet, Free showers, RV dump, Tents: $12/RVs: $17-26, Also cabins, 36 Full hookup sites, Generator hours: 0800-2300, Open Apr-Oct, Reservations accepted, Elev: 1394ft/425m, Tel: 712-732-8023, Nearest town: Storm Lake. GPS: 42.628114, -95.175374

47 • B2 | Sunset City Park

Total sites: 10, RV sites: 10, Elec sites: 10, Water at site, Flush toilet, Free showers, RV dump, Tents: $8/RVs: $15, 10 Full hookup, Elev: 1312ft/400m, Tel: 712-843-5613, Nearest town: Albert City. GPS: 42.786161, -94.952879

48 • B3 | Dows Pool Park

Total sites: 11, RV sites: 11, Elec sites: 11, Water at site, Flush toilet, Free showers, Tent & RV camping: Fee unk, 11 Full hookup, Elev: 1155ft/352m, Tel: 515-852-4327, Nearest town: Dows. GPS: 42.653538, -93.507605

49 • B3 | Eastside City Park

Total sites: 15, RV sites: 15, Elec sites: 15, Water available, Flush toilet, Free showers, RV dump, Tent & RV camping: Fee unk, Elev: 1119ft/341m, Nearest town: Rudd. GPS: 43.127217, -92.894402

50 • B3 | Galvin Memorial Park

Total sites: 12, RV sites: 12, Elec sites: 12, Central water, Flush toilet, Free showers, RV dump, Tent & RV camping: $10, Open May-Sep, Elev: 1092ft/333m, Tel: 641-892-4718, Nearest town: Sheffield. GPS: 42.885910, -93.221760

51 • B3 | George Wyatt City Park

Total sites: 31, RV sites: 31, Elec sites: 31, Water at site, Flush toilet, Free showers, RV dump, Tents: $12/RVs: $12-15, 4 Full hookup, Elev: 997ft/304m, Tel: 641-756-3718, Nearest town: Rockford. GPS: 43.053813, -92.946127

52 • B3 | Iowa River RV Park

Total sites: 24, RV sites: 24, Elec sites: 24, Water at site, Flush toilet, Free showers, RV dump, Tents: $8/RVs: $10-12, 8 Full hookup, Open Apr-Oct, Elev: 1168ft/356m, Tel: 641-444-3386, Nearest town: Belmond. GPS: 42.843531, -93.617623

53 • B3 | Marble Rock City Park

Total sites: 6, RV sites: 6, Elec sites: 6, Central water, RV dump, Tent & RV camping: Donation, Stay limit: 3 days, Open all year, Elev: 1015ft/309m, Tel: 641-315-2621, Nearest town: Marble Rock. GPS: 42.967583, -92.869647

54 • B3 | Margaret MacNider Park

Total sites: 95, RV sites: 75, Elec sites: 75, Water at site, Flush toilet, Free showers, RV dump, Tents: $12/RVs: $17-26, 20 Full hookup, Open Apr-Oct, Reservations not accepted, Elev: 1089ft/332m, Tel: 641-421-3673, Nearest town: Mason City. GPS: 43.158009, -93.183477

55 • B3 | Oak Park

Total sites: 44, RV sites: 44, Elec sites: 44, Flush toilet, Free showers, No RV dump, Tent & RV camping: $12, Pay at City Hall or Oak Park Clubhouse or the police when they patrol the area, Open Apr-Oct, Reservations not accepted, Elev: 1096ft/334m, Tel: 515-547-2711, Nearest town: Dayton. GPS: 42.256001, -94.068833

56 • B3 | Prairie Bridges City Park

Total sites: 120, RV sites: 120, Elec sites: 90, Water at site, Flush toilet, Free showers, RV dump, Tents: $8/RVs: $15, Reservations accepted, Elev: 1076ft/328m, Tel: 641-485-1623, Nearest town: Ackley. GPS: 42.560080, -93.057140

57 • B3 | South City Park

Total sites: 2, RV sites: 2, Elec sites: 2, No toilets, No showers, No

RV dump, Tent & RV camping: $15, Elev: 1243ft/379m, Tel: 515-679-4292, Nearest town: Wesley. GPS: 43.082677, -93.993500

58 • B3 | Stratford City Park

Total sites: 60, RV sites: 60, Central water, Flush toilet, Free showers, RV dump, Tent & RV camping: Fee unk, Open all year, Reservations not accepted, Elev: 1112ft/339m, Tel: 515-838-2311, Nearest town: Stratford. GPS: 42.270900, -93.930500

59 • B3 | Wilder City Park

Total sites: 62, RV sites: 54, Elec sites: 54, Water at site, Vault/pit toilet, Tents: $14/RVs: $18-22, 26 Full hookup, Reservations accepted, Elev: 1047ft/319m, Tel: 319-267-2245, Nearest town: Allison. GPS: 42.749851, -92.783705

60 • B3 | Wunsch Memorial Park

Total sites: 10, RV sites: 10, Elec sites: 10, Central water, Flush toilet, No showers, RV dump, No tents/RVs: $15, Limited services in winter, Open all year, Elev: 961ft/293m, Tel: 319-278-4237, Nearest town: Greene. GPS: 42.892863, -92.801601

61 • B4 | Airport Lake Park

Total sites: 75, RV sites: 70, Elec sites: 70, Central water, Vault/pit toilet, No showers, No RV dump, Tents: $12/RVs: $18, Open Apr-Oct, Reservations accepted, Elev: 1174ft/358m, Tel: 641-394-4714, Nearest town: New Hampton. GPS: 43.089991, -92.347549

62 • B4 | Big Woods Lake

Total sites: 55, RV sites: 55, Elec sites: 55, Water at site, RV dump, Tents: $13/RVs: $18-25, Also cabins, Full hookup sites, Reservations accepted, Elev: 876ft/267m, Tel: 319-433-7275, Nearest town: Cedar Falls. GPS: 42.555720, -92.429160

63 • B4 | Brad Niewoehner Memorial Park

Total sites: 3, RV sites: 3, Water at site, No toilets, No showers, RV dump, Tent & RV camping: $12, Reservations not accepted, Elev: 1098ft/335m, Tel: 563-237-5725, Nearest town: Fredricksburg. GPS: 42.959271, -92.195941

64 • B4 | Cedar View Park

Total sites: 37, RV sites: 37, Central water, Flush toilet, Free showers, No RV dump, Tents: $15/RVs: $20, Reservations not accepted, Elev: 974ft/297m, Tel: 641-435-4156, Nearest town: Nashua. GPS: 42.960203, -92.546943

65 • B4 | Deerwood City Park

Total sites: 118, RV sites: 94, Elec sites: 94, Central water, Flush toilet, Free showers, RV dump, Tents: $12/RVs: $15-19, Some Full hookup, Open May-Sep, Elev: 846ft/258m, Tel: 319-493-0655, Nearest town: Evansdale. GPS: 42.459971, -92.307444

66 • B4 | Elkader City Park

Total sites: 100, RV sites: 100, Elec sites: 60, Water at site, Flush toilet, Free showers, RV dump, Tents: $15/RVs: $25, Open Apr-Oct, Reservations not accepted, Elev: 722ft/220m, Tel: 563-245-2098, Nearest town: Elkader. GPS: 42.852222, -91.398363

67 • B4 | Fort Atkinson City CG

Total sites: 15, RV sites: 6, Elec sites: 6, Central water, Tents: $8/RVs: $12, Reservations not accepted, Elev: 1013ft/309m, Nearest town: Fort Atkinson. GPS: 43.153064, -91.929117

68 • B4 | Gateway City Park

Total sites: 6, RV sites: 6, Elec sites: 6, Central water, Vault/pit toilet, No showers, RV dump, Tent & RV camping: $10, Elev: 1197ft/365m, Tel: 563-539-2355, Nearest town: Monona. GPS: 43.041904, -91.391109

69 • B4 | Independence City RV Park

Total sites: 42, RV sites: 42, Elec sites: 42, Water at site, Flush toilet, Free showers, RV dump, Tents: $7/RVs: $21-23, 42 Full hookup, Open Apr-Oct, Reservations accepted, Elev: 906ft/276m, Tel: 319-440-0472, Nearest town: Independence. GPS: 42.461116, -91.890912

70 • B4 | Klocks Island City Park

Total sites: 20, RV sites: 20, Elec sites: 20, Water at site, Flush toilet, Free showers, RV dump, Tent & RV camping: $10, Dump fee: $2, Generator hours: 0730-2200, Open all year, Reservations not accepted, Elev: 1024ft/312m, Tel: 563-425-4316, Nearest town: Fayette. GPS: 42.844336, -91.816290

71 • B4 | Maynard City Park

Total sites: 21, RV sites: 21, Elec sites: 21, Central water, RV dump, Tent & RV camping: $12, Elev: 1116ft/340m, Tel: 563-637-2269, Nearest town: Maynard. GPS: 42.779813, -91.880542

72 • B4 | New Hampton City CG

Total sites: 7, RV sites: 7, Elec sites: 7, Water at site, Flush toilet, Free showers, RV dump, Tents: $10/RVs: $15, 7 Full hookup, Open Apr-Oct, Reservations not accepted, Elev: 1148ft/350m, Tel: 641-394-2758, Nearest town: New Hampton. GPS: 43.057857, -92.302855

73 • B4 | Oelwein City Park

Total sites: 40, RV sites: 40, Elec sites: 40, Water at site, Flush toilet, Free showers, RV dump, Tents: $8/RVs: $17-20, Seniors: $15-$19, Elev: 994ft/303m, Tel: 319-283-5440, Nearest town: Oelwein. GPS: 42.647146, -91.917802

74 • B4 | Quasqueton Veterans Memorial Park

Total sites: 44, RV sites: 28, Elec sites: 28, Water at site, Flush toilet, Free showers, No RV dump, Tent & RV camping: Fee unk, 16 Full hookup, RV dump nearby, Elev: 909ft/277m, Tel: 319-934-3340, Nearest town: Quasqueton. GPS: 42.393435, -91.766764

75 • B4 | Scout City Park

Total sites: 6, RV sites: 6, Elec sites: 6, No toilets, No showers, Tent & RV camping: $20, Elev: 1040ft/317m, Tel: 563-924-2194 Nearest town: Lamont. GPS: 42.597037, -91.638318

76 • B5 | Finley's Landing City Park

Total sites: 24, RV sites: 19, Elec sites: 19, Central water, Flush toilet, Free showers, RV dump, Tent & RV camping: $23, Limited services in winter, Open all year, Reservations accepted, Elev: 620ft/189m, Tel: 563-552 1571, Nearest town: Dubuque. GPS: 42.653809, -90.806396

77 • B5 | Miller Riverview City Park

Total sites: 97, RV sites: 97, Elec sites: 97, Water at site, Flush toilet, Free showers, RV dump, Tents: $15/RVs: $18, 97 Full hookup, Open Apr-Oct, Reservations accepted, Elev: 594ft/181m, Tel: 563-589-4238, Nearest town: Dubuque. GPS: 42.520684, -90.640362

78 • C1 | Missouri Valley City Park

Total sites: 90, RV sites: 90, Elec sites: 90, Central water, No toilets, No showers, RV dump, Tents: $5/RVs: $15, No open fires, Reservations not accepted, Elev: 997ft/304m, Tel: 712-642-3502, Nearest town: Missouri Valley. GPS: 41.557356, -95.905978

79 • C1 | Pisgah City Park

Total sites: 6, RV sites: 6, Elec sites: 6, Central water, No toilets, No showers, RV dump, Tents: $10/RVs: $20, Open Apr-Dec, Reservations not accepted, Elev: 1063ft/324m, Nearest town: Pisgah. GPS: 41.833187, -95.929984

80 • C2 | Adair City Park

Total sites: 50, RV sites: 50, Elec sites: 10, Flush toilet, Free showers, No RV dump, Tent & RV camping: $15, Reservations not accepted, Elev: 1444ft/440m, Tel: 641-746-3315, Nearest town: Adair. GPS: 41.498842, -94.641638

81 • C2 | Albert the Bull CG

Total sites: 40, RV sites: 40, Elec sites: 40, Central water, Flush toilet, Free showers, RV dump, Tent & RV camping: $15, Several Full hookup sites, Max Length: 48ft, Reservations not accepted, Elev: 1306ft/398m, Tel: 712-563-3856, Nearest town: Audubon. GPS: 41.710572, -94.926363

82 • C2 | Carson City Park

Total sites: 6, RV sites: 6, Elec sites: 6, Central water, Flush toilet, Free showers, RV dump, Tent & RV camping: $5, Open Apr-Oct, Elev: 1073ft/327m, Tel: 712-484-3636, Nearest town: Carson. GPS: 41.236738, -95.423818

83 • C2 | Casey City Park

Total sites: 3, RV sites: 3, Elec sites: 3, Central water, Flush toilet, Free showers, RV dump, Tent & RV camping: $10, Elev: 1289ft/393m, Tel: 641-746-3315, Nearest town: Casey. GPS: 41.509700, -94.517659

84 • C2 | Chautauqua City Park

Total sites: 6, RV sites: 6, Elec sites: 6, No water, Flush toilet, No showers, No RV dump, Tent & RV camping: $7, Open all year, Elev: 1082ft/330m, Tel: 712-482-6811, Nearest town: Oakland. GPS: 41.308486, -95.400068

85 • C2 | Cocklin Fish Farm

Total sites: 68, RV sites: 68, Elec sites: 55, Central water, Vault/pit toilet, No showers, RV dump, Tents: $10/RVs: $12, Open Apr-Oct, Elev: 1102ft/336m, Tel: 712-778-2615, Nearest town: Griswold. GPS: 41.254688, -95.135621

86 • C2 | Menlo City Park

Total sites: 7, RV sites: 7, Elec sites: 7, Central water, Flush toilet, No showers, No RV dump, Tent & RV camping: $5, Elev: 1247ft/380m, Tel: 641-524-2411, Nearest town: Menlo. GPS: 41.521664, -94.404468

87 • C2 | Schildberg RA

Total sites: 20, RV sites: 20, Elec sites: 20, Water at site, Flush toilet, Free showers, RV dump, Tent & RV camping: Fee unk, 20 Full hookup, Elev: 1150ft/351m, Nearest town: Atlantic. GPS: 41.414389, -95.014009

88 • C2 | Willow Creek City Park

Total sites: 6, RV sites: 6, Elec sites: 6, Water at site, No toilets, No showers, Tents: $10/RVs: $18, 6 Full hookup, Elev: 1316ft/401m, Tel: 712-655-3131, Nearest town: Manning. GPS: 41.906023, -95.052558

89 • C3 | Ashton Wildwood Park

Total sites: 5, RV sites: 5, No water, Vault/pit toilet, Tent & RV camping: Fee unk, Astronomy observatory, Open May-Sep, Reservations not accepted, Elev: 955ft/291m, Tel: 641-792-9780, Nearest town: Baxter. GPS: 41.813897, -93.289283

90 • C3 | Island Park City Park

Total sites: 42, RV sites: 32, Elec sites: 32, Water at site, Flush toilet, Free showers, RV dump, Tents: $17/RVs: $20-25, Open Apr-Oct, Reservations not accepted, Elev: 961ft/293m, Tel: 515-993-4525, Nearest town: Adel. GPS: 41.621121, -94.013581

91 • C3 | Pattee City Park

Total sites: 4, RV sites: 4, Elec sites: 4, Central water, Flush toilet, No showers, RV dump, Tent & RV camping: $10, Stay limit: 5 days, Reservations not accepted, Elev: 935ft/285m, Tel: 515-465-4636, Nearest town: Perry. GPS: 41.834862, -94.110348

92 • C3 | Riverview Park

Total sites: 30, RV sites: 30, Elec sites: 30, Water at site, Flush toilet, Free showers, RV dump, Tents: $15/RVs: $20-25, 10 Full hookup, Open Apr-Oct, Reservations not accepted, Elev: 869ft/265m, Tel: 641-754-5715, Nearest town: Marshalltown. GPS: 42.064586, -92.906728

93 • C3 | Winterset City Park

Total sites: 46, RV sites: 34, Elec sites: 34, Central water, Flush toilet, Free showers, RV dump, Tents: $15/RVs: $22, 34 Full hookup, Open Apr-Oct, Reservations accepted, Elev: 1129ft/344m, Tel: 515-462-3258, Nearest town: Winterset. GPS: 41.332335, -94.002331

94 • C4 | Kalona City CG

Total sites: 38, RV sites: 38, Elec sites: 38, Water at site, Flush toilet, Free showers, Tent & RV camping: $20, Open Apr-Oct, Reservations not accepted, Elev: 656ft/200m, Tel: 319-656-2310, Nearest town: Kalona. GPS: 41.482712, -91.697997

95 • C4 | Middle Amana City Park

Total sites: 24, RV sites: 24, Elec sites: 24, Central water, No RV dump, Tent & RV camping: $20, Reservations not accepted, Elev: 745ft/227m, Nearest town: Middle Amana. GPS: 41.799029, -91.899946

96 • C5 | Deep Creek CG

Total sites: 15, RV sites: 15, Elec sites: 8, Water at site, Flush toilet, Free showers, RV dump, Tent & RV camping: $19, 8 Full hookup, Open all year, Reservations not accepted, Elev: 676ft/206m,

Tel: 563-677-2710, Nearest town: Charlotte. GPS: 41.960481, -90.470232

97 • C5 | Horseshoe Pond

Total sites: 22, RV sites: 22, Elec sites: 22, Central water, Flush toilet, Free showers, RV dump, Tent & RV camping: $17, Stay limit: 14 days, Open Apr-Oct, Max Length: 50ft, Reservations not accepted, Elev: 696ft/212m, Tel: 563-652-2484, Nearest town: Maquoketa. GPS: 42.054739, -90.663912

98 • C5 | McCreight City Park

Total sites: 3, RV sites: 3, Elec sites: 3, No toilets, No showers, No RV dump, No tents/RVs: Free, Open all year, Elev: 748ft/228m, Nearest town: Oxford Junction. GPS: 41.983918, -90.956205

99 • C5 | North End City Park

Total sites: 10, RV sites: 5, Elec sites: 5, No RV dump, Tent & RV camping: $10, Open Apr-Oct, Reservations not accepted, Elev: 581ft/177m, Tel: 319-523-4091, Nearest town: Wapello. GPS: 41.187392, -91.191283

100 • C5 | Riverview City Park

Total sites: 30, RV sites: 30, Elec sites: 30, Water at site, Flush toilet, Free showers, RV dump, Tent & RV camping: $22, 2 Full hookup, No water Oct-Apr: $15, Near RR, Open all year, Reservations not accepted, Elev: 591ft/180m, Tel: 563-243-1260, Nearest town: Clinton. GPS: 41.851835, -90.184756

101 • D1 | Boehner Pond

Total sites: 10, RV sites: 6, Elec sites: 6, Water at site, Flush toilet, Tents: $5/RVs: $15, Open Mar-Oct, Reservations not accepted, Elev: 997ft/304m, Nearest town: Malvern. GPS: 41.004296, -95.592422

102 • D1 | Glenwood Lake City Park

Total sites: 20, RV sites: 20, Elec sites: 20, Water at site, Flush toilet, Free showers, RV dump, Tents: $7/RVs: $17-25, 12 Full hookup, Open Apr-Oct, Reservations not accepted, Elev: 984ft/300m, Tel: 712-520-7275, Nearest town: Glenwood. GPS: 41.044991, -95.737217

103 • D2 | Imogene TH

Total sites: 6, RV sites: 2, Elec sites: 2, Central water, Flush toilet, Free showers, Tent & RV camping: Free, Reservations not accepted, Elev: 1050ft/320m, Tel: 515-210-0269, Nearest town: Imogene. GPS: 40.879578, -95.429381

104 • D2 | Manti City Park

Dispersed sites, Central water, Vault/pit toilet, No showers, No RV dump, Tents only: Free, Walk-to sites, Unconfirmed, Elev: 981ft/299m, Tel: 712-246-1213, Nearest town: Shenandoah. GPS: 40.728242, -95.404117

105 • D2 | Marlin E. Fogle RA

Total sites: 45, RV sites: 45, Elec sites: 45, Central water, Flush toilet, Free showers, RV dump, Tent & RV camping: Fee unk, Also cabins, Open all year, Elev: 1174ft/358m, Tel: 641-734-5491, Nearest town: Diagonal. GPS: 40.818276, -94.348717

106 • D2 | McKinley City Park

Total sites: 38, RV sites: 38, Elec sites: 38, Water at site, RV dump, Tents: $8-10/RVs: $12-14, Stay limit: 14 days, Reservations not accepted, Elev: 1280ft/390m, Tel: 641-782-2000 x2, Nearest town: Creston. GPS: 41.049462, -94.385645

107 • D2 | Montgomery County Fairgrounds

Total sites: 18, RV sites: 18, Elec sites: 18, Central water, No toilets, No showers, RV dump, Tent & RV camping: $15, Elev: 1030ft/314m, Tel: 712-623-6514, Nearest town: Red Oak. GPS: 41.023061, -95.228267

108 • D2 | Three Lakes CG

Total sites: 9, RV sites: 9, Elec sites: 9, Water at site, Tent & RV camping: $15, 3 Full hookup, Stay limit: 14 days, Reservations not accepted, Elev: 1257ft/383m, Nearest town: Lenox. GPS: 40.896354, -94.552188

109 • D2 | Wabash Trace Park

Total sites: 10, RV sites: 5, Elec sites: 5, Central water, Flush toilet, Free showers, No RV dump, Tent & RV camping: $10, Plus $2/person, Elev: 991ft/302m, Tel: 712-583-3523, Nearest town: Coin. GPS: 40.658471, -95.230293

110 • D3 | Bobwhite CP

Total sites: 32, RV sites: 32, Elec sites: 19, Central water, Flush toilet, Free showers, No RV dump, Tent & RV camping: $15, Open Apr-Nov, Reservations not accepted, Elev: 1086ft/331m, Tel: 641-873-4670, Nearest town: Allerton. GPS: 40.710125, -93.393996

111 • D3 | Cinder Path RV Park

Total sites: 13, RV sites: 13, Elec sites: 13, Water at site, Flush toilet, Free showers, RV dump, Tent & RV camping: Fee unk, 13 Full hookup, Elev: 1096ft/334m, Tel: 641-877-6841, Nearest town: Humeston. GPS: 40.863274, -93.498781

112 • D3 | Lelah Bradley City Park

Total sites: 15, RV sites: 15, Elec sites: 12, Central water, No toilets, No showers, No RV dump, Tent & RV camping: Fee unk, Open May-Oct, Elev: 984ft/300m, Tel: 641-856-8528, Nearest town: Centerville. GPS: 40.715021, -92.886076

113 • D4 | Drakesville City Park

Total sites: 6, RV sites: 6, Elec sites: 6, No toilets, No showers, No RV dump, Tent & RV camping: Fee unk, Reservations not accepted, Elev: 888ft/271m, Tel: 641-722-3859, Nearest town: Drakesville. GPS: 40.800591, -92.480208

114 • D4 | Hubinger Landing Park

Total sites: 8, RV sites: 8, Elec sites: 8, Water at site, No toilets, No showers, RV dump, No tents/RVs: $16, $2 senior discount, Pay at Southside Boat Club, Near RR, Reservations not accepted, Elev: 500ft/152m, Tel: 319-524-2050, Nearest town: Keokuk. GPS: 40.389295, -91.382582

115 • D4 | Indian Lake City Park

Total sites: 40, RV sites: 32, Elec sites: 32, Water at site, Flush toilet, Free showers, RV dump, Tents: $8/RVs: $10-18, Also cabins, 1[illegible] Full hookup, Open all year, Reservations not accepted, Elev

594ft/181m, Tel: 319-878-3706, Nearest town: Farmington. GPS: 40.632610, -91.751880

116 • D4 | Lake Fisher City CG

Total sites: 10, RV sites: 6, Elec sites: 6, Central water, Tents: $5/RVs: $10, Stay limit: 10 days, Generator hours: 0800-2200, Reservations not accepted, Elev: 830ft/253m, Tel: 641-664-2260, x23, Nearest town: Bloomfield. GPS: 40.759426, -92.446027

117 • D4 | Ottumwa City Park

Total sites: 100, RV sites: 83, Elec sites: 83, Water at site, Flush toilet, Free showers, RV dump, Tents: $15/RVs: $18, RVs should use north entrance to access, No tents in RV section, Open Apr-Oct, Reservations not accepted, Elev: 641ft/195m, Tel: 641-682-1307, Nearest town: Ottumwa. GPS: 41.015627, -92.426799

118 • D4 | Victory Park

Total sites: 5, RV sites: 5, Elec sites: 5, Water at site, No toilets, No showers, RV dump, No tents/RVs: $16, 5 Full hookup, Near RR, Reservations accepted, Elev: 499ft/152m, Tel: 319-524-3553, Nearest town: Keokuk. GPS: 40.390622, -91.379515

119 • D4 | Waubonsie Trail Park

Total sites: 16, RV sites: 12, Elec sites: 12, Water at site, No toilets, No showers, RV dump, Tents: $10/RVs: $18, 11 Full hookup, Reservations accepted, Elev: 764ft/233m, Tel: 319-397-2193, Nearest town: Cantril. GPS: 40.645903, -92.075616

120 • D5 | Fort Madison City CG

Total sites: 20, RV sites: 20, Elec sites: 20, No water, Vault/pit toilet, No showers, No RV dump, Tents: $8/RVs: $15, Max Length: 48ft, Reservations not accepted, Elev: 698ft/213m, Tel: 319-372-7700, Nearest town: Fort Madison. GPS: 40.647056, -91.319422

Kansas

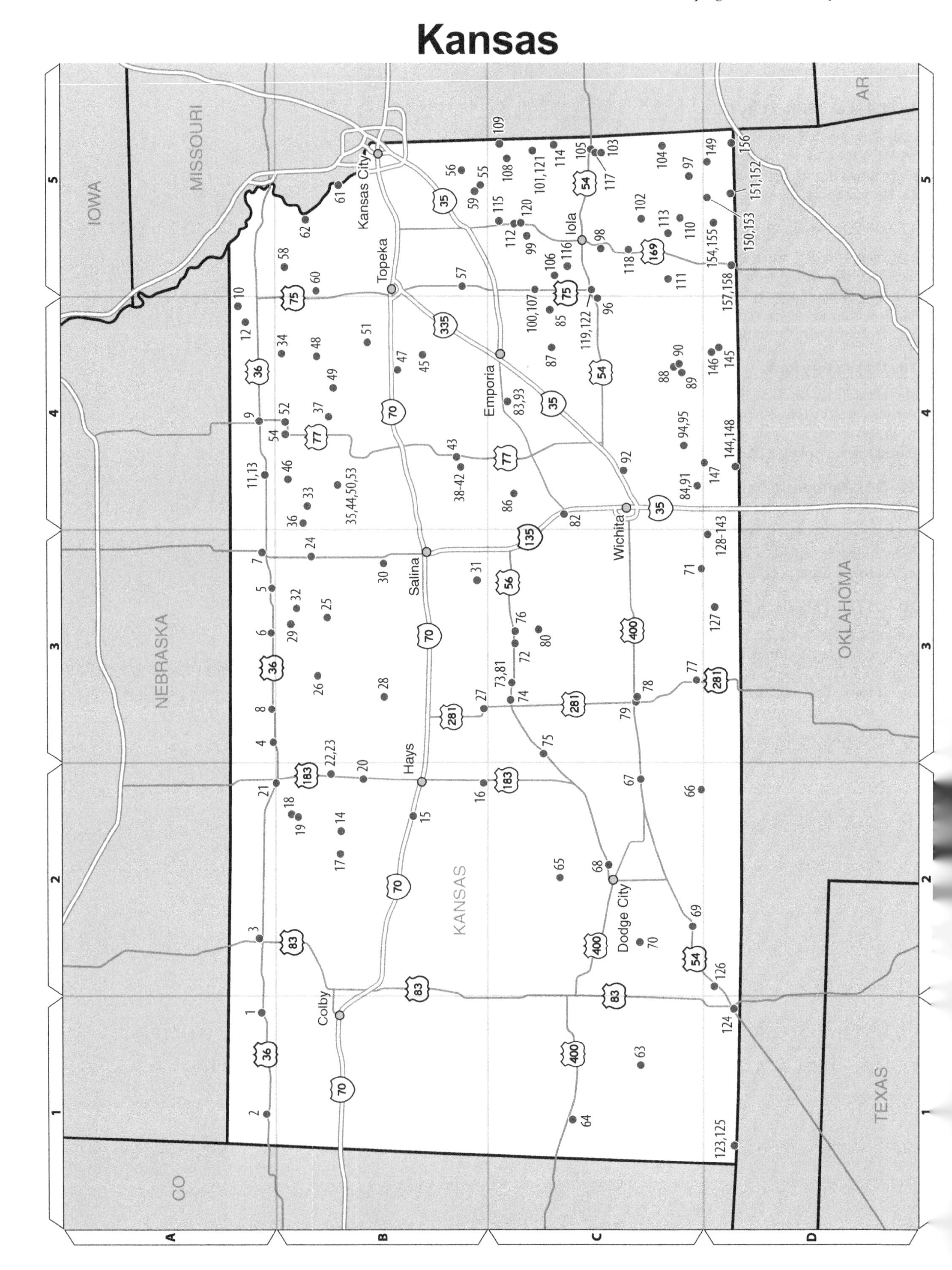
IOWA
MISSOURI
NEBRASKA
KANSAS
OKLAHOMA
TEXAS
CO
AR
Kansas City
Topeka
Emporia
Iola
Wichita
Salina
Hays
Dodge City
Colby

Map	ID	Map	ID
A1	1-2	C2	65-70
A2	3	C3	71-81
A3	4-8	C4	82-96
A4	9-13	C5	97-122
B2	14-23	D1	123-125
B3	24-32	D2	126
B4	33-54	D3	127-143
B5	55-62	D4	144-148
C1	63-64	D5	149-158

Alphabetical List of Camping Areas

Name	ID	Map
Airport Park - City	24	B3
Anthony City Lake	127	D3
Argonia River City Park	71	C3
Arkalon City Park	126	D2
Athletic Park - City	82	C4
Atwood Lions Club Park	1	A1
Bates Grove City Park	83	C4
Berner Memorial CG	33	B4
Big Brutus Museum	97	C5
Bogue Roadside Park	14	B2
Buckner Valley Park	65	C2
Camp Hunter City Park	98	C5
Cave Park	84	C4
Cedar Valley Reservoir	99	C5
Centralia City Lake	34	B4
Chase Roadside Park	72	C3
Chautauqua Park - City	25	B3
Clay County Fairgrounds	35	B4
Clyde City Park	36	B4
Coldwater Lake	66	C2
Columbus VFW City Park	149	D5
Danny Elliott City Park	150	D5
Davis City Park	67	C2
Dodge City Roadside Park	68	C2
Downs City Park	26	B3
Drake City Park	100	C5
East City Lake	101	C5
East River Park	151	D5
Elkhart City CG	123	D1
Ellinwood City Park	73	C3
Ellis Lakeside City CG	15	B2
Elmore Park	152	D5
Erie City Park CG	102	C5
Fort Scott Lake	103	C5
Fort Zarah Roadside Park	74	C3
Four Oaks City RV Park	104	C5
Frazier Park	63	C1
Grass Park	16	B2
Greenwood City Park	37	B4
Gridley City Lake	85	C4
Gunn Park	105	C5
Herington City Lakes - 400 Ave	38	B4
Herington City Lakes - Kandt's Point	39	B4
Herington City Lakes - Schmidt Point	40	B4
Herington City Lakes - Sun Lane	41	B4
Herington City Lakes - Ziebell Cove	42	B4
Herington RV Park	43	B4
Hill City Roadside Park	17	B2
Hillsboro Memorial Park	86	C4
Hoisington City Park	27	B3
Holiday Park - City	106	C5
Huntress City Park	44	B4
John Brown Memorial Park	55	B5
Kamp Siesta at Riverside Park	153	D5
Kelley City Park	107	C5
Kensington City Park	4	A3
La Cygne Community Park	108	C5
Lake Miola City Park	56	B5
Lake Wabaunsee	45	B4
Larned City Park	75	C3
Larsen City Park	5	A3
Linn City Park	46	B4
Linn CP	109	C5
Logan City Park	18	B2
Logan Lake Park	19	B2
Louie P. Gartner RA - North	154	D5
Louie P. Gartner RA - South	155	D5
Luray City Park	28	B3
Lyndon City Park	57	B5
Lyons City CG	76	C3
MAAG Memorial Park	29	B3
Madison City Lake	87	C4
Main St RV Park	20	B2
Mankato City Park	6	A3
Markley Grove City Park	30	B3
Marquette City Park	31	B3
Marvel City Park	110	C5
Mary Frame City Park	124	D1
Marysville City Park	9	A4
McKnight City Park	47	B4
Meade City Park	69	C2
Medicine Lodge City Park	77	C3
Mission Lake CG	58	B5
Moline City Lake (New - North)	88	C4
Moline City Lake (Old-South) - KDPW	89	C4
Moline City Park	90	C4
Napawalla Park - City	91	C4
Neodesha RV Park	111	C5
Newman City Park	144	D4
North Lake City Park	112	C5
Onaga City Park	48	B4
Oregon Trail RV Park	49	B4
Osawatomie City Lake	59	B5
Otto Unruh Stadium	50	B4
Parsons City Lake	113	C5
Phillipsburg City CG	21	B2
Pony Creek Lake	10	A4
Prairie Lake	60	B5
Prairie RV Park	125	D1
Prairie Wind City RV Park	70	C2
Pratt County Veterans Memorial Lake	78	C3
Prescott City Lake	114	C5
Randall City Park	32	B3
Richmond City Lake	115	C5
Riverfront City Park	61	B5

1 • A1 | Atwood Lions Club Park

Total sites: 9, RV sites: 9, Elec sites: 9, Central water, Flush toilet, Free showers, RV dump, Tent & RV camping: $25, Open all year, Reservations not accepted, Elev: 2877ft/877m, Tel: 785-626-3428, Nearest town: Atwood. GPS: 39.818291, -101.041888

2 • A1 | St Francis City CG

Total sites: 15, RV sites: 15, Elec sites: 10, Central water, Flush toilet, Free showers, RV dump, Tents: Free/RVs: $25, RVs can dry-camp for free, Stay limit: 3 days, Generator hours: 0700-2300, Reservations not accepted, Elev: 3373ft/1028m, Tel: 785-332-2961, Nearest town: St Francis. GPS: 39.765582, -101.801965

3 • A2 | Sappa City Park

Total sites: 14, RV sites: 14, Elec sites: 14, No water, Vault/pit toilet, Tent & RV camping: Free, Elev: 2543ft/775m, Tel: 785-475-3441, Nearest town: Oberlin. GPS: 39.839189, -100.495291

4 • A3 | Kensington City Park

Dispersed sites, No toilets, No tents/RVs: Fee unk, Unconfirmed, Elev: 1778ft/542m, Nearest town: Kensington. GPS: 39.770839, -99.028490

5 • A3 | Larsen City Park

Total sites: 2, RV sites: 2, Elec sites: 2, Water at site, No toilets, No showers, No RV dump, No tents/RVs: Free, 20-amp only, Near RR, Elev: 1501ft/458m, Nearest town: Courtland. GPS: 39.781087, -97.892733

6 • A3 | Mankato City Park

Total sites: 3, RV sites: 3, No water, No toilets, No showers, No RV dump, Tent & RV camping: Free, A place to park for a night or two, Reservations not accepted, Elev: 1754ft/535m, Nearest town: Mankato. GPS: 39.787445, -98.216705

7 • A3 | Rocky Pond Park

Total sites: 10, RV sites: 7, Elec sites: 7, Central water, Flush toilet, Free showers, RV dump, Tents: Free/RVs: $20, Reservations not accepted, Elev: 1509ft/460m, Tel: 785-527-2288, Nearest town: Belleville. GPS: 39.828598, -97.621643

8 • A3 | Smith Center Roadside Area

Total sites: 4, RV sites: 4, No water, No toilets, No tents/RVs: Free, Elev: 1798ft/548m, Nearest town: Smith Center. GPS: 39.784914, -98.793992

9 • A4 | Marysville City Park

Total sites: 4, RV sites: 4, Elec sites: 4, Central water, RV dump, Tent & RV camping: Free, Stay limit: 5 days, Reservations not accepted, Elev: 1152ft/351m, Tel: 785-562-3101, Nearest town: Marysville. GPS: 39.837635, -96.646193

10 • A4 | Pony Creek Lake

Dispersed sites, Central water, Vault/pit toilet, Tents: $5/RVs: $12 Reservations not accepted, Elev: 1165ft/355m, Tel: 785-284-2158 Nearest town: Sabetha. GPS: 39.947642, -95.782423

11 • A4 | Rotary Park

Dispersed sites, No water, No toilets, Tent & RV camping: Free Elev: 1289ft/393m, Nearest town: Washington. GPS: 39.813775 -97.036765

12 • A4 | Sabetha Lake

Total sites: 10, RV sites: 8, Elec sites: 8, Vault/pit toilet, Tents: $5

RVs: $12, Elev: 1220ft/372m, Tel: 785-284-2158, Nearest town: Sabetha. GPS: 39.908997, -95.902772

13 • A4 | Washington City Park

Total sites: 20, RV sites: 20, Elec sites: 20, Water at site, Flush toilet, Free showers, RV dump, Tent & RV camping: $15, Elev: 1300ft/396m, Tel: 785-325-2284, Nearest town: Washington. GPS: 39.808483, -97.054085

14 • B2 | Bogue Roadside Park

Total sites: 2, RV sites: 2, Elec sites: 2, Vault/pit toilet, No tents/RVs: Free, Reservations not accepted, Elev: 2039ft/621m, Nearest town: Bogue. GPS: 39.362725, -99.686056

15 • B2 | Ellis Lakeside City CG

Total sites: 17, RV sites: 17, Elec sites: 17, Water at site, Flush toilet, Free showers, RV dump, Tents: $15/RVs: $20, $5 off mid-Nov to mid-Apr - no water, Open all year, Reservations not accepted, Elev: 2159ft/658m, Tel: 785-726-4812, Nearest town: Ellis. GPS: 38.940186, -99.557861

16 • B2 | Grass Park

Total sites: 4, RV sites: 4, Elec sites: 4, Central water, Flush toilet, No showers, RV dump, Tent & RV camping: Fee unk, Reservations not accepted, Elev: 2077ft/633m, Tel: 785-222-2511, Nearest town: Lacrosse. GPS: 38.524794, -99.310812

17 • B2 | Hill City Roadside Park

Dispersed sites, Tent & RV camping: Free, Elev: 2238ft/682m, Tel: 785-421-5621, Nearest town: Hill City. GPS: 39.364527, -99.856727

18 • B2 | Logan City Park

Total sites: 4, RV sites: 4, Elec sites: 4, Central water, Flush toilet, No tents/RVs: Fee unk, Reservations not accepted, Elev: 2001ft/610m, Nearest town: Logan. GPS: 39.664653, -99.573332

19 • B2 | Logan Lake Park

Dispersed sites, Vault/pit toilet, No showers, Tents: Free/RVs: $10, Elev: 2070ft/631m, Tel: 785-689-4865, Nearest town: Logan. GPS: 39.627467, -99.582102

20 • B2 | Main St RV Park

Total sites: 11, RV sites: 11, Elec sites: 11, Water at site, Flush toilet, RV dump, No tents/RVs: $23, Elev: 2152ft/656m, Tel: 785-434-4886, Nearest town: Plainville. GPS: 39.236158, -99.301357

21 • B2 | Phillipsburg City CG

Total sites: 10, RV sites: 10, Elec sites: 10, Water at site, Flush toilet, Free showers, RV dump, Tent & RV camping: $10, Open Apr-Oct, Reservations not accepted, Elev: 1903ft/580m, Tel: 785-543-5234, Nearest town: Phillipsburg. GPS: 39.754772, -99.335809

22 • B2 | Rooks County Fairgrounds

Total sites: 30, RV sites: 30, Elec sites: 30, Central water, Flush toilet, Free showers, No tents/RVs: $20, Elev: 1779ft/542m, Tel: 785-425-6703, Nearest town: Stockton. GPS: 39.427729, -99.272944

23 • B2 | Stockton City Park

Total sites: 7, RV sites: 7, Elec sites: 7, Water at site, Flush toilet, Free showers, RV dump, Tent & RV camping: $10, Reservations not accepted, Elev: 1775ft/541m, Tel: 785-425-6703, Nearest town: Stockton. GPS: 39.436046, -99.280964

24 • B3 | Airport Park - City

Total sites: 16, RV sites: 16, Elec sites: 12, Water at site, No toilets, No showers, RV dump, Tent & RV camping: Donation, Stay limit: 7 days, Open all year, Reservations not accepted, Elev: 1446ft/441m, Tel: 785-243-2670, Nearest town: Concordia. GPS: 39.548179, -97.655736

25 • B3 | Chautauqua Park - City

Total sites: 30, RV sites: 30, Elec sites: 30, Water at site, RV dump, Tent & RV camping: Donation, Stay limit: 10 days, Reservations not accepted, Elev: 1384ft/422m, Tel: 785-738-2270, Nearest town: Beloit. GPS: 39.455071, -98.113568

26 • B3 | Downs City Park

Total sites: 4, RV sites: 4, Elec sites: 4, Flush toilet, No tents/RVs: Free, Stay limit: 3 days, Reservations not accepted, Elev: 1492ft/455m, Nearest town: Downs. GPS: 39.509087, -98.541125

27 • B3 | Hoisington City Park

Total sites: 12, RV sites: 12, Elec sites: 12, Water at site, Flush toilet, Free showers, RV dump, Tent & RV camping: $15, Elev: 1880ft/573m, Tel: 620-653-4134, Nearest town: Hoisington. GPS: 38.524046, -98.772751

28 • B3 | Luray City Park

Total sites: 4, RV sites: 4, Elec sites: 4, Central water, Tent & RV camping: $10, Elev: 1598ft/487m, Tel: 785-698-2264, Nearest town: Luray. GPS: 39.118574, -98.691858

29 • B3 | MAAG Memorial Park

Total sites: 5, RV sites: 5, Elec sites: 3, Central water, Flush toilet, Free showers, RV dump, No tents/RVs: Free, $10 for electric, Max Length: 27ft, Elev: 1572ft/479m, Nearest town: Jewell. GPS: 39.670006, -98.155262

30 • B3 | Markley Grove City Park

Total sites: 8, RV sites: 4, Elec sites: 4, Water available, Flush toilet, Free showers, RV dump, Tent & RV camping: $10, Elev: 1257ft/383m, Tel: 785-392-2176, Nearest town: Minneapolis. GPS: 39.118765, -97.710761

31 • B3 | Marquette City Park

Dispersed sites, Central water, Flush toilet, Free showers, No RV dump, Tents only: Free, For bicyclists, Elev: 1414ft/431m, Tel: 785-546-2205, Nearest town: Marquette. GPS: 38.556047, -97.834195

32 • B3 | Randall City Park

Total sites: 2, RV sites: 2, Elec sites: 2, Vault/pit toilet, No showers, No RV dump, No tents/RVs: Free, Unconfirmed, Elec may not work, Elev: 1450ft/442m, Nearest town: Randall. GPS: 39.639629, -98.043971

33 • B4 | Berner Memorial CG

Total sites: 2, RV sites: 2, Elec sites: 2, Flush toilet, Free showers, RV dump, Tent & RV camping: $10-12, Elev: 1280ft/390m, Tel: 785-455-3711, Nearest town: Clifton. GPS: 39.567395, -97.287570

34 • B4 | Centralia City Lake

Total sites: 30, RV sites: 30, Elec sites: 20, Central water, Vault/pit toilet, Tents: $1/RVs: $5-8, 10% senior discount, Elev: 1276ft/389m, Tel: 785-857-3764, Nearest town: Centralia. GPS: 39.703296, -96.151865

35 • B4 | Clay County Fairgrounds

Total sites: 4, RV sites: 4, Elec sites: 4, Water at site, RV dump, No tents/RVs: $20-25, Elev: 1201ft/366m, Tel: 785-632-3797, Nearest town: Clay Center. GPS: 39.368402, -97.113653

36 • B4 | Clyde City Park

Total sites: 2, RV sites: 2, Elec sites: 6, Central water, No toilets, No showers, No RV dump, Tent & RV camping: Free, Showers/toilets at nearby pool, Open all year, Elev: 1302ft/397m, Nearest town: Clyde. GPS: 39.595075, -97.404719

37 • B4 | Greenwood City Park

Total sites: 5, RV sites: 5, Elec sites: 5, Central water, Flush toilet, Free showers, RV dump, Tent & RV camping: $15, Reservations not accepted, Elev: 1398ft/426m, Tel: 785-468-3209, Nearest town: Olsburg. GPS: 39.429013, -96.622132

38 • B4 | Herington City Lakes - 400 Ave

Dispersed sites, No water, No toilets, Tent & RV camping: $8, Elev: 1328ft/405m, Tel: 785-258-2271, Nearest town: Herington. GPS: 38.652923, -96.990237

39 • B4 | Herington City Lakes - Kandt's Point

Total sites: 4, RV sites: 4, No toilets, Tent & RV camping: $8, Elev: 1371ft/418m, Tel: 785-258-2271, Nearest town: Herington. GPS: 38.647533, -97.010783

40 • B4 | Herington City Lakes - Schmidt Point

Total sites: 10, RV sites: 10, Vault/pit toilet, Tents: $8/RVs: $8-18, Elev: 1366ft/416m, Tel: 785-258-2271, Nearest town: Herington. GPS: 38.651153, -97.006025

41 • B4 | Herington City Lakes - Sun Lane

Total sites: 50, RV sites: 50, Vault/pit toilet, Tent & RV camping: $8, Elev: 1345ft/410m, Tel: 785-258-2271, Nearest town: Herington. GPS: 38.665147, -96.987638

42 • B4 | Herington City Lakes - Ziebell Cove

Total sites: 10, RV sites: 10, No toilets, Tent & RV camping: $8, Elev: 1355ft/413m, Tel: 785-258-2271, Nearest town: Herington. GPS: 38.657379, -97.005035

43 • B4 | Herington RV Park

Total sites: 16, RV sites: 16, Elec sites: 16, Water at site, RV dump, Tent & RV camping: $12, 8 Full hookup, Open all year, Elev: 1335ft/407m, Tel: 785-258-5987, Nearest town: Herington. GPS: 38.669491, -96.947218

44 • B4 | Huntress City Park

Total sites: 6, RV sites: 6, Elec sites: 6, Water at site, Flush toilet, No showers, No RV dump, No tents/RVs: Donation, 3-day limit, Reservations not accepted, Elev: 1200ft/366m, Tel: 785-632-3797, Nearest town: Clay Center. GPS: 39.379771, -97.137135

45 • B4 | Lake Wabaunsee

Total sites: 20, RV sites: 10, Elec sites: 5, Central water, RV dump, Tents: $6/RVs: $10-15, Elev: 1326ft/404m, Tel: 785-449-2507, Nearest town: Alma. GPS: 38.864949, -96.186582

46 • B4 | Linn City Park

Dispersed sites, Central water, Flush toilet, Free showers, No RV dump, Tent & RV camping: Free, Elev: 1444ft/440m, Tel: 785-348-5839, Nearest town: Linn. GPS: 39.683032, -97.081871

47 • B4 | McKnight City Park

Total sites: 3, RV sites: 3, Elec sites: 3, Water at site, Flush toilet, No showers, No RV dump, Tent & RV camping: Donation, Near RR, Reservations not accepted, Elev: 1060ft/323m, Tel: 785-765-3922, Nearest town: Alma. GPS: 39.009628, -96.285862

48 • B4 | Onaga City Park

Dispersed sites, Central water, Tents only: $8, Showers at pool, Elev: 1166ft/355m, Tel: 785-889-4456, Nearest town: Onaga. GPS: 39.496726, -96.168578

49 • B4 | Oregon Trail RV Park

Total sites: 16, RV sites: 16, Elec sites: 16, Central water, Flush toilet, Free showers, RV dump, Tents: $25/RVs: $25-35, 12 Full hookup, Reservations accepted, Elev: 1201ft/366m, Tel: 785-457-3361, Nearest town: Westmoreland. GPS: 39.397199, -96.408055

50 • B4 | Otto Unruh Stadium

Total sites: 2, RV sites: 2, Elec sites: 2, Central water, No toilets, No showers, No RV dump, No tents/RVs: Donation, 3-day limit, Elev: 1211ft/369m, Tel: 785-632-3797, Nearest town: Clay Center. GPS: 39.379545, -97.140716

51 • B4 | Riverside Park

Total sites: 3, RV sites: 3, Elec sites: 3, Water at site, No toilets, No showers, No RV dump, Tent & RV camping: $10, Refundable $25 electric box key fee, Dump at sewer station weekdays, Elev: 951ft/290m, Tel: 785-437-2311, Nearest town: St. Marys. GPS: 39.190027, -96.073193

52 • B4 | Riverside Park

Total sites: 6, RV sites: 6, Elec sites: 6, Central water, Flush toilet, Free showers, RV dump, Tent & RV camping: $10, Reservations not accepted, Elev: 1125ft/343m, Tel: 785-363-7991, Nearest town: Blue Rapids. GPS: 39.683465, -96.666485

53 • B4 | Water Tower Park

Total sites: 6, RV sites: 6, Elec sites: 6, Water at site, No toilets, No showers, RV dump, No tents/RVs: $12, 3-day limit, Elev: 1283ft/391m, Tel: 785-632-3797, Nearest town: Clay Center. GPS: 39.380523, -97.113887

54 • B4 | Waterville City CG

Total sites: 6, RV sites: 6, Elec sites: 6, Water at site, RV dump, Tent & RV camping: $10, Elev: 1168ft/356m, Tel: 785-363-2367, Nearest town: Waterville. GPS: 39.693173, -96.743685

55 • B5 | John Brown Memorial Park

Total sites: 35, RV sites: 35, Elec sites: 10, Central water, Flush toilet, No showers, RV dump, Tent & RV camping: Fee unk, Elev: 855ft/261m, Tel: 913-755-4460, Nearest town: Osawatomie. GPS: 38.499987, -94.958294

56 • B5 | Lake Miola City Park

Total sites: 24, RV sites: 24, Elec sites: 24, Central water, Flush toilet, Free showers, RV dump, Tents: $12/RVs: $17-19, Discount for local residents, Open Apr-Oct, Elev: 951ft/290m, Tel: 913-259-3665, Nearest town: Paola. GPS: 38.595534, -94.846063

57 • B5 | Lyndon City Park

Total sites: 3, RV sites: 3, Central water, No toilets, No showers, No RV dump, Tent & RV camping: Free, Open all year, Elev: 1064ft/324m, Tel: 785-828-3146, Nearest town: Lyndon. GPS: 38.614212, -95.685251

58 • B5 | Mission Lake CG

Total sites: 100, RV sites: 100, Elec sites: 100, Central water, Flush toilet, Free showers, RV dump, Tent & RV camping: $17, Open Apr-Oct, Reservations not accepted, Elev: 1050ft/320m, Tel: 785-486-2324, Nearest town: Horton. GPS: 39.671651, -95.513982

59 • B5 | Osawatomie City Lake

Total sites: 6, RV sites: 6, Elec sites: 6, No toilets, No showers, No RV dump, Tent & RV camping: $10, Elev: 896ft/273m, Tel: 913-755-4769, Nearest town: Osawatomie. GPS: 38.527661, -94.994427

60 • B5 | Prairie Lake

Total sites: 17, RV sites: 17, Elec sites: 11, Central water, Vault/pit toilet, Tents: $8/RVs: $8-10, Open Mar-Oct, Reservations not accepted, Elev: 1057ft/322m, Tel: 785-364-2721, Nearest town: Holton. GPS: 39.487929, -95.690903

61 • B5 | Riverfront City Park

Total sites: 20, RV sites: 13, Elec sites: 13, Central water, Flush toilet, Free showers, RV dump, Tent & RV camping: $15, Beware of RR crossing with longer trailers, $2(tent)-$3(RV) restroom key fee/night, $2 pet fee, Beside RR tracks, Stay limit: 7 days, Generator hours: 0700-2200, Open Apr-Oct, Reservations accepted, Elev: 794ft/242m, Tel: 913-290-0034, Nearest town: Leavenworth. GPS: 39.331520, -94.910540

62 • B5 | Warnock Park

Total sites: 16, RV sites: 16, Elec sites: 16, Central water, Flush toilet, Free showers, No RV dump, Tents: $5/RVs: $10, Elev: 938ft/286m, Tel: 913-367-5561, Nearest town: Atchison. GPS: 39.535019, -95.152001

63 • C1 | Frazier Park

Total sites: 9, RV sites: 9, Elec sites: 9, Water at site, Flush toilet, RV dump, Tent & RV camping: $15, 6 Full hookup, No open fires, Max Length: 40ft, Reservations accepted, Elev: 2995ft/913m, Tel: 620-356-3097, Nearest town: Ulysses. GPS: 37.564345, -101.336802

64 • C1 | Syracuse Sand Dunes

Total sites: 6, RV sites: 6, Elec sites: 6, Central water, Flush toilet, Free showers, Tents: $5/RVs: $15, Open all year, Reservations not accepted, Elev: 3235ft/986m, Tel: 620-384-2480, Nearest town: Syracuse. GPS: 37.960721, -101.758541

65 • C2 | Buckner Valley Park

Total sites: 15, RV sites: 5, Central water, No RV dump, Tent & RV camping: Fee unk, Elev: 2354ft/717m, Tel: 620-357-8344, Nearest town: Jetmore. GPS: 38.068159, -100.004809

66 • C2 | Coldwater Lake

Total sites: 100, RV sites: 100, Elec sites: 100, Water at site, Flush toilet, Free showers, RV dump, Tents: $18/RVs: $21-28, Full hookup sites, Elev: 2028ft/618m, Tel: 620-582-2702, Nearest town: Coldwater. GPS: 37.250545, -99.353332

67 • C2 | Davis City Park

Total sites: 8, RV sites: 8, Elec sites: 8, RV dump, Tent & RV camping: Fee unk, Shared electric, Elev: 2247ft/685m, Tel: 620-723-1110, Nearest town: Greensburg. GPS: 37.607031, -99.283062

68 • C2 | Dodge City Roadside Park

Dispersed sites, No toilets, No tents/RVs: Free, Elev: 2522ft/769m, Nearest town: Dodge City. GPS: 37.779584, -99.904715

69 • C2 | Meade City Park

Total sites: 5, RV sites: 5, Central water, Flush toilet, No showers, RV dump, No tents/RVs: Donation, Park on east side near RV sign, Open all year, Reservations not accepted, Elev: 2477ft/755m, Tel: 620-873-2091, Nearest town: Meade. GPS: 37.284190, -100.327620

70 • C2 | Prairie Wind City RV Park

Total sites: 5, RV sites: 5, Elec sites: 5, Water at site, No toilets, No showers, RV dump, Tent & RV camping: $10, Reservations not accepted, Elev: 2802ft/854m, Tel: 620-846-2267, Nearest town: Montezuma. GPS: 37.595756, -100.451579

71 • C3 | Argonia River City Park

Total sites: 24, RV sites: 24, Elec sites: 24, Water at site, Flush toilet, Free showers, RV dump, Tents: $5/RVs: $10-15, 6 Full hookup, Open all year, Reservations not accepted, Elev: 1234ft/376m, Tel: 620-435-6553, Nearest town: Argonia. GPS: 37.247155, -97.764333

72 • C3 | Chase Roadside Park

Dispersed sites, No water, No toilets, Tent & RV camping: Free, Elev: 1680ft/512m, Nearest town: Chase. GPS: 38.347321, -98.297758

73 • C3 | Ellinwood City Park

Total sites: 8, RV sites: 8, Elec sites: 8, Central water, No toilets, No showers, No RV dump, Tent & RV camping: $8, Max Length: 40ft, Elev: 1798ft/548m, Nearest town: Ellinwood. GPS: 38.361485, -98.590264

74 • C3 | Fort Zarah Roadside Park

Dispersed sites, No water, No tents/RVs: Free, Reservations not accepted, Elev: 1841ft/561m, Nearest town: Great Bend. GPS: 38.365498, -98.713838

75 • C3 | Larned City Park

Dispersed sites, Central water, Flush toilet, Free showers, Tents only: Free, Get permit at police station, Elev: 2007ft/612m, Nearest town: Larned. GPS: 38.173963, -99.105961

76 • C3 | Lyons City CG

Total sites: 18, RV sites: 18, Elec sites: 18, Central water, Flush toilet, Free showers, RV dump, Tent & RV camping: Free, Stay limit: 5 days, Open all year, Elev: 1709ft/521m, Tel: 620-257-2320, Nearest town: Lyons. GPS: 38.340201, -98.210389

77 • C3 | Medicine Lodge City Park

Total sites: 4, RV sites: 4, Elec sites: 4, Central water, No toilets, No showers, No RV dump, Tent & RV camping: Free, 2-night limit, Max Length: 40ft, Elev: 1464ft/446m, Tel: 620-895-6446, Nearest town: Medicine Lodge. GPS: 37.278614, -98.574837

78 • C3 | Pratt County Veterans Memorial Lake

Total sites: 41, RV sites: 20, Elec sites: 20, Water at site, RV dump, Tents: $5/RVs: $15, Generator hours: 0600-2300, Open all year, Reservations accepted, Elev: 1808ft/551m, Tel: 620-388-3528, Nearest town: Pratt. GPS: 37.629815, -98.684415

79 • C3 | Sixth Street Park

Total sites: 14, RV sites: 14, Elec sites: 14, Water at site, RV dump, No tents/RVs: $10, Reservations not accepted, Elev: 1852ft/564m, Tel: 620-672-6882, Nearest town: Pratt. GPS: 37.639181, -98.733133

80 • C3 | Sterling Lake Park

Total sites: 14, RV sites: 14, Elec sites: 14, Water at site, Flush toilet, Free showers, RV dump, Tent & RV camping: $20, 14 Full hookup, $10 Nov-Mar, Open all year, Reservations not accepted, Elev: 1654ft/504m, Tel: 620-278-3411, Nearest town: Sterling. GPS: 38.205151, -98.201902

81 • C3 | Wolf Pond Park - City

Total sites: 4, RV sites: 4, Elec sites: 4, Water at site, Tent & RV camping: $8, Reservations not accepted, Elev: 1811ft/552m, Tel: 620-564-3896, Nearest town: Ellinwood. GPS: 38.353741, -98.587597

82 • C4 | Athletic Park - City

Dispersed sites, RV dump, Tent & RV camping: Free, Stay limit: 2 days, Elev: 1423ft/434m, Tel: 316-284-6083, Nearest town: Newton. GPS: 38.046312, -97.356613

83 • C4 | Bates Grove City Park

Dispersed sites, No water, Vault/pit toilet, Tents only: Free, For cyclists in tents, Elev: 1188ft/362m, Tel: 620-273-6666, Nearest town: Cottonwood Falls. GPS: 38.375418, -96.540947

84 • C4 | Cave Park

Dispersed sites, No water, No toilets, Tents only: Free, Stay limit: 2 days, Open all year, Elev: 1184ft/361m, Tel: 620-455-2223, Nearest town: Oxford. GPS: 37.275081, -97.163115

85 • C4 | Gridley City Lake

Total sites: 7, RV sites: 7, Elec sites: 7, Water at site, Flush toilet, Free showers, Tents: $5/RVs: $15, Elev: 1137ft/347m, Tel: 620-836-3145, Nearest town: Gridley. GPS: 38.110633, -95.877209

86 • C4 | Hillsboro Memorial Park

Total sites: 4, RV sites: 4, Elec sites: 4, Central water, Flush toilet, RV dump, No tents/RVs: Fee unk, Contact police to unlock power, Elev: 1418ft/432m, Nearest town: Hillsboro. GPS: 38.346331, -97.208079

87 • C4 | Madison City Lake

Total sites: 16, RV sites: 16, Elec sites: 16, Central water, Flush toilet, No showers, No RV dump, Tent & RV camping: $12, Elev: 1181ft/360m, Tel: 620-437-2556, Nearest town: Madison. GPS: 38.108978, -96.149741

88 • C4 | Moline City Lake (New - North)

Dispersed sites, No water, Vault/pit toilet, Tent & RV camping: $3, Elev: 1096ft/334m, Tel: 620-647-3665, Nearest town: Moline. GPS: 37.391481, -96.308591

89 • C4 | Moline City Lake (Old-South) - KDPW

Dispersed sites, No water, Vault/pit toilet, Tent & RV camping: $3, Elev: 1135ft/346m, Tel: 620-647-3665, Nearest town: Moline. GPS: 37.350143, -96.343105

90 • C4 | Moline City Park

Total sites: 3, RV sites: 3, Elec sites: 3, RV dump, Tent & RV camping: $10, 3 Full hookup, Elev: 1050ft/320m, Tel: 620-647-3665, Nearest town: Moline. GPS: 37.363685, -96.297603

91 • C4 | Napawalla Park - City

Total sites: 10, RV sites: 10, Elec sites: 10, Central water, Flush toilet, No showers, RV dump, Tents: $4/RVs: $10, Restrooms closed Oct 15-Apr 15, Open all year, Reservations not accepted, Elev: 1172ft/357m, Tel: 620-455-2223, Nearest town: Oxford. GPS: 37.272163, -97.172865

92 • C4 | Santa Fe Lake

Total sites: 9, RV sites: 9, Elec sites: 9, Central water, Vault/pit toilet, No showers, RV dump, Tents: $11-20/RVs: $18-23, $20 holidays, Plus daily entrance fee: $8, Reservations not accepted Elev: 1289ft/393m, Tel: 316-775-9926, Nearest town: Augusta GPS: 37.703022, -97.053396

93 • C4 | Swope Park

Total sites: 5, RV sites: 5, Elec sites: 5, Water at site, Flush toilet Free showers, RV dump, Tent & RV camping: $15, Open all year Reservations not accepted, Elev: 1201ft/366m, Tel: 620-273-6666 Nearest town: Cottonwood Falls. GPS: 38.369166, -96.534241

94 • C4 | Winfield City Lake - North Shore

Total sites: 40, RV sites: 30, Elec sites: 30, Water at site, Flush toilet Free showers, RV dump, Tents: $3/RVs: $12, Full hookup sites Generator hours: 0600-2200, Elev: 1283ft/391m, Tel: 620-221-5635, Nearest town: Winfield. GPS: 37.359854, -96.876062

95 • C4 | Winfield City Lake - South Shore

Total sites: 24, RV sites: 24, Elec sites: 24, Water at site, Flush toilet, Free showers, RV dump, Tents: $3/RVs: $12, Full hookup sites, Generator hours: 0600-2200, Elev: 1273ft/388m, Tel: 620-221-5635, Nearest town: Winfield. GPS: 37.346546, -96.889083

96 • C4 | Yates Center Reservoir

Dispersed sites, Central water, Vault/pit toilet, Tent & RV camping: $10, Open all year, Elev: 1024ft/312m, Tel: 620-625-2118, Nearest town: Yates Center. GPS: 37.835378, -95.798642

97 • C5 | Big Brutus Museum

Total sites: 10, RV sites: 10, Elec sites: 10, Flush toilet, Free showers, RV dump, Tents: $7/RVs: $15, Restrooms only available when museum is open, Open all year, Reservations accepted, Elev: 899ft/274m, Tel: 620-827-6177, Nearest town: West Mineral. GPS: 37.273772, -94.938917

98 • C5 | Camp Hunter City Park

Total sites: 17, RV sites: 17, Elec sites: 17, Central water, Flush toilet, Free showers, Tent & RV camping: $10, 5-night limit, Pay at City Hall or Water Plant, Reservations not accepted, Elev: 971ft/296m, Tel: 620-473-3232, Nearest town: Humboldt. GPS: 37.806289, -95.446196

99 • C5 | Cedar Valley Reservoir

Total sites: 12, RV sites: 12, Elec sites: 12, Central water, Vault/pit toilet, No showers, No RV dump, Tents: $9/RVs: $14, Discount for local residents, Reservations not accepted, Elev: 974ft/297m, Tel: 785-448-5496, Nearest town: Garnett. GPS: 38.241912, -95.322977

100 • C5 | Drake City Park

Total sites: 8, RV sites: 8, Elec sites: 8, Water at site, Flush toilet, Free showers, Tent & RV camping: $10, $8 for seniors, Get permit at police station, Open all year, Reservations not accepted, Elev: 1022ft/312m, Tel: 620-364-2996, Nearest town: Burlington. GPS: 38.204821, -95.731389

101 • C5 | East City Lake

Dispersed sites, No water, Vault/pit toilet, Tents only: Free, Elev: 833ft/254m, Tel: 913-352-8257, Nearest town: Pleasanton. GPS: 38.193641, -94.692546

102 • C5 | Erie City Park CG

Total sites: 5, RV sites: 5, Elec sites: 5, Central water, Flush toilet, Free showers, RV dump, Tent & RV camping: $10, Elev: 906ft/276m, Tel: 620-244-3461, Nearest town: Erie. GPS: 37.566513, -95.241395

103 • C5 | Fort Scott Lake

Dispersed sites, No water, Vault/pit toilet, Tent & RV camping: $5, Reservations not accepted, Elev: 889ft/271m, Tel: 620-223-0550, Nearest town: Fort Scott. GPS: 37.787508, -94.761615

104 • C5 | Four Oaks City RV Park

Total sites: 12, RV sites: 12, Elec sites: 12, Water at site, Flush toilet, Free showers, RV dump, Tents: $10/RVs: $20, Reservations accepted, Elev: 932ft/284m, Tel: 620-230-5585, Nearest town: Pittsburg. GPS: 37.425374, -94.714642

105 • C5 | Gunn Park

Total sites: 14, RV sites: 14, Elec sites: 14, Water at site, Flush toilet, No RV dump, Tent & RV camping: $10, Can use dump station at Fairgrounds, Elev: 827ft/252m, Tel: 620-223-0550, Nearest town: Fort Scott. GPS: 37.827804, -94.723783

106 • C5 | Holiday Park - City

Total sites: 4, RV sites: 4, Elec sites: 4, No water, No toilets, No tents/RVs: $5, Open all year, Elev: 1017ft/310m, Tel: 620-964-2245, Nearest town: Leroy. GPS: 38.083848, -95.633429

107 • C5 | Kelley City Park

Total sites: 10, RV sites: 10, Elec sites: 10, Central water, Flush toilet, Free showers, RV dump, Tent & RV camping: $10, Large rigs should use entrance 1 block of main gate, $4 for seniors, Get permit at police station, Open all year, Reservations not accepted, Elev: 991ft/302m, Tel: 620-364-5334, Nearest town: Burlington. GPS: 38.188513, -95.733472

108 • C5 | La Cygne Community Park

Total sites: 5, RV sites: 5, Elec sites: 5, Water at site, Flush toilet, Free showers, Tents: $10/RVs: $17-19, 5 Full hookup, Reservations not accepted, Elev: 824ft/251m, Tel: 913-757-2144, Nearest town: La Cygne. GPS: 38.338132, -94.764406

109 • C5 | Linn CP

Total sites: 113, RV sites: 113, Elec sites: 113, Water at site, Flush toilet, Free showers, RV dump, Tents: $9/RVs: $14-16, Also cabins, Some Full hookup, Open all year, Reservations not accepted, Elev: 873ft/266m, Tel: 913-757-6633, Nearest town: La Cygne. GPS: 38.369302, -94.666965

110 • C5 | Marvel City Park

Total sites: 24, RV sites: 24, Elec sites: 24, Water at site, Flush toilet, Free showers, RV dump, Tent & RV camping: $10, Elev: 886ft/270m, Tel: 620-421-7030, Nearest town: Parsons. GPS: 37.335687, -95.245557

111 • C5 | Neodesha RV Park

Total sites: 4, RV sites: 4, Elec sites: 4, Water at site, No tents/RVs: $15, 3 Full hookup, Reservations not accepted, Elev: 804ft/245m, Tel: 620-325-2431, Nearest town: Neodesha. GPS: 37.417252, -95.674661

112 • C5 | North Lake City Park

Total sites: 50, RV sites: 30, Elec sites: 30, Central water, No toilets, No showers, RV dump, Tents: $9/RVs: $14, 22 Full hookup, Discount for local residents, Reservations accepted, Elev: 1011ft/308m, Tel: 785-448-6823, Nearest town: Garnett. GPS: 38.305623, -95.240985

113 • C5 | Parsons City Lake

Total sites: 50, RV sites: 18, Elec sites: 10, Water at site, Flush toilet, Free showers, RV dump, Tents: $5/RVs: $8-12, Stay limit: 10 days, Elev: 942ft/287m, Tel: 620-421-7031, Nearest town: Parsons. GPS: 37.406524, -95.349875

114 • C5 | Prescott City Lake

Dispersed sites, No water, Vault/pit toilet, Tents only: Free, Elev:

860ft/262m, Tel: 913-471-4521, Nearest town: Prescott. GPS: 38.059832, -94.678688

115 • C5 | Richmond City Lake

Dispersed sites, No water, Vault/pit toilet, Tent & RV camping: Free, Elev: 981ft/299m, Tel: 785-835-6425, Nearest town: Richmond. GPS: 38.392109, -95.223836

116 • C5 | Riverside Park

Total sites: 12, RV sites: 12, Central water, Flush toilet, No showers, Tents: $6/RVs: $12, Reservations not accepted, Elev: 981ft/299m, Tel: 620-795-4433, Nearest town: Neosho Falls. GPS: 38.009846, -95.552065

117 • C5 | Rock Creek Lake

Dispersed sites, No water, No toilets, Tents only: Free, Elev: 837ft/255m, Tel: 620-223-0550, Nearest town: Fort Scott. GPS: 37.815343, -94.751965

118 • C5 | Santa Fe Safari RV Park

Total sites: 34, RV sites: 28, Elec sites: 28, Central water, Flush toilet, Free showers, RV dump, Tents: Free/RVs: $10, 1st 2 nights free, Tents limited to 2 nights, Stay limit: 10 days, Reservations not accepted, Elev: 961ft/293m, Tel: 620-431-3350, Nearest town: Chanute. GPS: 37.646347, -95.453187

119 • C5 | South Owl Lake

Total sites: 12, RV sites: 12, Elec sites: 12, Water at site, No toilets, No showers, RV dump, Tent & RV camping: $10, 10 Full hookup, Open all year, Elev: 1099ft/335m, Tel: 620-625-2118, Nearest town: Yates Center. GPS: 37.868279, -95.744737

120 • C5 | Veterans Memorial Park (Crystal Lake)

Total sites: 5, RV sites: 5, Elec sites: 5, Water at site, No toilets, No showers, No RV dump, Tent & RV camping: $16, 5 Full hookup, Discount for local residents, Reservations accepted, Elev: 1056ft/322m, Tel: 785-448-5496, Nearest town: Garnett. GPS: 38.267606, -95.247688

121 • C5 | West City Lake

Dispersed sites, No water, Vault/pit toilet, Tents only: Fee unk, Elev: 860ft/262m, Tel: 913-352-8257, Nearest town: Pleasanton. GPS: 38.174239, -94.725887

122 • C5 | Yates Center RV Park

Total sites: 5, RV sites: 5, Elec sites: 5, Water at site, No toilets, No showers, RV dump, No tents/RVs: $10, Reservations not accepted, Elev: 1115ft/340m, Nearest town: Yates Center. GPS: 37.872157, -95.739754

123 • D1 | Elkhart City CG

Total sites: 6, RV sites: 6, Elec sites: 6, Water at site, No toilets, No showers, RV dump, Tent & RV camping: $10, Elev: 3618ft/1103m, Nearest town: Elkhart. GPS: 36.998587, -101.899494

124 • D1 | Mary Frame City Park

Total sites: 3, RV sites: 3, Central water, Flush toilet, Tent & RV camping: Free, 1-night limit, Elev: 2851ft/869m, Tel: 620-626-2206, Nearest town: Liberal. GPS: 37.031759, -100.919282

125 • D1 | Prairie RV Park

Total sites: 20, RV sites: 20, Elec sites: 20, Water at site, No toilets, No showers, RV dump, No tents/RVs: $20, 20 Full hookup, Elev: 3586ft/1093m, Tel: 620-697-4124, Nearest town: Elkhart. GPS: 37.008056, -101.884963

126 • D2 | Arkalon City Park

Total sites: 30, RV sites: 30, Elec sites: 30, Water at site, Flush toilet, Free showers, RV dump, Tents: $5/RVs: $5-10, Open Apr-Oct, Elev: 2589ft/789m, Tel: 620-626-0531, Nearest town: Liberal. GPS: 37.148008, -100.761479

127 • D3 | Anthony City Lake

Total sites: 66, RV sites: 66, Elec sites: 66, Central water, Flush toilet, Free showers, No RV dump, Tents: $5/RVs: $15, Cold showers, Generator hours: 0600-2300, Open all year, Elev: 1365ft/416m, Tel: 620-842-5434, Nearest town: Anthony. GPS: 37.175133, -98.049486

128 • D3 | Wellington Lake RA - Boy Scout Cove

Dispersed sites, No water, No toilets, Tent & RV camping: $9, Reservations not accepted, Elev: 1224ft/373m, Tel: 620-434-5454, Nearest town: Wellington. GPS: 37.221347, -97.517121

129 • D3 | Wellington Lake RA - Catfish Cove

Dispersed sites, No water, No toilets, Tent & RV camping: $9, Reservations not accepted, Elev: 1214ft/370m, Tel: 620-434-5454, Nearest town: Wellington. GPS: 37.204124, -97.522319

130 • D3 | Wellington Lake RA - Driftwood Bank

Dispersed sites, No water, No toilets, Tent & RV camping: $9, Reservations not accepted, Elev: 1215ft/370m, Tel: 620-434-5454, Nearest town: Wellington. GPS: 37.232485, -97.514847

131 • D3 | Wellington Lake RA - Eagle Cove

Total sites: 60, RV sites: 60, Elec sites: 50, Water at site, Flush toilet, Tents: $9/RVs: $9-12, Reservations not accepted, Elev: 1226ft/374m, Tel: 620-434-5454, Nearest town: Wellington. GPS: 37.216461, -97.520488

132 • D3 | Wellington Lake RA - Forest Cove

Total sites: 20, RV sites: 20, Elec sites: 20, Water at site, No toilets, No showers, No RV dump, Tents: $9/RVs: $9-12, Reservations not accepted, Elev: 1223ft/373m, Tel: 620-434-5454, Nearest town: Wellington. GPS: 37.211797, -97.521777

133 • D3 | Wellington Lake RA - Hay Meadow

Dispersed sites, No water, No toilets, Tent & RV camping: $9 Reservations not accepted, Elev: 1215ft/370m, Tel: 620-434-5454 Nearest town: Wellington. GPS: 37.234489, -97.519424

134 • D3 | Wellington Lake RA - J C Point

Dispersed sites, No water, Vault/pit toilet, Tent & RV camping: $9 Reservations not accepted, Elev: 1214ft/370m, Tel: 620-434-5454 Nearest town: Wellington. GPS: 37.220104, -97.524177

135 • D3 | Wellington Lake RA - Lillypad Cove

Total sites: 10, RV sites: 4, No water, No toilets, No showers, No RV dump, Tent & RV camping: $9, Reservations not accepted

Elev: 1221ft/372m, Tel: 620-434-5454, Nearest town: Wellington. GPS: 37.223397, -97.515856

136 • D3 | Wellington Lake RA - Mallard Cove

Total sites: 4, RV sites: 4, Central water, Vault/pit toilet, No showers, No RV dump, Tent & RV camping: $9, Reservations not accepted, Elev: 1218ft/371m, Tel: 620-434-5454, Nearest town: Wellington. GPS: 37.206475, -97.521287

137 • D3 | Wellington Lake RA - Old West

Total sites: 27, RV sites: 27, Elec sites: 20, Water at site, Flush toilet, Free showers, RV dump, Tents: $9/RVs: $9-12, Reservations not accepted, Elev: 1243ft/379m, Tel: 620-434-5454, Nearest town: Wellington. GPS: 37.217303, -97.528429

138 • D3 | Wellington Lake RA - Pioneer Cove

Dispersed sites, No water, No toilets, Tent & RV camping: $9, Reservations not accepted, Elev: 1216ft/371m, Tel: 620-434-5454, Nearest town: Wellington. GPS: 37.219505, -97.518912

139 • D3 | Wellington Lake RA - Rocky Bank

Total sites: 6, RV sites: 6, Central water, No toilets, No showers, No RV dump, Tents: $9/RVs: $9-12, Reservations not accepted, Elev: 1216ft/371m, Tel: 620-434-5454, Nearest town: Wellington. GPS: 37.212968, -97.522644

140 • D3 | Wellington Lake RA - Roundabout Cove/The Island

Total sites: 25, RV sites: 25, Central water, Vault/pit toilet, No showers, No RV dump, Tent & RV camping: $9, Reservations not accepted, Elev: 1218ft/371m, Tel: 620-434-5454, Nearest town: Wellington. GPS: 37.207099, -97.532586

141 • D3 | Wellington Lake RA - Sandy Point

Dispersed sites, No water, No toilets, Tent & RV camping: $9, Reservations not accepted, Elev: 1216ft/371m, Tel: 620-434-5454, Nearest town: Wellington. GPS: 37.230569, -97.519977

142 • D3 | Wellington Lake RA - Single Tree Cove

Dispersed sites, No water, Vault/pit toilet, Tent & RV camping: $9, Reservations not accepted, Elev: 1212ft/369m, Tel: 620-434-5454, Nearest town: Wellington. GPS: 37.225519, -97.520752

143 • D3 | Wellington Lake RA - Sunset View

Total sites: 4, RV sites: 4, Central water, Flush toilet, No showers, No RV dump, Tent & RV camping: $9, Reservations not accepted, Elev: 1220ft/372m, Tel: 620-434-5454, Nearest town: Wellington. GPS: 37.209594, -97.521889

144 • D4 | Newman City Park

Total sites: 8, RV sites: 8, Elec sites: 8, Central water, RV dump, Tent & RV camping: $15, Reservations not accepted, Elev: 1070ft/326m, Tel: 620-441-4470, Nearest town: Arkansas City. GPS: 37.041325, -97.039414

145 • D4 | Sedan City Park

Total sites: 15, RV sites: 15, Elec sites: 15, Central water, Flush toilet, Free showers, RV dump, Tent & RV camping: $10, 20 Amp only, Elev: 873ft/266m, Tel: 620-725-3193, Nearest town: Sedan. GPS: 37.127981, -96.184046

146 • D4 | Sedan Old City Lake

Total sites: 6, RV sites: 6, Elec sites: 2, Vault/pit toilet, Tent & RV camping: $10, Elev: 934ft/285m, Tel: 620-725-3193, Nearest town: Sedan. GPS: 37.170087, -96.219548

147 • D4 | Tunnel Mill Park

Dispersed sites, Vault/pit toilet, Tent & RV camping: $3, Elev: 1119ft/341m, Tel: 620-221-5525, Nearest town: Winfield. GPS: 37.228536, -97.005369

148 • D4 | Walnut City Park

Total sites: 16, RV sites: 16, Elec sites: 16, Central water, Flush toilet, No tents/RVs: $15, Reservations not accepted, Elev: 1066ft/325m, Tel: 620-441-4470, Nearest town: Arkansas City. GPS: 37.057248, -97.026336

149 • D5 | Columbus VFW City Park

Total sites: 6, RV sites: 6, Elec sites: 6, Water at site, RV dump, Tent & RV camping: $12, Elev: 906ft/276m, Tel: 620-429-1492, Nearest town: Columbus. GPS: 37.164129, -94.841365

150 • D5 | Danny Elliott City Park

Total sites: 4, RV sites: 4, Elec sites: 4, Water at site, No toilets, No showers, No RV dump, Tent & RV camping: $15, Can use dump at Kamp Siesta, Elev: 820ft/250m, Tel: 620-795-4433, Nearest town: Oswego. GPS: 37.176973, -95.103767

151 • D5 | East River Park

Total sites: 40, RV sites: 40, Elec sites: 40, Water at site, RV dump, Tents: $5/RVs: $15, Reservations accepted, Elev: 794ft/242m, Tel: 620-236-7541, Nearest town: Chetopa. GPS: 37.036034, -95.077945

152 • D5 | Elmore Park

Total sites: 26, RV sites: 26, Elec sites: 26, Water at site, Flush toilet, RV dump, Tents: $5/RVs: $15, Reservations accepted, Elev: 827ft/252m, Tel: 620-236-7541, Nearest town: Chetopa. GPS: 37.047408, -95.083982

153 • D5 | Kamp Siesta at Riverside Park

Total sites: 42, RV sites: 42, Elec sites: 42, Water at site, Flush toilet, Free showers, RV dump, Tent & RV camping: $15, Open all year, Reservations not accepted, Elev: 866ft/264m, Tel: 620-795-4433, Nearest town: Oswego. GPS: 37.173027, -95.104422

154 • D5 | Louie P. Gartner RA - North

Total sites: 9, RV sites: 9, Elec sites: 9, Water at site, Flush toilet, Free showers, RV dump, Tent & RV camping: $10, 9 Full hookup, Generator hours: 0800-2200, Reservations accepted, Elev: 898ft/274m, Tel: 620-784-5582, Nearest town: Altamont. GPS: 37.142741, -95.288243

155 • D5 | Louie P. Gartner RA - South

Total sites: 11, RV sites: 11, Elec sites: 11, Water at site, Flush toilet, Free showers, RV dump, Tent & RV camping: $10, 11 Full hookup, Generator hours: 0800-2200, Reservations accepted, Elev: 896ft/273m, Tel: 620-784-5582, Nearest town: Altamont. GPS: 37.139655, -95.286527

156 • D5 | Riverside Park

Total sites: 7, RV sites: 7, Elec sites: 7, Central water, RV dump, Tents: $5/RVs: $10, Pay at police station, Reservations not accepted, Elev: 800ft/244m, Tel: 620-856-2112, Nearest town: Baxter Springs. GPS: 37.022902, -94.719796

157 • D5 | Walter Johnson City Park - Rivercrest

Total sites: 62, RV sites: 62, Elec sites: 62, Water at site, Flush toilet, Free showers, RV dump, Tent & RV camping: $15, 62 Full hookup, Reservations not accepted, Elev: 704ft/215m, Tel: 620-252-6108, Nearest town: Coffeyville. GPS: 37.037119, -95.589219

158 • D5 | Walter Johnson City Park - The Woods

Total sites: 56, RV sites: 56, Elec sites: 56, Water at site, Flush toilet, Free showers, RV dump, Tent & RV camping: $8, Open all year, Reservations not accepted, Elev: 725ft/221m, Tel: 620-252-6108, Nearest town: Coffeyville. GPS: 37.036311, -95.594577

Kentucky

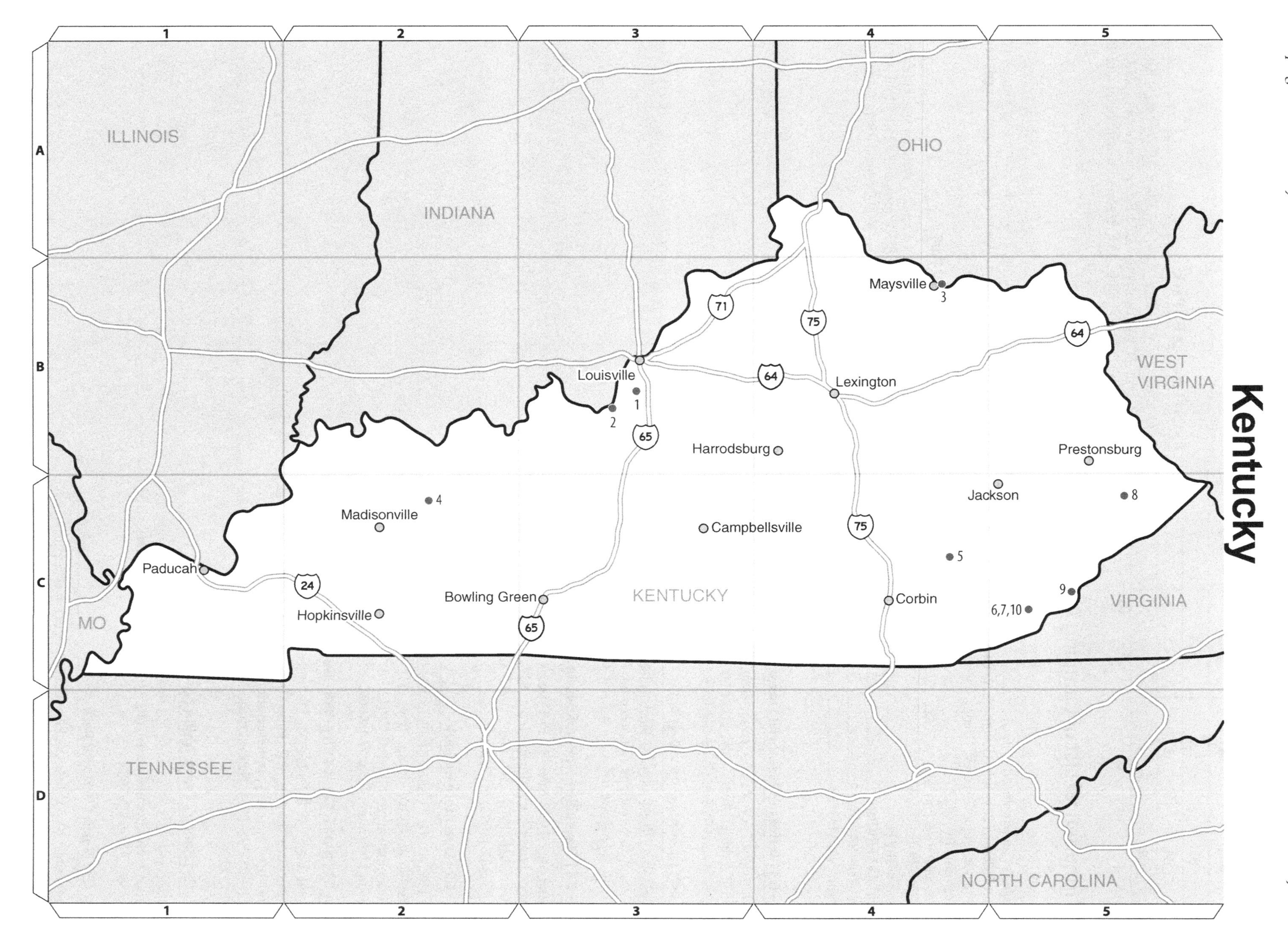
ILLINOIS
INDIANA
OHIO
WEST VIRGINIA
VIRGINIA
NORTH CAROLINA
TENNESSEE
MO
KENTUCKY
Maysville
3
71
75
64
Louisville
1
2
Lexington
65
Harrodsburg
Prestonsburg
Jackson
8
4
Madisonville
Campbellsville
5
Paducah
24
Bowling Green
Corbin
9
6,7,10
Hopkinsville
1 2 3 4 5
A B C D

Map	ID	Map	ID
B3	1-2	C4	5
B4	3	C5	6-10
C2	4		

Alphabetical List of Camping Areas

1 • B3 | Jefferson Memorial Forest - Tom Wallace Lake

Total sites: 7, RV sites: 0, Central water, Vault/pit toilet, No showers, No RV dump, Tents only: $15, Elev: 656ft/200m, Tel: 502-368-5404, Nearest town: Louisville. GPS: 38.085477, -85.774055

2 • B3 | Salt River RA - West Point

Total sites: 20, RV sites: 10, Flush toilet, Tents: $10/RVs: $25, Open all year, Reservations not accepted, Elev: 423ft/129m, Tel: 502-773-4056, Nearest town: West Point. GPS: 37.998676, -85.940275

3 • B4 | Maysville River Park Marina

Total sites: 43, RV sites: 43, Elec sites: 43, Water at site, Flush toilet, Free showers, RV dump, Tents: $15/RVs: $30, Open Apr-Oct, Elev: 502ft/153m, Tel: 606-541-6283, Nearest town: Maysville. GPS: 38.641893, -83.730888

4 • C2 | Livermore RV Park

Total sites: 31, RV sites: 31, Elec sites: 31, Water at site, Flush toilet, Free showers, RV dump, Tents: $10/RVs: $25-28, Full hookup sites, Open all year, Elev: 382ft/116m, Tel: 270-278-2113, Nearest town: Livermore. GPS: 37.486069, -87.144812

5 • C4 | Bert T. Combs City Park - Governor's RV Park

Total sites: 39, RV sites: 31, Elec sites: 31, Water at site, Flush toilet, Free showers, RV dump, Tents: $15/RVs: $20-23, 24 Full hookup, Open all year, Reservations accepted, Elev: 921ft/281m, Tel: 606-598-1554, Nearest town: Manchester. GPS: 37.170649, -83.712286

6 • C5 | Bailey's Creek Trailhead - City

Dispersed sites, No water, No toilets, Tent & RV camping: Fee unk, Open all year, Elev: 1670ft/509m, Nearest town: Evarts. GPS: 36.882794, -83.197087

7 • C5 | North Evarts RV Park

Total sites: 20, RV sites: 20, Elec sites: 20, Water at site, Flush toilet, Free showers, RV dump, Tents: $15/RVs: $20, 20 Full hookup, Elev: 1309ft/399m, Tel: 606-837-0609, Nearest town: Evarts. GPS: 36.869384, -83.190557

8 • C5 | Pikeville RV Park

Total sites: 21, RV sites: 21, Elec sites: 21, Water at site, RV dump, Tent & RV camping: $25, Reservations accepted, Elev: 928ft/283m, Tel: 606-444-5131, Nearest town: Pikeville. GPS: 37.471048, -82.541921

9 • C5 | Portal #31 RV Park

Total sites: 20, RV sites: 12, Elec sites: 12, Central water, Flush toilet, No showers, RV dump, Tent & RV camping: $15, Open all year, Elev: 1877ft/572m, Tel: 606-848-1530, Nearest town: Lynch. GPS: 36.966173, -82.918084

10 • C5 | South Evarts RV Park

Total sites: 23, RV sites: 23, Elec sites: 23, Water at site, Flush toilet, Free showers, RV dump, Tent & RV camping: $25, 23 Full hookup, Elev: 1289ft/393m, Tel: 606-837-0609, Nearest town: Evarts. GPS: 36.863519, -83.197827

Louisiana

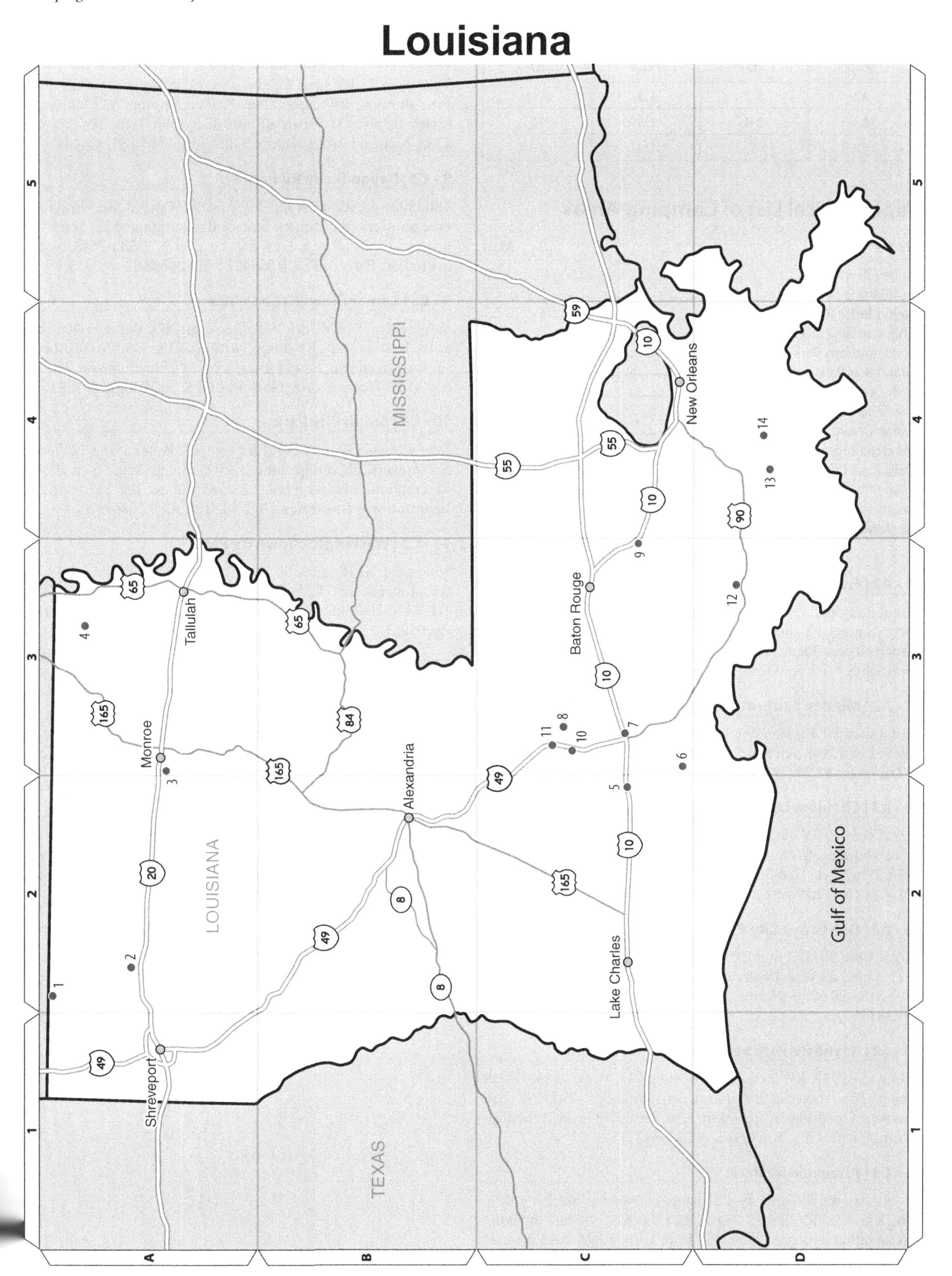
MISSISSIPPI
LOUISIANA
TEXAS
Gulf of Mexico
Shreveport
Monroe
Tallulah
Alexandria
Lake Charles
Baton Rouge
New Orleans
1
2
3
4
5
6
7
8
9
10
11
12
13
14
49
20
165
65
84
8
10
55
59
90
A
B
C
D

Map	ID	Map	ID
A2	1-2	C3	6-11
A3	3-4	D3	12
C2	5	D4	13-14

Alphabetical List of Camping Areas

1 • A2 | Frank Anthony Park

Total sites: 30, RV sites: 30, Elec sites: 30, Water at site, Flush toilet, Free showers, RV dump, Tent & RV camping: $25, 30 Full hookup, Open all year, Elev: 249ft/76m, Tel: 318-539-5646, Nearest town: Springhill. GPS: 33.002461, -93.462991

2 • A2 | Minden Fairgrounds

Total sites: 90, RV sites: 90, Elec sites: 90, No tents/RVs: Fee unk, Elev: 259ft/79m, Tel: 318-377-2144, Nearest town: Minden. GPS: 32.627868, -93.292799

3 • A3 | Cheniere Lake City Park

Total sites: 8, RV sites: 8, Elec sites: 8, Water at site, Flush toilet, Free showers, No tents/RVs: $34, Reservations accepted, Elev: 95ft/29m, Tel: 318-387-2383, Nearest town: Monroe. GPS: 32.478045, -92.198691

4 • A3 | Oak Grove City Park

Total sites: 30, RV sites: 30, Elec sites: 30, Tent & RV camping: $11, Open all year, Reservations not accepted, Elev: 125ft/38m, Tel: 318-428-3276, Nearest town: Oak Grove. GPS: 32.865179, -91.384617

5 • C2 | Rayne RV Park at Gossen Memorial Park

Total sites: 737, RV sites: 737, Elec sites: 737, Water at site, Flush toilet, Free showers, RV dump, No tents/RVs: $30, 229 Full hookup, Open all year, Elev: 39ft/12m, Tel: 337-334-3121, Nearest town: Rayne. GPS: 30.249916, -92.273847

6 • C3 | Abbeville RV Park

Total sites: 49, RV sites: 49, Elec sites: 48, Water at site, No toilets, No showers, RV dump, No tents/RVs: $24, 49 Full hookup, Reservations accepted, Elev: 49ft/15m, Tel: 337-898-4042, Nearest town: Abbeville. GPS: 29.978087, -92.162673

7 • C3 | Acadiana Park

Total sites: 75, RV sites: 75, Elec sites: 75, Water at site, Flush toilet, Free showers, RV dump, Tent & RV camping: $25, Generator hours: 0800-2300, Open all year, Elev: 59ft/18m, Tel: 337-291-8388, Nearest town: Lafayette. GPS: 30.257306, -91.988134

8 • C3 | Bayou Teche RV Park

Total sites: 48, RV sites: 48, Elec sites: 48, Water at site, Flush toilet, Free showers, RV dump, Tent & RV camping: $25, Some Full hookup, Open all year, Elev: 26ft/8m, Tel: 337-585-7646, Nearest town: Port Barre. GPS: 30.559421, -91.956598

9 • C3 | Lamar Dixon Expo Center

Total sites: 300, RV sites: 300, Elec sites: 300, Water at site, Flush toilet, Free showers, RV dump, No tents/RVs: $35-45, Full hookup sites, Open all year, Reservations accepted, Elev: 20ft/6m, Tel: 225-621-1700, Nearest town: Gonzales. GPS: 30.193641, -90.953668

10 • C3 | South City Park

Total sites: 67, RV sites: 67, Elec sites: 67, Water at site, No toilets, No showers, RV dump, Tent & RV camping: $10, Open all year, Reservations not accepted, Elev: 85ft/26m, Tel: 337-948-2562, Nearest town: Opelousas. GPS: 30.519234, -92.086981

11 • C3 | Washington Town RV Park

Total sites: 50, RV sites: 50, Elec sites: 50, Water at site, Tent & RV camping: Fee unk, 50 Full hookup, Open all year, Elev: 35ft/11m, Tel: 337-826-3626, Nearest town: Washington. GPS: 30.614241, -92.049137

12 • D3 | Lake End City Park

Total sites: 167, RV sites: 147, Elec sites: 147, Water at site, Flush toilet, Free showers, RV dump, Tents: $24/RVs: $40, Some Full hookup, Open all year, Reservations accepted, Elev: 3ft/1m, Tel: 985-380-4623, Nearest town: Morgan City. GPS: 29.719720, -91.188260

13 • D4 | Grand Bois Park

Total sites: 50, RV sites: 44, Elec sites: 44, Water at site, Flush toilet, Free showers, RV dump, Tent & RV camping: $15, Open all year, Max Length: 40ft, Elev: 33ft/10m, Tel: 985-594-7410, Nearest town: Bourg. GPS: 29.551231, -90.561473

14 • D4 | Kelly Grove CG

Total sites: 12, RV sites: 12, Elec sites: 12, Water at site, No tents/RVs: $35, Open all year, Elev: 5ft/2m, Tel: 985-693-7355, Nearest town: Larose. GPS: 29.575437, -90.375625

Maine

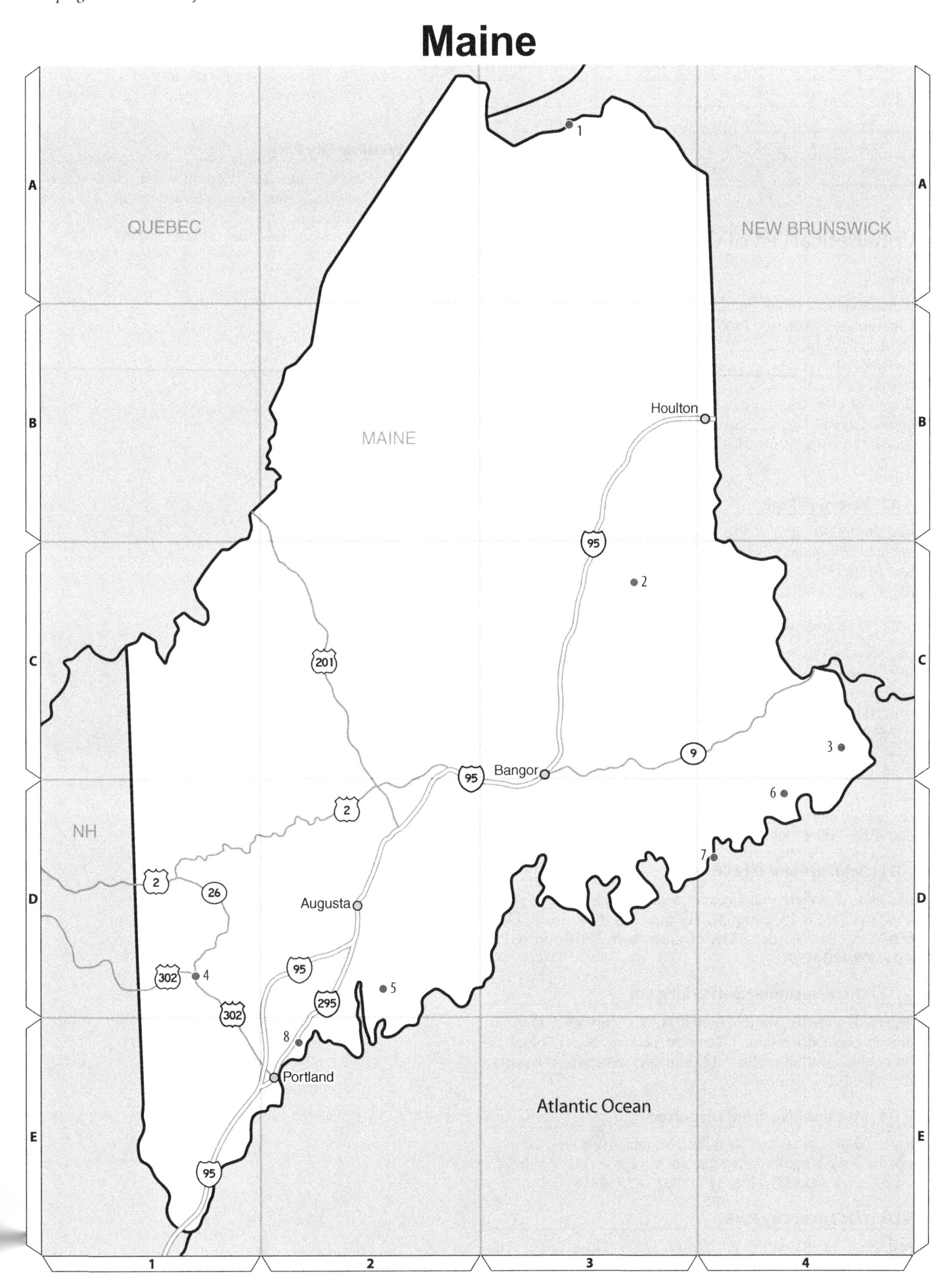
QUEBEC
NEW BRUNSWICK
MAINE
NH
Houlton
Bangor
Augusta
Portland
Atlantic Ocean
95
201
2
9
26
302
295
1
2
3
4
5
6
7
8
A
B
C
D
E
1
2
3
4

Map	ID	Map	ID
A3	1	D2	5
C3	2	D4	6-7
C4	3	E2	8
D1	4		

Alphabetical List of Camping Areas

1 • A3 | Riverside Park

Total sites: 8, RV sites: 8, Elec sites: 8, Central water, RV dump, Tent & RV camping: $20, Open May-Nov, Reservations accepted, Elev: 515ft/157m, Tel: 207-834-5678, Nearest town: Fort Kent. GPS: 47.254524, -68.594188

2 • C3 | Mattawamkeag Wilderness Park CG

Total sites: 50, RV sites: 50, Elec sites: 14, Central water, Flush toilet, Free showers, RV dump, Tents: $22/RVs: $30-35, 6 Full hookup, Open May-Sep, Reservations not accepted, Elev: 351ft/107m, Tel: 207-736-2465, Nearest town: Lincoln. GPS: 45.523682, -68.264160

3 • C4 | Reversing Falls Park

Dispersed sites, No water, No toilets, Tent & RV camping: Free, Reservations not accepted, Elev: 27ft/8m, Nearest town: Pembroke. GPS: 44.883299, -67.133216

4 • D1 | Salmon Point City CG

Total sites: 55, RV sites: 51, Elec sites: 51, Flush toilet, Free showers, RV dump, Tent & RV camping: Fee unk, Mostly seasonal, Elev: 285ft/87m, Tel: 207-647-5229, Nearest town: Bridgton. GPS: 44.050408, -70.679976

5 • D2 | Wiscasset Municipal Parking Lot

Dispersed sites, No water, No toilets, No tents/RVs: Free, At harbormasters discretion, Overnight parking also allowed at library and courthouse, Elev: 12ft/4m, Nearest town: Wiscasset. GPS: 43.999795, -69.665649

6 • D4 | Machias Riverfront Dispersed

Dispersed sites, No water, No toilets, No tents/RVs: Free, 1-night, park in back row, Reservations not accepted, Elev: 10ft/3m, Nearest town: Machias. GPS: 44.715062, -67.456814

7 • D4 | McClellan City Park

Total sites: 12, RV sites: 12, Central water, Flush toilet, Free showers, No RV dump, Tent & RV camping: $10, Open May-Oct, Max Length: 25ft, Reservations not accepted, Elev: 24ft/7m, Tel: 207-546-2688, Nearest town: Millbridge. GPS: 44.484315, -67.854254

8 • E2 | Winslow City Park

Total sites: 100, RV sites: 100, Central water, Flush toilet, Pay showers, RV dump, Tents: $25-30/RVs: $30-35, Also cabins, Residents: 50% discount, Open May-Oct, Elev: 12ft/4m, Tel: 207-865-4198, Nearest town: Freeport. GPS: 43.801433, -70.116083

Maryland

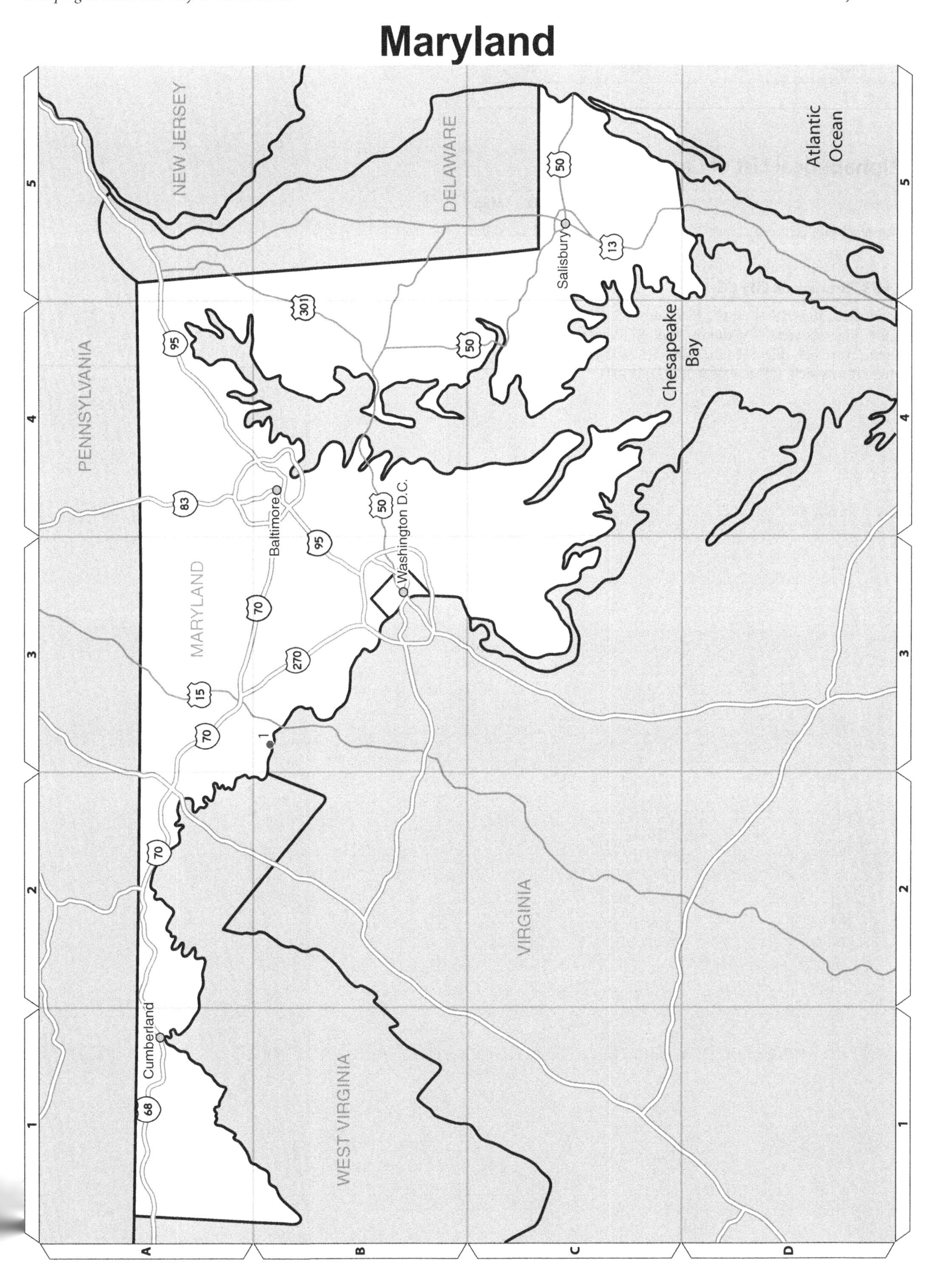
PENNSYLVANIA
NEW JERSEY
DELAWARE
MARYLAND
WEST VIRGINIA
VIRGINIA
Atlantic Ocean
Chesapeake Bay
Baltimore
Washington D.C.
Salisbury
Cumberland
1
95
83
70
270
15
68
50
301
13
A
B
C
D
1
2
3
4
5

Map	ID	Map	ID
B3	1		

Alphabetical List of Camping Areas

1 • B3 | Brunswick City CG

Total sites: 365, RV sites: 65, Elec sites: 65, Water at site, Flush toilet, Free showers, RV dump, Tent & RV camping: Fee unk, Open Apr-Nov, Elev: 249ft/76m, Tel: 301-834-8050, Nearest town: Brunswick. GPS: 39.306626, -77.613021

Massachusetts

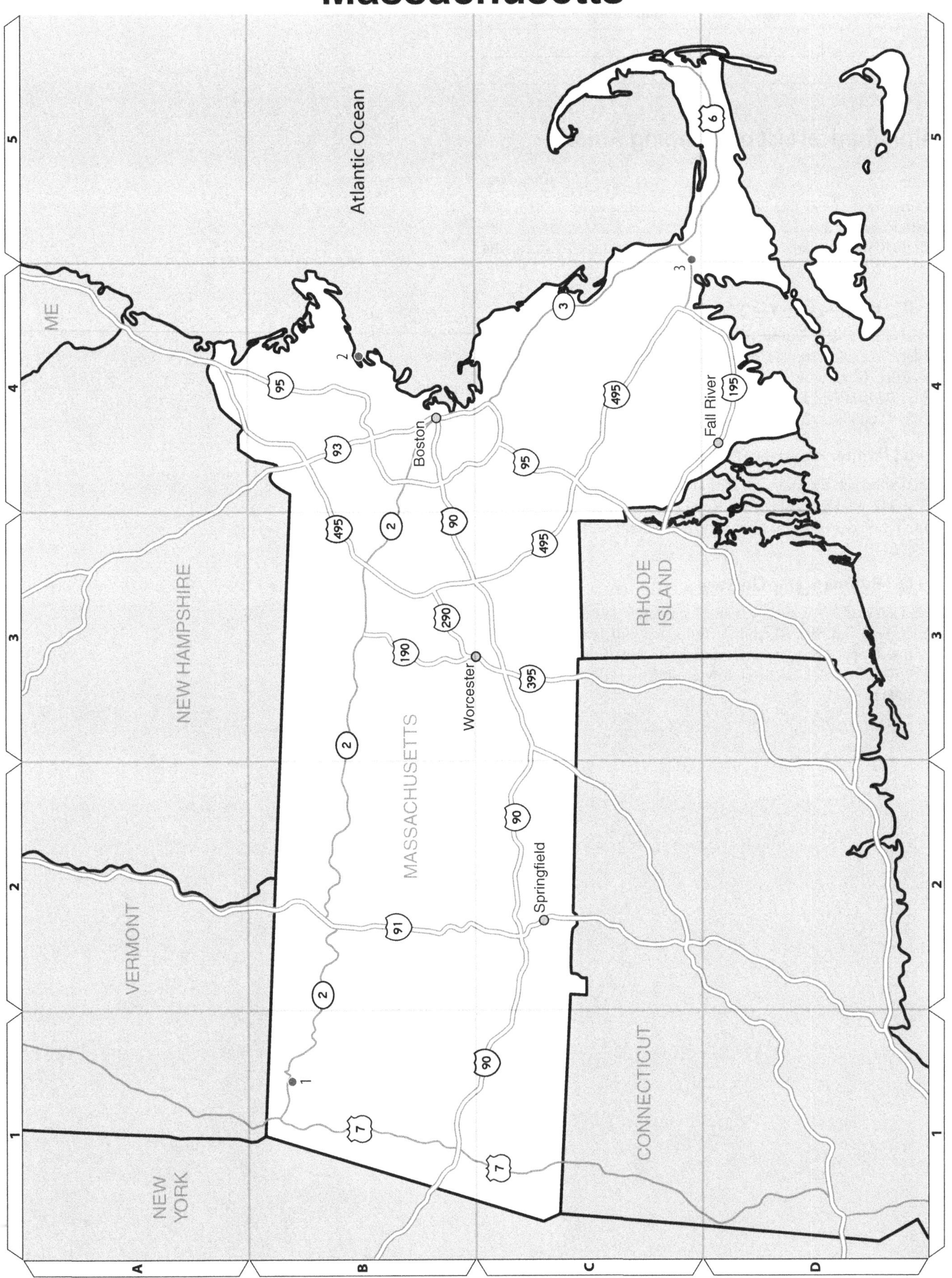

Map	ID	Map	ID
B1	1	C5	3
B4	2		

Alphabetical List of Camping Areas

1 • B1 | Historic Valley City CG

Total sites: 114, RV sites: 100, Elec sites: 100, Water at site, Flush toilet, Free showers, RV dump, Tents: $25/RVs: $30-40, 94 Full hookup, Generator hours: 0800-2200, Reservations accepted, Elev: 988ft/301m, Tel: 413-662-3198, Nearest town: North Adams. GPS: 42.685081, -73.091714

2 • B4 | Winter Island City Park

Total sites: 59, RV sites: 29, Elec sites: 34, RV dump, Tents: $35/ RVs: $42-50, Open May-Oct, Reservations accepted, Elev: 10ft/ 3m, Tel: 978-745-9430, Nearest town: Salem. GPS: 42.531070, -70.868120

3 • C5 | Bourne Scenic City Park

Total sites: 439, RV sites: 439, Elec sites: 408, Water at site, Flush toilet, Free showers, RV dump, Tents: $50-58/RVs: $64-72, Also cabins, Open Apr-Oct, Reservations accepted, Elev: 46ft/14m, Tel: 508-759-7873, Nearest town: Bourne. GPS: 41.749822, -70.589649

Michigan

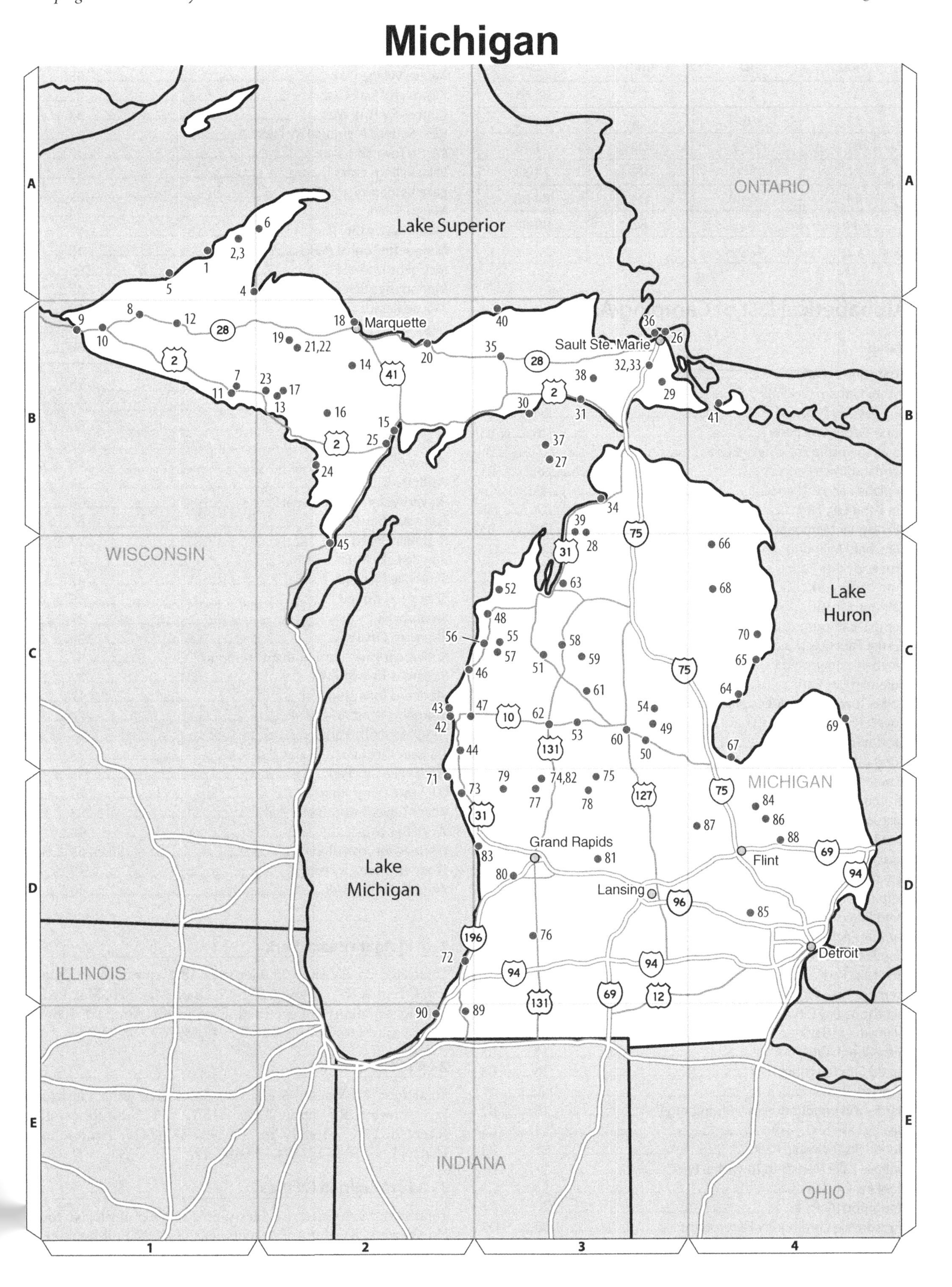
Lake Superior
ONTARIO
WISCONSIN
Lake Huron
Lake Michigan
MICHIGAN
ILLINOIS
INDIANA
OHIO
Marquette
Sault Ste. Marie
Grand Rapids
Lansing
Flint
Detroit

Map	ID	Map	ID
A1	1-5	C3	48-63
A2	6	C4	64-70
B1	7-12	D2	71-73
B2	13-25	D3	74-83
B3	26-40	D4	84-88
B4	41	E2	89-90
C2	42-47		

Alphabetical List of Camping Areas

Name	ID	Map
Agate Beach Park	1	A1
Arthur Latham City Park	84	D4
Au Gres City Park and CG	64	C4
Aune-Osborn RV Park	26	B3
Bates Township Park/Sunset Lake	7	B1
Bergland Town Park	8	B1
Beulah Beach RV Park	43	C3
Big Bend City Park	74	D3
Bill Wagner Memorial Park	27	B3
Blanchard Millpond City Park	75	D3
Brookside City Park	76	D3
Buttersville Park	42	C2
Calhoun City CG	45	C3
Camp Dearborn	85	D4
Cartier Park CG	43	C2
Claybanks Township Park	71	D2
Coleman City Park	47	C3
Colfax Township Park/Lester A. Barnes Memorial Park	48	C3
Covert Park Beach and CG	72	D2
Croton Township Park	77	D3
Curry City Park	9	B1
Dawson Lake City Park	13	B2
Drummond Island Township Park	41	B4
East Jordan Tourist Park	28	B3
East Tawas City Park	65	C4
Eddy Park	10	B1
Emerick City Park	66	C4
Empire Township CG	49	C3
Evart Riverside Park	50	C3
Farquar-Metsa Tourist Park	14	B2
Finn Road City CG	67	C4
First Lake Park	78	D3
Fremont Lake City Park	79	D3
Gladstone Bay City CG	15	B2
Gladwin City Park	51	C3
Glen Gough City Park	29	B3
Gould City Township Park	30	B3
Hancock RA	2	A1
Hardwood Impoundment – Stromberg Park	16	B2
Healey Lake SFC - City	52	C3
Hendricks Township Park	31	B3
Holmes Lake Mansfield Township Park	17	B2
Hopkins City Park	53	C3
Houghton RV Park	3	A1
Hudsonville Community Fairgrounds	80	D3
Ionia Free Fairgrounds	81	D3
John Gurney City Park	44	C2
Kaleva Village Park	55	C3
Kinross RV Park East	32	B3
Kinross RV Park West	33	B3
Klint Safford Memorial RV Park	11	B1
L'Anse Township Park	4	A1
Lake Billings City CG	56	C3
Lake Linden Village Park	6	A2
Magnus Park	34	B3
Maple Grove City Park	57	C3
Marquette Tourist Park	18	B2
McCollum Lake SFC	68	C4
Menominee River City Park	45	C2
Moose Rapids CG	19	B2
Munising Municipal Tourist Park	20	B2
North Park CG	69	C4
Northern Lights City CG	21	B2
Old Orchard City Park	70	C4
Ontonagon Township Park	5	A1
Otter Lake City Park	86	D4
Oxbow City Park	82	D3
Penny Park	46	C2
Pettit Park	59	C3
Powers Veterans Memorial Park	60	C3
Rambadt City Park	61	C3
Republic Beach	22	B2
Runkle Lake Municipal Park	23	B2
Scottville Riverside Park	47	C2
Seney Township CG	35	B3
Shamrock City Park	89	E2
Sherman City Park	36	B3
Showboat Park - Tom Graham Memorial CG	87	D4
St. James Township CG	37	B3
Stannard Township Park	12	B1
Sturgeon Bend Town Park	24	B2
Tanglefoot City Park	83	D3
Trailway City CG	73	D2
Trout Lake City Park	38	B3
U.P. State Fairgrounds	25	B2
Water Tower Travel Trailer Park	88	D4
Weko Beach	90	E2
Whitewater Township Park	63	C3
Wooden Shoe City Park	39	B3
Woodland City Park	40	B3

1 • A1 | Agate Beach Park

Total sites: 25, RV sites: 25, Elec sites: 18, Central water, Vault/pi toilet, Tent & RV camping: $12-15, Open May-Sep, Max Length 20ft, Reservations not accepted, Elev: 650ft/198m, Tel: 906-482-8319, Nearest town: Toivola. GPS: 47.039762, -88.925114

2 • A1 | Hancock RA

Total sites: 71, RV sites: 56, Elec sites: 56, Central water, Flush toilet Free showers, RV dump, Tents: $15/RVs: $22-25, Reservation accepted, Elev: 646ft/197m, Tel: 906-482-7413, Nearest town Hancock. GPS: 47.132884, -88.618749

3 • A1 | Houghton RV Park

Total sites: 22, RV sites: 22, Elec sites: 22, Water at site, No toilets No showers, RV dump, No tents/RVs: $45, 22 Full hookup, N pop-ups, No generators, Open May-Oct, Reservations accepted, Elev: 594ft/181m, Tel: 906-482-8745, Nearest town: Houghton. GPS: 47.120325, -88.588814

4 • A1 | L'Anse Township Park

Total sites: 30, RV sites: 30, Elec sites: 30, Central water, Flush toilet, Free showers, RV dump, Tents: $15/RVs: $20, Open May-Oct, Elev: 699ft/213m, Tel: 906-524-6985, Nearest town: L'Anse. GPS: 46.785047, -88.436954

5 • A1 | Ontonagon Township Park

Total sites: 79, RV sites: 79, Elec sites: 79, Water at site, Flush toilet, Pay showers, RV dump, Tents: $15-20/RVs: $21-35, Local residents discount: $2-$5, Stay limit: 9-16 days, Generator hours: 0800-2300, Open May-Oct, Max Length: 35ft, Reservations not accepted, Elev: 614ft/187m, Tel: 906-884-2930, Nearest town: Ontonagon. GPS: 46.884359, -89.299761

6 • A2 | Lake Linden Village Park

Total sites: 26, RV sites: 20, Water at site, Flush toilet, Free showers, RV dump, Tents: $15/RVs: $25, Elev: 620ft/189m, Nearest town: Lake Linden. GPS: 47.189222, -88.404201

7 • B1 | Bates Township Park/Sunset Lake

Total sites: 13, RV sites: 13, Central water, Flush toilet, Free showers, No RV dump, Tent & RV camping: $12, Smaller RVs only, Open all year, Reservations accepted, Elev: 1578ft/481m, Tel: 906-265-2787, Nearest town: Iron River. GPS: 46.129430, -88.589580

8 • B1 | Bergland Town Park

Total sites: 15, RV sites: 15, Elec sites: 15, Central water, Flush toilet, Free showers, RV dump, Tent & RV camping: $12, Open May-Oct, Reservations not accepted, Elev: 1322ft/403m, Tel: 906-575-8733, Nearest town: Bergland. GPS: 46.590845, -89.573798

9 • B1 | Curry City Park

Total sites: 56, RV sites: 30, Elec sites: 30, Water at site, Flush toilet, Free showers, RV dump, Tents: $10/RVs: $15-25, 9 Full hookup, $10 dump fee, $10 water-fill fee, Elev: 1447ft/441m, Tel: 906-932-5050, Nearest town: Ironwood. GPS: 46.463997, -90.185117

10 • B1 | Eddy Park

Total sites: 79, RV sites: 63, Elec sites: 63, Water at site, Flush toilet, Free showers, Tents: $10/RVs: $20-30, Open May-Sep, Reservations accepted, Elev: 1555ft/474m, Tel: 906-224-4481, Nearest town: Wakefield. GPS: 46.484101, -89.944975

11 • B1 | Klint Safford Memorial RV Park

Total sites: 32, RV sites: 32, Elec sites: 32, Water at site, Flush toilet, Free showers, RV dump, Tent & RV camping: $30-39, 12 Full hookup, $20 Nov-Apr, Generator hours: 0700-2200, Open Apr-Nov, Max Length: 100ft, Reservations accepted, Elev: 1470ft/448m, Tel: 906-265-3822, Nearest town: Iron River. GPS: 46.090181, -88.636482

12 • B1 | Stannard Township Park

Total sites: 12, RV sites: 8, Elec sites: 8, Water at site, Flush toilet, Pay showers, RV dump, Tent & RV camping: $10, Open May-Oct, Reservations not accepted, Elev: 1138ft/347m, Tel: 906-827-3778, Nearest town: Bruce Crossing. GPS: 46.536668, -89.176809

13 • B2 | Dawson Lake City Park

Total sites: 10, RV sites: 10, Tent & RV camping: Fee unk, Max Length: 30ft, Elev: 1345ft/410m, Tel: 906-875-3553, Nearest town: Crystal Falls. GPS: 46.078065, -88.182882

14 • B2 | Farquar-Metsa Tourist Park

Total sites: 28, RV sites: 20, Elec sites: 20, Water at site, Flush toilet, Free showers, RV dump, Tents: $12/RVs: $22-28, 20 Full hookup, Reservations required, Elev: 1116ft/340m, Tel: 906-346-3267, Nearest town: Gwinn. GPS: 46.283378, -87.438099

15 • B2 | Gladstone Bay City CG

Total sites: 61, RV sites: 51, Elec sites: 51, Water at site, Flush toilet, Free showers, RV dump, Tents: $15/RVs: $25-33, 26 Full hookup, Generator hours: 0600-2300, Open May-Sep, Reservations accepted, Elev: 581ft/177m, Tel: 906-428-1211, Nearest town: Gladstone. GPS: 45.846781, -87.004974

16 • B2 | Hardwood Impoundment – Stromberg Park

Total sites: 5, RV sites: 5, Water available, Vault/pit toilet, No showers, Tent & RV camping: Fee unk, Open all year, Elev: 1102ft/336m, Nearest town: Hardwood. GPS: 45.971376, -87.679965

17 • B2 | Holmes Lake Mansfield Township Park

Total sites: 10, RV sites: 10, No water, No toilets, Tent & RV camping: Fee unk, Small RVs or, Open all year, Max Length: 30ft, Elev: 1411ft/430m, Tel: 906-875-6101, Nearest town: Mansfield. GPS: 46.106295, -88.126289

18 • B2 | Marquette Tourist Park

Total sites: 110, RV sites: 100, Elec sites: 100, Water at site, Flush toilet, Free showers, RV dump, Tents: $20/RVs: $35-40, 38 Full hookup, Stay limit: 14 days, Open May-Oct, Reservations accepted, Elev: 643ft/196m, Tel: 906-228-0465, Nearest town: Marquette. GPS: 46.568755, -87.412434

19 • B2 | Moose Rapids CG

Total sites: 11, RV sites: 11, No water, Vault/pit toilet, Tent & RV camping: $5, Elev: 1506ft/459m, Tel: 906-376-8827, Nearest town: North Republic. GPS: 46.457502, -88.073441

20 • B2 | Munising Municipal Tourist Park

Total sites: 127, RV sites: 104, Elec sites: 104, Water at site, Flush toilet, Free showers, RV dump, Tents: $25/RVs: $25-41, 26 Full hookup, Open May-Oct, Reservations accepted, Elev: 600ft/183m, Tel: 906-387-3145, Nearest town: Munising. GPS: 46.440624, -86.677511

21 • B2 | Northern Lights City CG

Total sites: 24, RV sites: 12, Elec sites: 12, Water at site, Vault/pit toilet, No showers, RV dump, Tents: $5/RVs: $20, Reservations accepted, Elev: 1514ft/461m, Tel: 906-376-8827, Nearest town: Republic. GPS: 46.405428, -87.981322

22 • B2 | Republic Beach

Dispersed sites, Tent & RV camping: $5, Reservations not

accepted, Elev: 1503ft/458m, Nearest town: Republic. GPS: 46.411534, -87.993537

23 • B2 | Runkle Lake Municipal Park

Total sites: 57, RV sites: 57, Elec sites: 17, Water at site, Flush toilet, Free showers, RV dump, Tents: $20/RVs: $20-25, 17 Full hookup, Open May-Sep, Elev: 1375ft/419m, Tel: 906-875-6647, Nearest town: Crystal Falls. GPS: 46.101563, -88.306396

24 • B2 | Sturgeon Bend Town Park

Total sites: 13, RV sites: 13, Central water, Vault/pit toilet, No showers, No RV dump, Tent & RV camping: $6, Reservations not accepted, Elev: 797ft/243m, Nearest town: Faithorn. GPS: 45.616284, -87.784385

25 • B2 | U.P. State Fairgrounds

Total sites: 765, RV sites: 765, Elec sites: 415, Water at site, Flush toilet, Free showers, RV dump, Tent & RV camping: $25, 120 Full hookup, Not available 3rd week of Aug - Fair Week, Open all year, Elev: 610ft/186m, Tel: 906-786-4011, Nearest town: Escanaba. GPS: 45.760788, -87.081708

26 • B3 | Aune-Osborn RV Park

Total sites: 100, RV sites: 100, Elec sites: 100, Water at site, Flush toilet, Free showers, RV dump, Tent & RV camping: $30-32, Open May-Oct, Reservations accepted, Elev: 574ft/175m, Tel: 906-632-3268, Nearest town: Sault Ste Marie. GPS: 46.488182, -84.306501

27 • B3 | Bill Wagner Memorial Park

Total sites: 22, RV sites: 22, Central water, Vault/pit toilet, No showers, No RV dump, Tent & RV camping: $5, Reservations not accepted, Elev: 574ft/175m, Tel: 231-448-2505, Nearest town: Beaver Island. GPS: 45.656326, -85.494658

28 • B3 | East Jordan Tourist Park

Total sites: 102, RV sites: 90, Elec sites: 90, Water at site, Flush toilet, Free showers, RV dump, Tents: $18/RVs: $26-36, 75 Full hookup, Open Apr-Oct, Reservations accepted, Elev: 574ft/175m, Tel: 231-536-2561, Nearest town: East Jordan. GPS: 45.156735, -85.141933

29 • B3 | Glen Gough City Park

Total sites: 18, RV sites: 18, Elec sites: 18, Water available, Flush toilet, Free showers, RV dump, Tent & RV camping: $12, Dump fee: $2, Reservations accepted, Elev: 607ft/185m, Tel: 906-647-3361, Nearest town: Pickford. GPS: 46.162203, -84.355227

30 • B3 | Gould City Township Park

Total sites: 6, RV sites: 0, Central water, Vault/pit toilet, No showers, No RV dump, Tents only: Free, Open May-Oct, Reservations not accepted, Elev: 587ft/179m, Nearest town: Gould City. GPS: 45.964476, -85.687916

31 • B3 | Hendricks Township Park

Total sites: 5, RV sites: 5, No water, Vault/pit toilet, Tent & RV camping: $10, Reservations not accepted, Elev: 584ft/178m, Nearest town: Epoufette. GPS: 46.057744, -85.171299

32 • B3 | Kinross RV Park East

Total sites: 64, RV sites: 64, Elec sites: 64, Water at site, Flush toilet, Free showers, RV dump, Tents: $15/RVs: $20, 64 Full hookup, $3 discount for seniors 65+, Open all year, Elev: 778ft/237m, Tel: 906-495-3023, Nearest town: Kincheloe. GPS: 46.261827, -84.460537

33 • B3 | Kinross RV Park West

Total sites: 70, RV sites: 52, Elec sites: 52, Water at site, Flush toilet, Free showers, RV dump, Tents: $15/RVs: $20, $3 discount for seniors 65+, Open all year, Elev: 794ft/242m, Tel: 906-495-3023, Nearest town: Kincheloe. GPS: 46.269011, -84.491416

34 • B3 | Magnus Park

Total sites: 72, RV sites: 72, Water at site, Flush toilet, Free showers, RV dump, Tents: $25/RVs: $27-50, Some Full hookup, Reservations accepted, Elev: 577ft/176m, Tel: 231-347-1027, Nearest town: Petoskey. GPS: 45.373290, -84.974360

35 • B3 | Seney Township CG

Total sites: 25, RV sites: 15, Elec sites: 15, Water at site, Flush toilet, No showers, No RV dump, Tent & RV camping: $15, Open May-Nov, Reservations not accepted, Elev: 728ft/222m, Tel: 906-499-3332, Nearest town: Seney. GPS: 46.353616, -85.962757

36 • B3 | Sherman City Park

Total sites: 25, RV sites: 25, Central water, Vault/pit toilet, No showers, No RV dump, Tent & RV camping: $20, $15 for local residents, Open May-Oct, Reservations not accepted, Elev: 607ft/185m, Tel: 906-632-5768, Nearest town: Sault Ste Marie. GPS: 46.485698, -84.419575

37 • B3 | St. James Township CG

Total sites: 12, RV sites: 12, Central water, Vault/pit toilet, No showers, No RV dump, Tent & RV camping: $5, Ferry to island, Open Apr-Nov, Reservations not accepted, Elev: 627ft/191m, Tel: 231-448-2505, Nearest town: Beaver Island. GPS: 45.748212, -85.539027

38 • B3 | Trout Lake City Park

Total sites: 83, RV sites: 83, Elec sites: 60, Central water, Flush toilet, Free showers, RV dump, Tents: $17/RVs: $22, Open May-Oct, Elev: 837ft/255m, Tel: 906-569-3299, Nearest town: Trout Lake. GPS: 46.191194, -85.042116

39 • B3 | Wooden Shoe City Park

Total sites: 52, RV sites: 45, Elec sites: 45, Water at site, Flush toilet, Free showers, RV dump, Tents: $20/RVs: $30, Open May-Sep, Reservations accepted, Elev: 640ft/195m, Tel: 231-588-6382 Nearest town: Banks. GPS: 45.164262, -85.238896

40 • B3 | Woodland City Park

Total sites: 151, RV sites: 132, Elec sites: 132, Water at site, Flush toilet, Pay showers, RV dump, Tents: $21/RVs: $27-30, Open Apr-Oct, Reservations not accepted, Elev: 591ft/180m, Tel: 906-494-2613, Nearest town: Grand Marais. GPS: 46.674060, -85.991470

41 • B4 | Drummond Island Township Park

Total sites: 43, RV sites: 43, Elec sites: 30, Central water, Vault/pit toilet, No showers, Tents: $14-16/RVs: $14-19, Ferry access, Max Length: 31ft, Reservations not accepted, Elev: 587ft/179m, Tel: 906-493-5245, Nearest town: Drummond Island. GPS: 45.997834, -83.787806

42 • C2 | Buttersville Park

Total sites: 56, RV sites: 44, Elec sites: 44, Central water, Flush toilet, Pay showers, RV dump, Tent & RV camping: $25, 16 seasonal sites, Open May-Oct, Reservations accepted, Elev: 676ft/206m, Tel: 231-843-2114, Nearest town: Ludington. GPS: 43.934858, -86.450776

43 • C2 | Cartier Park CG

Total sites: 185, RV sites: 185, Elec sites: 94, Water at site, Flush toilet, Free showers, RV dump, Tents: $24/RVs: $24-32, Full hookup sites, No generators, Open May-Oct, Reservations accepted, Elev: 597ft/182m, Tel: 231-845-1522, Nearest town: Ludington. GPS: 43.977073, -86.457839

44 • C2 | John Gurney City Park

Total sites: 88, RV sites: 88, Elec sites: 84, Water at site, Flush toilet, Free showers, RV dump, Tents: $20-23/RVs: $25-33, 10 Full hookup, Open Apr-Oct, Max Length: 76ft, Reservations accepted, Elev: 673ft/205m, Tel: 231-873-4959, Nearest town: Hart. GPS: 43.705515, -86.357944

45 • C2 | Menominee River City Park

Total sites: 58, RV sites: 58, Elec sites: 58, Water at site, RV dump, Tents: $20/RVs: $25-35, Full hookup sites, Open May-Oct, Reservations accepted, Elev: 587ft/179m, Tel: 906-863-5101, Nearest town: Menominee. GPS: 45.104481, -87.620359

46 • C2 | Penny Park

Total sites: 37, RV sites: 37, Elec sites: 10, Central water, Flush toilet, Free showers, No RV dump, Tents: $15/RVs: $21, Reservations not accepted, Elev: 577ft/176m, Tel: 231-723-9558, Nearest town: Eastlake. GPS: 44.251721, -86.297696

47 • C2 | Scottville Riverside Park

Total sites: 60, RV sites: 50, Elec sites: 50, Water at site, Flush toilet, Free showers, RV dump, Tents: $28/RVs: $33, Open May-Oct, Reservations accepted, Elev: 614ft/187m, Tel: 231-757-2429, Nearest town: Scottville. GPS: 43.943148, -86.276356

48 • C3 | Beulah Beach RV Park

Total sites: 20, RV sites: 20, Elec sites: 20, Water at site, Flush toilet, Free showers, RV dump, No tents/RVs: Fee unk, 20 Full hookup, Elev: 597ft/182m, Tel: 231-882-4451, Nearest town: Beulah. GPS: 44.627712, -86.098391

49 • C3 | Calhoun City CG

Total sites: 92, RV sites: 67, Elec sites: 58, Water at site, Flush toilet, Free showers, RV dump, Tents: $17/RVs: $25, Full hookup sites, Open May-Oct, Reservations accepted, Elev: 709ft/216m, Tel: 989-312-4401, Nearest town: Beaverton. GPS: 43.875645, -84.507722

50 • C3 | Coleman City Park

Dispersed sites, No tents/RVs: Free, Free - 3 nights, Reservations not accepted, Elev: 761ft/232m, Tel: 989-465-6961, Nearest town: Coleman. GPS: 43.758935, -84.584012

51 • C3 | Colfax Township Park/Lester A. Barnes Memorial Park

Dispersed sites, Tent & RV camping: Fee unk, Elev: 1304ft/397m, Nearest town: Mesick. GPS: 44.347674, -85.563415

52 • C3 | Empire Township CG

Total sites: 60, RV sites: 60, Elec sites: 9, Central water, Flush toilet, Pay showers, No RV dump, Tents: $25-28/RVs: $30, 3 group sites: $45, Open May-Sep, Reservations accepted, Elev: 942ft/287m, Tel: 231-326-5285, Nearest town: Empire. GPS: 44.787564, -86.003134

53 • C3 | Evart Riverside Park

Total sites: 15, RV sites: 15, Elec sites: 15, Water at site, Flush toilet, Free showers, RV dump, Tents: $12/RVs: $20-25, $5 discount RV sites for city residents, Open May-Sep, Reservations accepted, Elev: 992ft/302m, Tel: 231-734-2181, Nearest town: Evart. GPS: 43.896788, -85.257648

54 • C3 | Gladwin City Park

Total sites: 60, RV sites: 60, Central water, Flush toilet, Free showers, RV dump, Tent & RV camping: $27, Open May-Nov, Reservations accepted, Elev: 794ft/242m, Tel: 989-426-8126, Nearest town: South Cayuga. GPS: 43.978516, -84.491455

55 • C3 | Healey Lake SFC - City

Total sites: 24, RV sites: 24, Central water, Vault/pit toilet, No showers, No RV dump, Tent & RV camping: $20, Open May-Nov, Max Length: 20ft, Reservations not accepted, Elev: 800ft/244m, Tel: 231-864-2531, Nearest town: Copemish. GPS: 44.437465, -85.997666

56 • C3 | Hopkins City Park

Total sites: 30, RV sites: 30, Elec sites: 30, Central water, Flush toilet, Pay showers, RV dump, Tent & RV camping: $22-27, Reservations accepted, Elev: 758ft/231m, Tel: 231-383-2402, Nearest town: Bear Lake. GPS: 44.424057, -86.147753

57 • C3 | Kaleva Village Park

Total sites: 32, RV sites: 32, Elec sites: 6, Central water, Tents: $15/RVs: $20, Open all year, Max Length: 42ft, Reservations not accepted, Elev: 761ft/232m, Tel: 616-362-3366, Nearest town: Kaleva. GPS: 44.370242, -86.018031

58 • C3 | Lake Billings City CG

Total sites: 85, RV sites: 85, Elec sites: 85, Water at site, Flush toilet, Free showers, RV dump, Tent & RV camping: $24-26, 37 Full hookup, Open Apr-Oct, Elev: 1116ft/340m, Tel: 231-824-6454, Nearest town: Manton. GPS: 44.412473, -85.393814

59 • C3 | Maple Grove City Park

Total sites: 33, RV sites: 33, Elec sites: 33, Water at site, Flush toilet, Free showers, RV dump, Tent & RV camping: $20, 33 Full hookup, Open May-Nov, Reservations accepted, Elev: 1253ft/382m, Tel: 231-839-4429, Nearest town: Lake City. GPS: 44.331113, -85.207438

60 • C3 | Pettit Park

Total sites: 21, RV sites: 21, Elec sites: 16, Central water, No toilets, No showers, RV dump, Tents: $20/RVs: $25, Dump fee: $5, Reservations not accepted, Elev: 843ft/257m, Tel: 989-386-7541, Nearest town: Clare. GPS: 43.829607, -84.770816

61 • C3 | Powers Veterans Memorial Park

Total sites: 12, RV sites: 12, Elec sites: 12, Water at site, Flush toilet,

Free showers, RV dump, Tents: $14/RVs: $20, 12 Full hookup, Open Apr-Nov, Elev: 1095ft/334m, Tel: 231-667-0100, Nearest town: Marion. GPS: 44.098984, -85.150046

62 • C3 | Rambadt City Park

Total sites: 12, RV sites: 12, Elec sites: 12, Water at site, Flush toilet, Free showers, RV dump, Tents: $12/RVs: $20, Open May-Oct, Reservations not accepted, Elev: 1040ft/317m, Tel: 231-832-2245, Nearest town: Reed City. GPS: 43.885446, -85.515102

63 • C3 | Whitewater Township Park

Total sites: 53, RV sites: 53, Elec sites: 53, Central water, Flush toilet, Pay showers, RV dump, Tent & RV camping: $25-30, Open May-Sep, Reservations accepted, Elev: 617ft/188m, Tel: 231-267-5091, Nearest town: Williamsburg. GPS: 44.817122, -85.387059

64 • C4 | Au Gres City Park and CG

Total sites: 109, RV sites: 109, Elec sites: 109, Water at site, Flush toilet, Free showers, RV dump, Tent & RV camping: $29-33, 26 Full hookup, Open Apr-Oct, Reservations accepted, Elev: 581ft/177m, Tel: 989-876-8310, Nearest town: Au Gres. GPS: 44.049856, -83.688406

65 • C4 | East Tawas City Park

Total sites: 178, RV sites: 178, Elec sites: 178, Water at site, Flush toilet, Free showers, RV dump, Tent & RV camping: $35-40, 178 Full hookup, $20 15 Oct-1 May, Open all year, Max Length: 37ft, Reservations not accepted, Elev: 591ft/180m, Tel: 989-362-5562, Nearest town: East Tawas. GPS: 44.278430, -83.494990

66 • C4 | Emerick City Park

Total sites: 38, RV sites: 34, Elec sites: 34, Water at site, Flush toilet, Free showers, RV dump, Tents: $12/RVs: $16-20, 12 Full hookup, Reservations accepted, Elev: 771ft/235m, Tel: 989-733-0613, Nearest town: Hillman. GPS: 45.060091, -83.902095

67 • C4 | Finn Road City CG

Total sites: 56, RV sites: 56, Elec sites: 56, Water at site, Flush toilet, Free showers, RV dump, Tent & RV camping: $26-27, 56 Full hookup, Open May-Oct, Reservations accepted, Elev: 587ft/179m, Tel: 989-894-0055, Nearest town: Essexville. GPS: 43.627704, -83.778815

68 • C4 | McCollum Lake SFC

Total sites: 20, RV sites: 17, Central water, Vault/pit toilet, No showers, No RV dump, Tent & RV camping: $20, Also walk-to sites, Max Length: 40ft, Reservations not accepted, Elev: 932ft/284m, Tel: 989-848-8545, Nearest town: Clinton. GPS: 44.771014, -83.900483

69 • C4 | North Park CG

Total sites: 184, RV sites: 184, Elec sites: 184, Water at site, Flush toilet, Free showers, RV dump, Tents: $21/RVs: $25-26, 184 Full hookup, Reservations accepted, Elev: 594ft/181m, Tel: 989-479-9554, Nearest town: Harbor Beach. GPS: 43.855957, -82.656250

70 • C4 | Old Orchard City Park

Total sites: 525, RV sites: 231, Elec sites: 231, Water at site, Flush toilet, Free showers, RV dump, Tents: $21-23/RVs: $28-35, Also cabins, Open Mar-Nov, Reservations accepted, Elev: 659ft/201m, Tel: 989-739-7814, Nearest town: Oscoda. GPS: 44.444133, -83.482326

71 • D2 | Claybanks Township Park

Total sites: 68, RV sites: 68, Elec sites: 42, Central water, No toilets, No showers, RV dump, Tent & RV camping: $25, Open May-Sep, Reservations accepted, Elev: 653ft/199m, Tel: 231-861-8885, Nearest town: New Era. GPS: 43.530349, -86.485587

72 • D2 | Covert Park Beach and CG

Total sites: 62, RV sites: 53, Elec sites: 53, Water at site, Flush toilet, Free showers, RV dump, Tents: $31-40/RVs: $34, Also cabins, Pet fee: $4, $5 discount for county residents, Open May-Oct, Reservations accepted, Elev: 689ft/210m, Tel: 269-764-1421, Nearest town: Covert. GPS: 42.299620, -86.325530

73 • D2 | Trailway City CG

Total sites: 53, RV sites: 53, Elec sites: 50, Water at site, Flush toilet, Free showers, RV dump, No tents/RVs: $45, Bicycle tenters allowed, 50 Full hookup, Open May-Oct, Reservations accepted, Elev: 594ft/181m, Tel: 231-894-4903, Nearest town: Montague. GPS: 43.416453, -86.353175

74 • D3 | Big Bend City Park

Total sites: 225, RV sites: 225, Elec sites: 225, Water at site, Flush toilet, Free showers, RV dump, Tent & RV camping: $25-26, $15 Oct-Apr, Open Apr-Oct, Reservations accepted, Elev: 869ft/265m, Tel: 231-689-6325, Nearest town: White Cloud. GPS: 43.523709, -85.582258

75 • D3 | Blanchard Millpond City Park

Dispersed sites, Central water, No toilets, No showers, RV dump, Tent & RV camping: $5, Reservations accepted, Elev: 925ft/282m, Tel: 989-561-5050, Nearest town: Blanchard. GPS: 43.524912, -85.071213

76 • D3 | Brookside City Park

Total sites: 4, RV sites: 4, Elec sites: 4, Vault/pit toilet, No tents/RVs: $15, Register at police station, Reservations not accepted, Elev: 705ft/215m, Tel: 269-692-3391, Nearest town: Otsego. GPS: 42.455452, -85.684632

77 • D3 | Croton Township Park

Total sites: 150, Central water, Flush toilet, Free showers, RV dump, Tents: $18/RVs: $24-27, Open Apr-Oct, Max Length: 36ft Reservations accepted, Elev: 778ft/237m, Tel: 231-652-4642 Nearest town: Newaygo. GPS: 43.447925, -85.658723

78 • D3 | First Lake Park

Total sites: 10, RV sites: 10, Tent & RV camping: Fee unk Unconfirmed, Elev: 921ft/281m, Tel: 989-365-3555, Nearest town: Six Lakes. GPS: 43.435796, -85.143787

79 • D3 | Fremont Lake City Park

Total sites: 98, RV sites: 98, Elec sites: 98, Water at site, Flush toilet Free showers, RV dump, Tents: $15/RVs: $30, Open Apr-Oct Elev: 768ft/234m, Tel: 231-924-2101, Nearest town: Fremont GPS: 43.457769, -85.960972

80 • D3 | Hudsonville Community Fairgrounds

Total sites: 83, RV sites: 83, Elec sites: 83, Central water, Flush toilet, Free showers, RV dump, No tents/RVs: $15, Max Length: 35ft, Elev: 633ft/193m, Tel: 616-669-1630, Nearest town: Hudsonville. GPS: 42.864661, -85.878579

81 • D3 | Ionia Free Fairgrounds

Total sites: 430, RV sites: 430, Elec sites: 340, RV dump, No tents/RVs: $25, Open Apr-Oct, Elev: 636ft/194m, Tel: 616-527-1310, Nearest town: Ionia. GPS: 42.976467, -85.070991

82 • D3 | Oxbow City Park

Total sites: 197, RV sites: 190, Elec sites: 190, Water at site, Flush toilet, Free showers, RV dump, Tents: $15/RVs: $25, Open Apr-Oct, Reservations accepted, Elev: 856ft/261m, Tel: 231-856-4279, Nearest town: Newaygo. GPS: 43.504296, -85.608554

83 • D3 | Tanglefoot City Park

Total sites: 38, RV sites: 38, Elec sites: 38, Water at site, Flush toilet, Free showers, RV dump, No tents/RVs: $55, 38 Full hookup, Open Apr-Oct, Reservations accepted, Elev: 591ft/180m, Tel: 616-842-1393, Nearest town: Spring Lake. GPS: 43.075046, -86.201824

84 • D4 | Arthur Latham City Park

Total sites: 4, RV sites: 4, Tent & RV camping: $8, Open May-Sep, Reservations not accepted, Elev: 735ft/224m, Tel: 989-871-2459, Nearest town: Millington. GPS: 43.281343, -83.547567

85 • D4 | Camp Dearborn

Total sites: 191, RV sites: 191, Elec sites: 191, Flush toilet, Free showers, RV dump, Tent & RV camping: $26-42, Also cabins, Open May-Oct, Reservations accepted, Elev: 997ft/304m, Tel: 248-684-6000, Nearest town: Milford. GPS: 42.580747, -83.635633

86 • D4 | Otter Lake City Park

Total sites: 38, RV sites: 38, Elec sites: 34, Water at site, Flush toilet, Free showers, RV dump, Tents: $25/RVs: $33-38, 34 Full hookup, No generators, Open Apr-Oct, Reservations accepted, Elev: 850ft/259m, Tel: 810-793-4258, Nearest town: Otter Lake. GPS: 43.214069, -83.458987

87 • D4 | Showboat Park - Tom Graham Memorial CG

Total sites: 40, RV sites: 22, Elec sites: 22, Central water, Flush toilet, Free showers, Tents: $22/RVs: $25, Open May-Oct, Reservations accepted, Elev: 621ft/189m, Tel: 989-845-3800, Nearest town: Chesaning. GPS: 43.176867, -84.114734

88 • D4 | Water Tower Travel Trailer Park

Total sites: 30, RV sites: 30, Elec sites: 30, Water at site, Flush toilet, Free showers, RV dump, Tents: $17/RVs: $28, Full hookup sites, Dump fee - $10, Water fill - $10, Open May-Oct, Reservations accepted, Elev: 820ft/250m, Tel: 810-667-7163, Nearest town: Lapeer. GPS: 43.066282, -83.318086

89 • E2 | Shamrock City Park

Total sites: 124, RV sites: 124, Elec sites: 99, Water at site, Flush toilet, Free showers, RV dump, Tents: $25/RVs: $30-35, Also cabins, 69 Full hookup, Open all year, Elev: 607ft/185m, Tel: 269-473-5691, Nearest town: Berrien Springs. GPS: 41.953375, -86.331644

90 • E2 | Weko Beach

Total sites: 70, RV sites: 70, Elec sites: 43, Water at site, Flush toilet, Free showers, RV dump, Tents: $30/RVs: $30-35, Also cabins, Open Apr-Oct, Reservations accepted, Elev: 627ft/191m, Tel: 269-465-5407, Nearest town: Bridgman. GPS: 41.941911, -86.581366

Minnesota

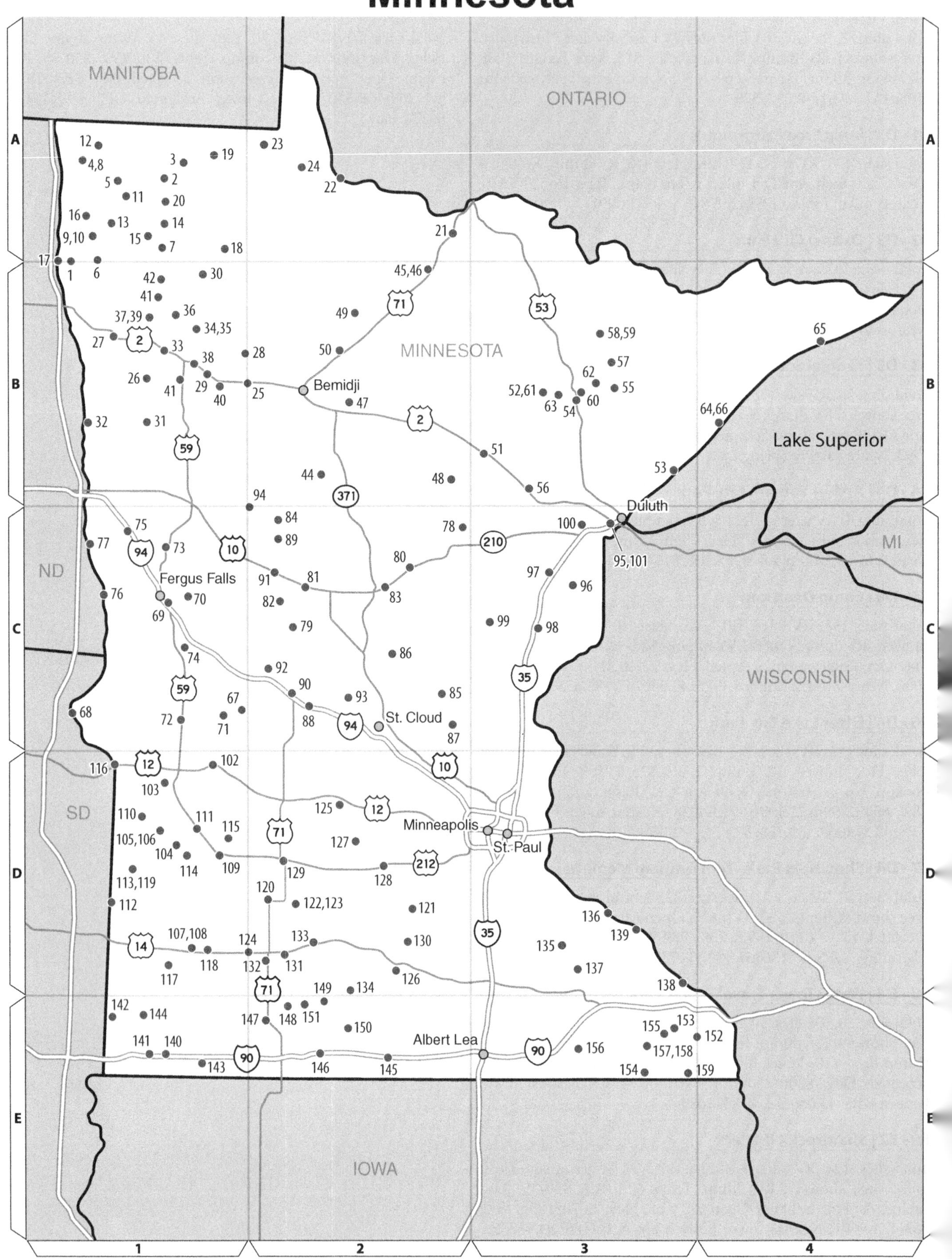
MANITOBA
ONTARIO
MINNESOTA
Lake Superior
ND
SD
WISCONSIN
MI
IOWA
Bemidji
Duluth
Fergus Falls
St. Cloud
Minneapolis
St. Paul
Albert Lea
A
B
C
D
E
1
2
3
4

Map	ID	Map	ID
A1	1-20	C3	95-101
A2	21-24	D1	102-119
B1	25-43	D2	120-134
B2	44-50	D3	135-139
B3	51-63	E1	140-144
B4	64-66	E2	145-151
C1	67-77	E3	152-159
C2	78-94		

Alphabetical List of Camping Areas

1 • A1 | Alvarado City Park

Total sites: 6, RV sites: 6, Elec sites: 6, Water at site, No toilets, No showers, RV dump, Tent & RV camping: $15, Full hookup sites, Elev: 812ft/247m, Tel: 218-965-4911, Nearest town: Alvarado. GPS: 48.189612, -97.000793

2 • A1 | American Legion Park

Total sites: 16, RV sites: 6, Elec sites: 6, Water at site, Flush toilet, Free showers, RV dump, Tents: $10/RVs: $15, Elev: 1073ft/327m, Tel: 218-782-2570, Nearest town: Greenbush. GPS: 48.693793, -96.194127

3 • A1 | Durgin Memorial Park

Total sites: 6, RV sites: 6, Elec sites: 3, Water at site, No toilets, No showers, RV dump, Tents: $8/RVs: $12, Near RR, Open May-Sep, Reservations not accepted, Elev: 1066ft/325m, Tel: 218-528-3670, Nearest town: Badger. GPS: 48.782421, -96.017441

4 • A1 | Gilbert Olson Park

Total sites: 36, RV sites: 36, Elec sites: 36, Water available, Flush toilet, Free showers, RV dump, Tent & RV camping: $20, Some seasonal sites, Open May-Sep, Reservations accepted, Elev: 810ft/247m, Tel: 218-843-2737, Nearest town: Hallock. GPS: 48.770041, -96.934313

5 • A1 | Halma City Park

Dispersed sites, Vault/pit toilet, Tent & RV camping: Fee unk, Reservations not accepted, Elev: 998ft/304m, Tel: 218-436-2738, Nearest town: Halma. GPS: 48.661359, -96.599863

6 • A1 | Holiday City Park

Total sites: 80, RV sites: 65, Elec sites: 80, Water at site, Flush toilet, Free showers, RV dump, Tents: $16/RVs: $27-32, 31 Full hookup, Open May-Sep, Reservations accepted, Elev: 863ft/263m, Tel: 218-201-0743, Nearest town: Warren. GPS: 48.204379, -96.760824

7 • A1 | Holt Park

Dispersed sites, No water, Vault/pit toilet, Tent & RV camping: Fee unk, Open all year, Elev: 1152ft/351m, Tel: 218-449-3015, Nearest town: Holt. GPS: 48.291889, -96.192614

8 • A1 | Horseshoe Park

Total sites: 11, RV sites: 11, Elec sites: 11, Water available, Flush toilet, Free showers, RV dump, Tent & RV camping: $20, Some seasonal sites, Open May-Sep, Reservations accepted, Elev: 810ft/247m, Tel: 218-843-2737, Nearest town: Hallock. GPS: 48.776926, -96.945979

9 • A1 | Island Park

Total sites: 4, RV sites: 4, Elec sites: 4, Water at site, No toilets No showers, No RV dump, Tents: $8/RVs: $9, Open May-Oct Elev: 843ft/257m, Tel: 218-437-6621, Nearest town: Argyle. GPS 48.336821, -96.812356

10 • A1 | John Kurz Memorial Park

Total sites: 4, RV sites: 4, Elec sites: 4, Central water, No toilets, No showers, No RV dump, Tent & RV camping: $6, Open May-Oct Reservations not accepted, Elev: 830ft/253m, Tel: 218-437-6621 Nearest town: Argyle. GPS: 48.339723, -96.817409

11 • A1 | Karlstad Moose Park

Total sites: 12, RV sites: 12, Elec sites: 12, Water at site, No toilets No showers, RV dump, Tent & RV camping: $10, Near RR Reservations not accepted, Elev: 1037ft/316m, Tel: 218-436-217[illegible] Nearest town: Karlstad. GPS: 48.581096, -96.525742

12 • A1 | Lancaster City Park

Total sites: 28, RV sites: 28, Elec sites: 28, Central water, Flush toilet, Free showers, RV dump, Tents: $15/RVs: $20, Elev: 912ft/278m, Tel: 218-754-7585, Nearest town: Lancaster. GPS: 48.863404, -96.798284

13 • A1 | Marshall CP at Florian

Total sites: 104, RV sites: 104, Elec sites: 104, Water at site, Flush toilet, Free showers, RV dump, Tents: $15/RVs: $25-30, Open May-Sep, Reservations accepted, Elev: 928ft/283m, Tel: 218-478-3658, Nearest town: Stephen. GPS: 48.428367, -96.655714

14 • A1 | Middle River City Park

Total sites: 12, RV sites: 12, Elec sites: 12, Central water, Flush toilet, Free showers, RV dump, Tent & RV camping: $20, Open Apr-Nov, Elev: 1135ft/346m, Tel: 218-222-3511, Nearest town: Middle River. GPS: 48.433988, -96.166147

15 • A1 | Newfolden City Park

Total sites: 6, RV sites: 3, Elec sites: 3, Water at site, No toilets, No showers, RV dump, Tent & RV camping: $16, No campfires, Open May-Nov, Reservations accepted, Elev: 1086ft/331m, Tel: 218-874-7405, Nearest town: Newfolden. GPS: 48.351509, -96.324842

16 • A1 | Northwest Acres City CG

Total sites: 27, RV sites: 27, Elec sites: 27, Water at site, Flush toilet, Free showers, RV dump, Tents: $6/RVs: $20, 27 Full hookup, Reservations accepted, Elev: 824ft/251m, Tel: 218-478-3614, Nearest town: Stephen. GPS: 48.451776, -96.881576

17 • A1 | Oslo City Park

Total sites: 6, RV sites: 6, Elec sites: 6, Water at site, No toilets, No showers, No RV dump, Tent & RV camping: Fee unk, Elev: 804ft/245m, Tel: 218-695-3841, Nearest town: Oslo. GPS: 48.192941, -97.130949

18 • A1 | Ralph J. Klein City Park

Total sites: 6, RV sites: 6, Elec sites: 6, Water at site, Flush toilet, Free showers, RV dump, Tents: $15/RVs: $25, 6 Full hookup, Reservations accepted, Elev: 1168ft/356m, Tel: 218-294-6292, Nearest town: Grygla. GPS: 48.301953, -95.622946

19 • A1 | Roseau City Park

Total sites: 20, RV sites: 10, Elec sites: 10, Water at site, Flush toilet, Free showers, RV dump, Tent & RV camping: $10, Elev: 1050ft/320m, Tel: 218-463-1542, Nearest town: Roseau. GPS: 48.835128, -95.749875

20 • A1 | Strathcona City Park

Total sites: 3, RV sites: 3, Elec sites: 3, Water at site, Vault/pit toilet, No showers, No RV dump, Tent & RV camping: Fee unk, Reservations not accepted, Elev: 1124ft/343m, Tel: 218-781-2242, Nearest town: Strathcona. GPS: 48.552379, -96.168695

21 • A2 | Lofgren Memorial Park

Total sites: 12, RV sites: 12, Elec sites: 12, Water at site, Flush toilet, Free showers, Tents: $15/RVs: $15-20, Open Apr-Oct, Elev: 1125ft/343m, Tel: 916-764-5954, Nearest town: Little Fork. GPS: 48.399835, -93.564088

22 • A2 | Timber Mill Community Park CG

Total sites: 38, RV sites: 38, Elec sites: 16, Water available, Flush toilet, Pay showers, RV dump, Tents: $20/RVs: $35, Open May-Oct, Reservations accepted, Elev: 1089ft/332m, Tel: 218-634-1850, Nearest town: Baudette. GPS: 48.719345, -94.601235

23 • A2 | Warroad City CG

Total sites: 182, RV sites: 172, Elec sites: 92, Water at site, Flush toilet, Free showers, RV dump, Tents: $25/RVs: $30-40, Unk # Full hookup, Open May-Oct, Reservations accepted, Elev: 1060ft/323m, Tel: 218-386-1004, Nearest town: Warroad. GPS: 48.906291, -95.301238

24 • A2 | Williams City Park

Total sites: 25, RV sites: 10, Elec sites: 10, Central water, No toilets, No showers, RV dump, Tents: $11/RVs: $22, 10 Full hookup, Open May-Nov, Reservations accepted, Elev: 1152ft/351m, Tel: 218-783-3271, Nearest town: Williams. GPS: 48.771915, -94.957914

25 • B1 | Bagley City Park

Total sites: 50, RV sites: 40, Elec sites: 40, Central water, Flush toilet, Free showers, RV dump, Tents: $15/RVs: $25, Open May-Oct, Reservations accepted, Elev: 1463ft/446m, Tel: 218-694-2871, Nearest town: Bagley. GPS: 47.528330, -95.399810

26 • B1 | Cannon Park

Total sites: 4, RV sites: 4, Elec sites: 4, Central water, Flush toilet, Pay showers, No RV dump, No tents/RVs: $15, Showers at Nature Center, Open May-Sep, Elev: 1142ft/348m, Tel: 218-945-3136, Nearest town: Fertile. GPS: 47.531926, -96.282577

27 • B1 | Central City Park

Total sites: 16, RV sites: 16, Elec sites: 16, Central water, Flush toilet, Free showers, RV dump, Tents: $15/RVs: $20, Open May-Oct, Reservations not accepted, Elev: 850ft/259m, Tel: 218-281-1232, Nearest town: Crookston. GPS: 47.773682, -96.601563

28 • B1 | Clearbrook City Park

Total sites: 35, RV sites: 15, Elec sites: 15, Water at site, Flush toilet, Free showers, RV dump, Tents: $10/RVs: $20, 15 Full hookup, Open Apr-Oct, Reservations not accepted, Elev: 1335ft/407m, Tel: 218-776-2323, Nearest town: Clearbrook. GPS: 47.696947, -95.428096

29 • B1 | Fosston City CG

Total sites: 10, RV sites: 10, Elec sites: 10, Central water, Flush toilet, Free showers, RV dump, Tents: $5/RVs: $16, Open May-Oct, Reservations not accepted, Elev: 1293ft/394m, Tel: 218-435-1959, Nearest town: Fosston. GPS: 47.573975, -95.754639

30 • B1 | Goodridge Lions Park

Total sites: 4, RV sites: 4, Elec sites: 4, Water at site, No toilets, No showers, No RV dump, Tent & RV camping: Fee unk, Reservations not accepted, Elev: 1168ft/356m, Tel: 218-378-4646, Nearest town: Goodridge. GPS: 48.143558, -95.809115

31 • B1 | Heiberg Park

Total sites: 5, RV sites: 5, Elec sites: 5, Vault/pit toilet, Tent & RV camping: $10, Reservations not accepted, Elev: 1010ft/308m,

Tel: 218-584-5254, Nearest town: Twin Valley. GPS: 47.283102, -96.275861

32 • B1 | Hendrum Community Park

Total sites: 4, RV sites: 4, Elec sites: 4, Water at site, Flush toilet, No showers, RV dump, Tent & RV camping: $15, Free 1st night, Max Length: 35ft, Elev: 866ft/264m, Tel: 218-861-6210, Nearest town: Hendrum. GPS: 47.269079, -96.791651

33 • B1 | Mentor City Park

Dispersed sites, Central water, Vault/pit toilet, No showers, No RV dump, Tent & RV camping: Fee unk, Elev: 1155ft/352m, Tel: 218-637-2911, Nearest town: Mentor. GPS: 47.700507, -96.141817

34 • B1 | Oklee City Park - North

Dispersed sites, Tent & RV camping: Fee unk, Elev: 1155ft/352m, Tel: 218-796-5183, Nearest town: Oklee. GPS: 47.844668, -95.858211

35 • B1 | Oklee City Park - South

Dispersed sites, No toilets, Tent & RV camping: Fee unk, Elev: 1148ft/350m, Tel: 218-796-5183, Nearest town: Oklee. GPS: 47.815418, -95.858168

36 • B1 | Plummer Park

Total sites: 4, RV sites: 4, Elec sites: 4, Water at site, Flush toilet, Free showers, RV dump, Tent & RV camping: $10, Reservations not accepted, Elev: 1119ft/341m, Tel: 218-465-4231, Nearest town: Plummer. GPS: 47.910552, -96.038792

37 • B1 | Riverside City Park

Total sites: 14, RV sites: 14, Elec sites: 14, Water at site, Flush toilet, Free showers, RV dump, Tents: $20/RVs: $28-30, 9 Full hookup, Elev: 965ft/294m, Tel: 218-253-2684, Nearest town: Red Lake Falls. GPS: 47.887301, -96.275135

38 • B1 | Roholt McIntosh City Park

Total sites: 7, RV sites: 7, Elec sites: 7, Central water, Flush toilet, Free showers, RV dump, Tents: $6/RVs: $6-12, Open May-Oct, Reservations not accepted, Elev: 1218ft/371m, Tel: 218-563-3043, Nearest town: McIntosh. GPS: 47.633956, -95.883703

39 • B1 | Sportsman Park

Total sites: 40, RV sites: 17, Elec sites: 17, Water at site, Flush toilet, Free showers, RV dump, Tents: $20/RVs: $28-30, 10 Full hookup, Reservations accepted, Elev: 955ft/291m, Tel: 218-253-2684, Nearest town: Red Lake Falls. GPS: 47.890539, -96.282678

40 • B1 | Spring Lake City Park

Dispersed sites, No toilets, Tent & RV camping: Fee unk, Elev: 1357ft/414m, Tel: 218-668-2219, Nearest town: Lengby. GPS: 47.505615, -95.639007

41 • B1 | St. Hilaire City Park

Total sites: 35, RV sites: 35, Elec sites: 35, Water at site, Flush toilet, Free showers, RV dump, Tent & RV camping: Fee unk, 30 Full hookup, Reservations accepted, Elev: 1066ft/325m, Tel: 218-964-5257, Nearest town: St Hilaire. GPS: 48.009976, -96.210332

42 • B1 | Thief River Falls Tourist Park

Total sites: 72, RV sites: 72, Elec sites: 72, Water at site, Flush toilet, Free showers, RV dump, Tents: $20/RVs: $25-30, 16 Full hookup, Open May-Oct, Reservations accepted, Elev: 1122ft/342m, Tel: 218-681-2519, Nearest town: Thief River Falls. GPS: 48.110070, -96.186210

43 • B1 | Winger Depot Park

Dispersed sites, Central water, No RV dump, Tent & RV camping: Fee unk, Beside RR, Elev: 1239ft/378m, Tel: 218-938-4150, Nearest town: Winger. GPS: 47.537785, -95.985806

44 • B2 | Akeley City CG

Total sites: 42, RV sites: 28, Elec sites: 28, Water at site, Flush toilet, Free showers, RV dump, Tents: $30/RVs: $45, No water in winter, Open all year, Reservations accepted, Elev: 1408ft/429m, Tel: 218-252-4570, Nearest town: Akeley. GPS: 47.007413, -94.733913

45 • B2 | Big Falls City CG - Family

Total sites: 30, RV sites: 18, Elec sites: 18, Water at site, Flush toilet, Free showers, RV dump, Tents: $20/RVs: $30, Open May-Oct, Reservations accepted, Elev: 1165ft/355m, Tel: 218-276-3300, Nearest town: Big Falls. GPS: 48.194978, -93.802181

46 • B2 | Big Falls City CG - Horse Camp

Total sites: 6, RV sites: 6, Elec sites: 6, Water at site, Flush toilet, Free showers, Tent & RV camping: $30, Showers across road, Generator hours: 0700-2200, Open May-Oct, Reservations accepted, Elev: 1198ft/365m, Tel: 218-276-3300, Nearest town: Big Falls. GPS: 48.194855, -93.799067

47 • B2 | Camp Cassaway - City

Total sites: 4, RV sites: 4, Tent & RV camping: Fee unk, Elev: 1293ft/394m, Nearest town: Cass Lake. GPS: 47.422176, -94.497473

48 • B2 | Hill City Park

Total sites: 34, RV sites: 14, Elec sites: 14, Water available, Flush toilet, Free showers, No RV dump, Tents: $20/RVs: $35-45, 5 Full hookup, Dump Station at Sunny's (corner of HWY 169 & HWY 200): $10, Open May-Oct, Elev: 1283ft/391m, Tel: 218-697-2301, Nearest town: Hill City. GPS: 46.994136, -93.591051

49 • B2 | Paul Bunyan Memorial Park

Total sites: 6, RV sites: 6, Elec sites: 6, Water at site, Flush toilet Free showers, RV dump, Tents: $10/RVs: $20, 6 Full hookup Reservations accepted, Elev: 1358ft/414m, Tel: 218-647-8470 Nearest town: Kelliher. GPS: 47.939888, -94.448142

50 • B2 | Pine Tree City Park

Total sites: 32, RV sites: 23, Elec sites: 23, Central water, Flush toilet Free showers, RV dump, Tents: $22/RVs: $27-30, Reservation accepted, Elev: 1384ft/422m, Tel: 218-835-4803, Nearest town Blackduck. GPS: 47.731541, -94.586766

51 • B3 | American Legion Park

Total sites: 10, RV sites: 10, Elec sites: 10, Water at site, Flush toilet, Free showers, RV dump, Tents: $25-30/RVs: $25-35, 7 Fu hookup, Elev: 1283ft/391m, Tel: 218-326-6420, Nearest town Warba. GPS: 47.137789, -93.299719

52 • B3 | Buhl City Park

Total sites: 8, RV sites: 3, Tent & RV camping: Fee unk, Open May-Sep, Reservations not accepted, Elev: 1519ft/463m, Tel: 218-258-3226, Nearest town: Buhl. GPS: 47.489174, -92.781024

53 • B3 | Burlington Bay City Campsite

Total sites: 146, RV sites: 136, Elec sites: 136, Water at site, Flush toilet, Free showers, RV dump, Tents: $26-30/RVs: $36-41, 70 Full hookup, Open May-Oct, Reservations accepted, Elev: 640ft/195m, Tel: 218-834 2021, Nearest town: Two Harbors. GPS: 47.027115, -91.660442

54 • B3 | Eveleth Veterans Memorial Park

Total sites: 38, RV sites: 31, Elec sites: 31, Water at site, Flush toilet, Free showers, RV dump, Tent & RV camping: $25, Open May-Sep, Reservations accepted, Elev: 1402ft/427m, Tel: 218-744-7491, Nearest town: Eveleth. GPS: 47.438067, -92.504666

55 • B3 | Fisherman's Point City CG

Total sites: 70, RV sites: 70, Elec sites: 67, Flush toilet, Free showers, Tents: $15/RVs: $25-30, No water in off-season- $13, Open Apr-Sep, Reservations accepted, Elev: 1444ft/440m, Tel: 218-225-3337, Nearest town: Hoyt Lakes. GPS: 47.504639, -92.171387

56 • B3 | Floodwood Municipal CG

Total sites: 9, RV sites: 9, Elec sites: 9, Flush toilet, Free showers, RV dump, Tent & RV camping: $20, Open May-Sep, Reservations accepted, Elev: 1249ft/381m, Tel: 218-476-2751, Nearest town: Floodwood. GPS: 46.930171, -92.911052

57 • B3 | Heritage City Park

Total sites: 17, RV sites: 10, Elec sites: 10, Water at site, Flush toilet, Free showers, RV dump, Tents: $15/RVs: $22, Open May-Sep, Elev: 1447ft/441m, Tel: 218-984-2084, Nearest town: Embarrass. GPS: 47.662681, -92.193486

58 • B3 | Hoodoo Point City CG

Total sites: 85, RV sites: 85, Elec sites: 77, Water at site, Flush toilet, Free showers, RV dump, Tents: $31/RVs: $31-45, Open May-Sep, Reservations accepted, Elev: 1365ft/416m, Tel: 218-753-6868, Nearest town: Tower. GPS: 47.819421, -92.299122

59 • B3 | McKinley City Park

Total sites: 60, RV sites: 52, Elec sites: 52, Water at site, Flush toilet, Free showers, RV dump, Tents: $27/RVs: $45, Open May-Sep, Elev: 1375ft/419m, Tel: 218-753-5921, Nearest town: Soudan. GPS: 47.827966, -92.273511

60 • B3 | Sherwood Forest City CG

Total sites: 50, RV sites: 44, Elec sites: 44, Water at site, Flush toilet, Free showers, RV dump, Tents: $20/RVs: $22-25, 32 Full hookup, 5 sites available in winter, Open May-Oct, Reservations accepted, Elev: 1499ft/457m, Tel: 218-748-2221, Nearest town: Gilbert. GPS: 47.484229, -92.463971

61 • B3 | Stubler Beach

Total sites: 8, Central water, Vault/pit toilet, No showers, No RV dump, Tents only: $7, Open May-Sep, Reservations not accepted, Elev: 1472ft/449m, Tel: 218-258-3226, Nearest town: Buhl. GPS: 47.489995, -92.788455

62 • B3 | Vermilion Trail CG

Total sites: 54, RV sites: 46, Elec sites: 46, Water available, Flush toilet, Free showers, RV dump, Tent & RV camping: $19-22, Open May-Sep, Reservations accepted, Elev: 1434ft/437m, Tel: 218-865-6705, Nearest town: Biwabik. GPS: 47.530842, -92.326637

63 • B3 | West Two River Park

Total sites: 49, RV sites: 49, Elec sites: 49, Central water, Flush toilet, Free showers, Tent & RV camping: $35, Generator hours: 0800-2200, Open May-Sep, Reservations accepted, Elev: 1417ft/432m, Tel: 218-748-7570, Nearest town: Mountain Iron. GPS: 47.481238, -92.662033

64 • B4 | Black Beach City CG

Total sites: 49, RV sites: 49, Elec sites: 49, Water at site, Flush toilet, Free showers, No RV dump, Tents: $30/RVs: $30-40, 34 Full hookup, Dump station in town, Generator hours: 0800-2200, Open May-Oct, Max Length: 75ft, Reservations accepted, Elev: 695ft/212m, Nearest town: Silver Bay. GPS: 47.299264, -91.250893

65 • B4 | Grand Marais City RV Park

Total sites: 300, RV sites: 243, Elec sites: 243, Water at site, Flush toilet, Free showers, RV dump, Tents: $22-33/RVs: $39-56, 161 Full hookup, May-Jun 14 & Oct: Tents: $17-$28/RVs: $34-$51, Open all year, Reservations accepted, Elev: 604ft/184m, Tel: 218-387-1712, Nearest town: Grand Marais. GPS: 47.746094, -90.345215

66 • B4 | Silver Bay RV Parking

Total sites: 5, RV sites: 5, No toilets, RV dump, No tents/RVs: Free, Near RR, Elev: 945ft/288m, Nearest town: Silver Bay. GPS: 47.291069, -91.266357

67 • C1 | Barsness City Park

Total sites: 50, RV sites: 37, Elec sites: 1, Water at site, Flush toilet, Free showers, RV dump, Tents: $27/RVs: $42-27, Some Full hookup sites, Stay limit: 14 days, Open May-Sep, Elev: 1230ft/375m, Tel: 320-634-5433, Nearest town: Glenwood. GPS: 45.641205, -95.380116

68 • C1 | Browns Valley City Park

Total sites: 4, RV sites: 4, Elec sites: 4, Water at site, Flush toilet, No showers, RV dump, Tents: $10/RVs: $15, Open May-Oct, Reservations not accepted, Elev: 978ft/298m, Tel: 320-695-2110, Nearest town: Browns Valley. GPS: 45.595516, -96.841875

69 • C1 | Delagoon City CG

Total sites: 36, RV sites: 14, Elec sites: 14, Central water, No toilets, No showers, Tents: $10/RVs: $20, Open May-Oct, Reservations not accepted, Elev: 1224ft/373m, Tel: 218-739-3205, Nearest town: Fergus Falls. GPS: 46.257767, -96.037211

70 • C1 | Eagle Stone City CG

Total sites: 10, Central water, Flush toilet, Tent & RV camping: $10, Reservations not accepted, Elev: 1329ft/405m, Nearest town: Underwood. GPS: 46.288061, -95.871319

71 • C1 | Hobo Park - Starbuck CG

Total sites: 104, RV sites: 102, Elec sites: 102, Water at site, Flush toilet, Free showers, RV dump, Tents: $21/RVs: $34-45, 55 seasonal sites, Open May-Sep, Elev: 1135ft/346m, Tel: 320-239-2336, Nearest town: Starbuck. GPS: 45.607888, -95.528872

72 • C1 | Pomme De Terre City Park

Total sites: 28, RV sites: 28, Elec sites: 28, Central water, Flush toilet, Free showers, No RV dump, Tents: $15/RVs: $20, Reservations not accepted, Elev: 1089ft/332m, Tel: 320-589-3141, Nearest town: Morris. GPS: 45.572155, -95.881908

73 • C1 | Sherin Memorial City CG

Total sites: 11, RV sites: 10, Elec sites: 10, Central water, Flush toilet, Free showers, RV dump, Tents: $15/RVs: $20, Stay limit: 14 days, Open May-Sep, Elev: 1339ft/408m, Tel: 218-863-6571, Nearest town: Pelican Rapids. GPS: 46.570166, -96.079141

74 • C1 | Tipsinah Mounds City Park

Total sites: 79, RV sites: 29, Elec sites: 29, Water at site, Flush toilet, Free showers, RV dump, Tents: $26/RVs: $42-49, Also cabins, Some Full hookup, Open May-Sep, Reservations accepted, Elev: 1181ft/360m, Tel: 218-685-5114, Nearest town: Elbow Lake. GPS: 45.998595, -95.887296

75 • C1 | Wagner Park

Total sites: 78, RV sites: 28, Elec sites: 28, Water at site, Flush toilet, Pay showers, RV dump, Tents: $12/RVs: $25, 28 Full hookup, $15 in winter, Open all year, Reservations accepted, Elev: 1030ft/314m, Tel: 800-354-2292, Nearest town: Barnesville. GPS: 46.661102, -96.407531

76 • C1 | Welles Memorial Park

Total sites: 11, RV sites: 7, Elec sites: 7, Central water, Vault/pit toilet, No showers, No RV dump, Tents: $10/RVs: $20, Open May-Oct, Reservations not accepted, Elev: 955ft/291m, Tel: 218-643-3455, Nearest town: Breckenridge. GPS: 46.265041, -96.595844

77 • C1 | Wolverton City Park

Total sites: 4, RV sites: 4, Elec sites: 4, Water at site, Tent & RV camping: $10, Reservations not accepted, Elev: 931ft/284m, Tel: 218-995-2526, Nearest town: Wolverton. GPS: 46.565604, -96.735557

78 • C2 | Berglund CP

Total sites: 9, RV sites: 9, Elec sites: 9, Central water, Flush toilet, Free showers, RV dump, Tent & RV camping: $20, $5 donation appreciated for RV dump use, Elev: 1211ft/369m, Tel: 218-927-7364, Nearest town: Palisade. GPS: 46.709957, -93.486216

79 • C2 | Clarissa City Park

Total sites: 5, RV sites: 5, Elec sites: 5, Water at site, No toilets, No showers, RV dump, Tent & RV camping: Donation, 1 week free - then $5/day, Open May-Sep, Reservations not accepted, Elev: 1319ft/402m, Tel: 218-756-2450, Nearest town: Clarissa. GPS: 46.131093, -94.949606

80 • C2 | Crosby Memorial City Park

Total sites: 26, RV sites: 20, Elec sites: 20, Water at site, Flush toilet, Free showers, RV dump, Tent & RV camping: $25, 20 Full hookup, Open May-Oct, Elev: 1243ft/379m, Tel: 218-546-5021, Nearest town: Crosby. GPS: 46.479248, -93.957031

81 • C2 | Dower Lake RA

Total sites: 45, RV sites: 34, Elec sites: 34, Central water, Flush toilet, Free showers, RV dump, Tents: $15/RVs: $25, 14 Full hookup seasonal sites, Open May-Sep, Reservations not accepted, Elev: 1293ft/394m, Tel: 218-894-2553, Nearest town: Staples. GPS: 46.353672, -94.849353

82 • C2 | Glenn Johnson Memorial Park

Total sites: 8, RV sites: 8, Elec sites: 8, Water at site, Flush toilet, Free showers, RV dump, Tents: $15/RVs: $25, Elev: 1398ft/426m, Tel: 218-924-4454, Nearest town: Bertha. GPS: 46.268439, -95.068126

83 • C2 | Lum City Park

Total sites: 18, RV sites: 18, Elec sites: 18, Water at site, Flush toilet, Free showers, RV dump, No tents/RVs: $35, $5 senior discount, Elev: 1201ft/366m, Tel: 218-828-2320, Nearest town: Brainerd. GPS: 46.369581, -94.164201

84 • C2 | Memorial Forest Park

Total sites: 24, RV sites: 24, Elec sites: 11, Water at site, Flush toilet, Free showers, RV dump, Tents: $20/RVs: $32, Dump fee $10, Reservations accepted, Elev: 1411ft/430m, Tel: 218-564-4557, Nearest town: Menahga. GPS: 46.742235, -95.101999

85 • C2 | Milaca City Park

Total sites: 4, RV sites: 4, Elec sites: 4, Water at site, Flush toilet, Free showers, No RV dump, Tent & RV camping: Fee unk, RV dump at Jim's Mille Lacs Disposal (205 2nd Ave NE) - no dumping 0700-1700, Generator hours: 0700-2200, Elev: 1050ft/320m, Tel: 320-983-3141, Nearest town: Milaca. GPS: 45.755709, -93.659493

86 • C2 | Pierz City Park

Total sites: 38, RV sites: 38, Elec sites: 38, Water at site, Flush toilet, Free showers, Tents: $25/RVs: $40, Elev: 1142ft/348m, Tel: 320-468-2662, Nearest town: Pierz. GPS: 45.977574, -94.091003

87 • C2 | Riverside City Park

Total sites: 23, RV sites: 13, Elec sites: 13, Central water, Flush toilet, No showers, RV dump, Tents: $20-25/RVs: $30-40, Lower rate is for 1st 10 nights, Open May-Oct, Reservations accepted, Elev: 965ft/294m, Tel: 763-389-2040, Nearest town: Princeton. GPS: 45.572205, -93.578742

88 • C2 | Sauk River City Park

Total sites: 32, RV sites: 12, Elec sites: 12, Water at site, No toilets, No showers, RV dump, Tents: $10/RVs: $20, Stay limit: 7 days, Open May-Sep, Reservations not accepted, Elev: 1181ft/360m, Tel: 320-256-4278, Nearest town: Melrose. GPS: 45.675471, -94.806523

89 • C2 | Sebeka City Park

Total sites: 24, RV sites: 10, Elec sites: 10, Water at site, Flush toilet, Free showers, RV dump, Tents: $15/RVs: $25, 5 Full hookup, Open May-Sep, Elev: 1368ft/417m, Tel: 218-837-5773, Nearest town: Sebeka. GPS: 46.627427, -95.094615

90 • C2 | Sinclair Lewis City CG

Total sites: 80, RV sites: 76, Elec sites: 76, Water at site, Flush toilet, Free showers, RV dump, Tents: $15/RVs: $30-35, 46 Full hookup

Open May-Sep, Reservations accepted, Elev: 1211ft/369m, Tel: 320-333-9546, Nearest town: Sauk Centre. GPS: 45.740444, -94.959112

91 • C2 | Sunnybrook City Park

Total sites: 35, RV sites: 30, Elec sites: 30, Water at site, Flush toilet, Free showers, RV dump, Tents: $15/RVs: $30, Also cabins, 30 Full hookup, Near RR, Open May-Sep, Reservations accepted, Elev: 1345ft/410m, Tel: 218-632-2755, Nearest town: Wadena. GPS: 46.438685, -95.119951

92 • C2 | Two Mile Trailer Park and CG

Total sites: 28, RV sites: 28, Elec sites: 28, Water at site, Flush toilet, Free showers, RV dump, Tent & RV camping: Fee unk, 28 Full hookup, Open May-Sep, Elev: 1322ft/403m, Tel: 320-815-0411, Nearest town: Osakis. GPS: 45.886820, -95.157732

93 • C2 | Veterans Memorial Park

Total sites: 12, RV sites: 8, Elec sites: 8, Central water, No toilets, No showers, No RV dump, Tents: $15/RVs: $35, Stay limit: 7 days, Reservations accepted, Elev: 1158ft/353m, Tel: 320-293-6687, Nearest town: Holdingford. GPS: 45.725912, -94.476001

94 • C2 | Wolf Lake Park

Total sites: 15, RV sites: 8, Elec sites: 8, Central water, Flush toilet, Free showers, No RV dump, Tents: $25/RVs: $40, Sun-Thu: $15/$30, Open May-Oct, Elev: 1535ft/468m, Tel: 218-538-9500, Nearest town: Wolf Lake. GPS: 46.812892, -95.362533

95 • C3 | Indian Point CG

Total sites: 45, RV sites: 45, Elec sites: 45, Water at site, Flush toilet, Free showers, RV dump, Tents: $35-44/RVs: $40-63, 7 Full hookup, Concessionaire, Open May-Oct, Elev: 597ft/182m, Tel: 218-628-4977, Nearest town: Duluth. GPS: 46.721680, -92.183594

96 • C3 | Jackie Berger Park

Total sites: 6, RV sites: 6, Elec sites: 6, No water, Vault/pit toilet, No showers, No RV dump, Tent & RV camping: Donation, Near RR, Reservations not accepted, Elev: 1135ft/346m, Nearest town: Duquette. GPS: 46.372333, -92.555371

97 • C3 | Moose Lake City Park

Total sites: 87, RV sites: 70, Elec sites: 70, Water at site, Flush toilet, Free showers, RV dump, Tents: $15/RVs: $30-40, 22 Full hookup, Open May-Sep, Reservations accepted, Elev: 1043ft/318m, Tel: 218-485-4761, Nearest town: Moose Lake. GPS: 46.454171, -92.754155

98 • C3 | Robinson Park

Total sites: 3, RV sites: 0, Central water, Flush toilet, No showers, No RV dump, Tents only: $10, Also boat-in and group sites, 2 group sites: $30, Reservations not accepted, Elev: 960ft/293m, Tel: 320-245-5241, Nearest town: Sandstone. GPS: 46.132953, -92.857635

99 • C3 | Snake River County CG

Total sites: 12, RV sites: 12, Central water, Vault/pit toilet, No showers, No RV dump, Tent & RV camping: $15, Reservations not accepted, Elev: 1191ft/363m, Tel: 218-927-7364, Nearest town: McGrath. GPS: 46.169861, -93.259137

100 • C3 | Spafford City Park

Total sites: 25, RV sites: 24, Elec sites: 24, Water at site, Flush toilet, Free showers, RV dump, Tents: $15/RVs: $25, Open May-Oct, Elev: 1174ft/358m, Tel: 218-879-3347, Nearest town: Cloquet. GPS: 46.726807, -92.464600

101 • C3 | Spirit Mountain City CG

Total sites: 73, RV sites: 73, Elec sites: 73, Water at site, Flush toilet, Free showers, RV dump, Tents: $30/RVs: $42-46, Open May-Oct, Reservations accepted, Elev: 1250ft/381m, Tel: 218-624-8544, Nearest town: Duluth. GPS: 46.713918, -92.222563

102 • D1 | Ambush City Park

Total sites: 13, RV sites: 13, Elec sites: 13, Water at site, Flush toilet, Free showers, RV dump, Tents: $15/RVs: $20, 13 Full hookup, Generator hours: 0600-2200, Open May-Sep, Reservations accepted, Elev: 1027ft/313m, Tel: 320-843-4775, Nearest town: Benson. GPS: 45.320884, -95.617635

103 • D1 | Appleton Municipal CG - Mill Pond Park

Total sites: 12, RV sites: 12, Elec sites: 12, Central water, Flush toilet, Free showers, Tents: $15/RVs: $25, Reservations not accepted, Elev: 996ft/304m, Tel: 320-289-1363, Nearest town: Appleton. GPS: 45.204353, -96.019999

104 • D1 | Boyd City Park

Total sites: 12, RV sites: 12, No toilets, Tent & RV camping: Fee unk, Elev: 1050ft/320m, Tel: 320-855-2242, Nearest town: Boyd. GPS: 44.851438, -95.896523

105 • D1 | Dawson City Park

Total sites: 10, RV sites: 10, Elec sites: 10, Water at site, Flush toilet, Free showers, RV dump, Tent & RV camping: $25, No water in winter, Reservations accepted for June Riverfest only, Open all year, Reservations not accepted, Elev: 1050ft/320m, Tel: 320-769-2154, Nearest town: Dawson. GPS: 44.935015, -96.044814

106 • D1 | Dawson Veterans Park

Total sites: 6, RV sites: 6, Elec sites: 6, Water at site, No toilets, Tent & RV camping: $25, Reservations not accepted, Elev: 1050ft/320m, Tel: 320-769-2387, Nearest town: Dawson. GPS: 44.926801, -96.054626

107 • D1 | Garvin CP - Lower CG

Total sites: 18, RV sites: 18, Elec sites: 18, Water at site, Flush toilet, Free showers, RV dump, Tents: $10/RVs: $15, Elev: 1381ft/421m, Tel: 507-629-4081, Nearest town: Garvin. GPS: 44.272415, -95.741057

108 • D1 | Garvin CP - Upper CG

Total sites: 12, RV sites: 12, Elec sites: 12, Water at site, Flush toilet, Free showers, RV dump, Tents: $10/RVs: $15, Elev: 1384ft/422m, Tel: 507-629-4081, Nearest town: Garvin. GPS: 44.263195, -95.745972

109 • D1 | Granite Falls Memorial Park

Total sites: 22, RV sites: 12, Elec sites: 12, Central water, Flush toilet, Free showers, RV dump, Tents: $10/RVs: $12, Open May-Oct, Max Length: 34ft, Reservations not accepted, Elev:

896ft/273m, Tel: 320-564-3011, Nearest town: Granite Falls. GPS: 44.801123, -95.538961

110 • D1 | J F Jacobson City Park

Total sites: 8, RV sites: 8, Tent & RV camping: Fee unk, Elev: 1102ft/336m, Tel: 320-598-7373, Nearest town: Madison. GPS: 45.007502, -96.195727

111 • D1 | Lagoon City Park

Total sites: 10, RV sites: 10, Elec sites: 8, Water at site, Flush toilet, Free showers, RV dump, Tent & RV camping: $12, Reservations not accepted, Elev: 958ft/292m, Tel: 320-269-6575, Nearest town: Montevideo. GPS: 44.951090, -95.727610

112 • D1 | Lake Hendricks City Park

Total sites: 27, RV sites: 27, Elec sites: 27, Water at site, Flush toilet, Free showers, RV dump, Tents: $18/RVs: $25, Also cabins, Reservations accepted, Elev: 1755ft/535m, Tel: 507-275-3192, Nearest town: Hendricks. GPS: 44.506765, -96.434783

113 • D1 | Lake Sylvan Park

Total sites: 6, RV sites: 6, Elec sites: 6, Central water, No toilets, No showers, RV dump, Tent & RV camping: $10, Open May-Oct, Elev: 1217ft/371m, Tel: 507-223-7595, Nearest town: Canby. GPS: 44.705271, -96.280891

114 • D1 | Lion's RV Park

Total sites: 12, RV sites: 10, Elec sites: 10, Water at site, Flush toilet, Free showers, No RV dump, Tents: $5/RVs: $15, Reservations accepted, Elev: 1092ft/333m, Tel: 320-669-4435, Nearest town: Clarkfield. GPS: 44.796674, -95.806496

115 • D1 | Maynard Lions Park

Total sites: 5, RV sites: 5, Flush toilet, Tent & RV camping: Donation, Elev: 1017ft/310m, Tel: 320-367-2140, Nearest town: Maynard. GPS: 44.901969, -95.464868

116 • D1 | Riverside City Park

Total sites: 5, RV sites: 5, Central water, No toilets, No showers, RV dump, Tent & RV camping: $10, Reservations not accepted, Elev: 972ft/296m, Nearest town: Orttonville. GPS: 45.302645, -96.450613

117 • D1 | Swenson CP

Total sites: 18, RV sites: 18, Elec sites: 18, Central water, Vault/pit toilet, No showers, RV dump, Tent & RV camping: $17, Open Apr-Oct, Reservations not accepted, Elev: 1670ft/509m, Tel: 507-836-6148, Nearest town: Balaton. GPS: 44.166661, -95.939866

118 • D1 | Swift Lake Park

Total sites: 12, RV sites: 12, Elec sites: 10, Water at site, Flush toilet, Free showers, Tent & RV camping: Fee unk, Open May-Oct, Elev: 1316ft/401m, Tel: 507-629-5528, Nearest town: Tracy. GPS: 44.246427, -95.604793

119 • D1 | Triangle Municipal Park

Total sites: 20, RV sites: 20, Elec sites: 20, Central water, No toilets, No showers, RV dump, Tent & RV camping: $10, Open May-Sep, Elev: 1201ft/366m, Tel: 507-223-7295, Nearest town: Canby. GPS: 44.718762, -96.261016

120 • D2 | Alexander Ramsey Municipal Park

Total sites: 40, RV sites: 31, Elec sites: 31, Central water, Flush toilet, Free showers, RV dump, Tents: $15/RVs: $24, Open May-Oct, Reservations accepted, Elev: 928ft/283m, Tel: 507-644-2333, Nearest town: Redwood Falls. GPS: 44.552109, -95.122692

121 • D2 | Allanson's Park

Total sites: 18, RV sites: 18, Elec sites: 18, Water at site, Flush toilet, Free showers, RV dump, Tents: $10/RVs: $30, Open May-Oct, Max Length: 45ft, Reservations accepted, Elev: 751ft/229m, Tel: 507-248-3234, Nearest town: Henderson. GPS: 44.521891, -93.907023

122 • D2 | Franklin City CG - Ball Park

Total sites: 3, RV sites: 3, Elec sites: 3, Central water, Flush toilet, Free showers, No RV dump, Tent & RV camping: Free, Stay limit: 3 days, Open May-Oct, Reservations not accepted, Elev: 1010ft/308m, Tel: 507-557-2259, Nearest town: Franklin. GPS: 44.530027, -94.879352

123 • D2 | Franklin City CG - Landing

Dispersed sites, No water, No toilets, Tent & RV camping: Free, Stay limit: 7 days, Open May-Oct, Reservations not accepted, Elev: 869ft/265m, Tel: 507-557-2259, Nearest town: Franklin. GPS: 44.518319, -94.884679

124 • D2 | Kuhar City Park

Total sites: 4, RV sites: 4, Elec sites: 4, Water at site, Tent & RV camping: $10, Reservations not accepted, Elev: 1056ft/322m, Tel: 507-752-7601, Nearest town: Lamberton. GPS: 44.246393, -95.270217

125 • D2 | Lake Ripley CG

Total sites: 33, RV sites: 33, Elec sites: 33, Water at site, Flush toilet, Free showers, RV dump, Tent & RV camping: $20-25, 12 Full hookup, Open Apr-Oct, Reservations accepted, Elev: 1125ft/343m, Tel: 320-221-0957, Nearest town: Litchfield. GPS: 45.103469, -94.529733

126 • D2 | Land of Memories City Park

Total sites: 39, RV sites: 31, Elec sites: 31, Central water, Flush toilet, Free showers, No RV dump, Tents: $17/RVs: $27, Generator hours: 0800-2200, Reservations accepted, Elev: 775ft/236m, Tel: 507-387-8600, Nearest town: Mankato. GPS: 44.161301, -94.040291

127 • D2 | Masonic/West River City Park

Total sites: 32, RV sites: 24, Elec sites: 22, Water at site, Flush toilet, Free showers, RV dump, Tents: $15/RVs: $25-35, 14 Full hookup, Stay limit: 14 days, Open May-Oct, Reservations accepted, Elev: 1037ft/316m, Tel: 320-587-2975, Nearest town: Hutchinson. GPS: 44.891846, -94.386719

128 • D2 | Oak Leaf Park

Total sites: 17, RV sites: 15, Elec sites: 17, Central water, Flush toilet, Free showers, RV dump, Tents: $20/RVs: $28, Open May-Oct, Reservations accepted, Elev: 991ft/302m, Tel: 320-864-5586, Nearest town: Glencoe. GPS: 44.759284, -94.160985

129 • D2 | Olivia Memorial Park

Total sites: 6, RV sites: 6, Central water, Flush toilet, No showers, RV dump, Tents: $10/RVs: $20, Stay limit: 3 days, Open Apr-Oct, Reservations not accepted, Elev: 1070ft/326m, Tel: 320-523-2361, Nearest town: Olivia. GPS: 44.775905, -95.006561

130 • D2 | Riverside City Park

Total sites: 16, RV sites: 11, Elec sites: 11, Central water, Flush toilet, Free showers, RV dump, Tents: $17/RVs: $27, Open Mar-Sep, Reservations not accepted, Elev: 738ft/225m, Tel: 507-931-1550, Nearest town: St. Peter. GPS: 44.321983, -93.952251

131 • D2 | Rothenburg CG at Riverside Park

Total sites: 47, RV sites: 40, Elec sites: 40, Water at site, Flush toilet, Free showers, RV dump, Tents: $15/RVs: $30-35, 32 Full hookup, Reservations accepted, Elev: 1027ft/313m, Tel: 507-723-3517, Nearest town: Springfield. GPS: 44.236408, -94.973688

132 • D2 | Sailors and Soldiers Memorial Park

Total sites: 30, RV sites: 24, Elec sites: 24, Water at site, Flush toilet, Free showers, RV dump, Tents: $15/RVs: $25, Open May-Oct, Elev: 1079ft/329m, Tel: 507-430-6514, Nearest town: Sandborn. GPS: 44.204966, -95.129745

133 • D2 | Sleep Eye Sportsmen's Park

Total sites: 24, RV sites: 24, Elec sites: 24, Water at site, No toilets, No showers, No RV dump, Tent & RV camping: $30, Open May-Oct, Reservations accepted, Elev: 1001ft/305m, Tel: 507-794-4040, Nearest town: Sleepy Eye. GPS: 44.309515, -94.728322

134 • D2 | Watona City Park

Total sites: 54, RV sites: 54, Elec sites: 54, Water at site, Flush toilet, Free showers, RV dump, Tents: $15/RVs: $20-30, 24 Full hookup, Open Apr-Nov, Reservations accepted, Elev: 978ft/298m, Tel: 507-642-3314, Nearest town: Madelia. GPS: 44.041910, -94.421310

135 • D3 | Covered Bridge City Park

Total sites: 50, RV sites: 50, Elec sites: 24, Water at site, Flush toilet, Free showers, RV dump, Tents: $15/RVs: $25, Open May-Nov, Reservations not accepted, Elev: 965ft/294m, Tel: 507-732-7318, Nearest town: Zumbrota. GPS: 44.299669, -92.674782

136 • D3 | Hok-Si-La City Park

Total sites: 41, RV sites: 0, Central water, Flush toilet, Free showers, No RV dump, Tents only: $33-44, $5/day dog fee, Pre-Memorial Day and Post-Labor Day $22-$33, Open Apr-Oct, Reservations accepted, Elev: 712ft/217m, Tel: 651-345-3855, Nearest town: Lake City. GPS: 44.471105, -92.291101

137 • D3 | Oronoco City Park

Total sites: 8, RV sites: 8, Central water, Vault/pit toilet, No showers, No RV dump, Tent & RV camping: $15, $25 during Gold Rush, Open May-Sep, Reservations not accepted, Elev: 984ft/300m, Tel: 507-367-4405. GPS: 44.167780, -92.540000

138 • D3 | Prairie Island City CG

Total sites: 171, RV sites: 171, Elec sites: 106, Water at site, Flush toilet, Free showers, RV dump, Tents: $15-26/RVs: $31-38, Reservations accepted, Elev: 650ft/198m, Tel: 507-452-4501, Nearest town: Winona. GPS: 44.075994, -91.679209

139 • D3 | Wabasha Municipal CG

Total sites: 51, RV sites: 51, Elec sites: 51, Water at site, Flush toilet, Free showers, RV dump, No tents/RVs: $35, 51 Full hookup, Only 2 transient sites, Open Apr-Oct, Reservations not accepted, Elev: 673ft/205m, Tel: 651-565-4568, Nearest town: Wabasha. GPS: 44.385436, -92.038458

140 • E1 | Adrian City CG

Total sites: 121, RV sites: 121, Elec sites: 121, Water at site, Flush toilet, Free showers, RV dump, Tents: $18/RVs: $28-33, Some Full hookup, Open Apr-Oct, Elev: 1522ft/464m, Tel: 507-483-2820, Nearest town: Adrian. GPS: 43.640395, -95.939604

141 • E1 | Magnolia City CG

Total sites: 20, RV sites: 10, Elec sites: 10, Water at site, Flush toilet, Free showers, RV dump, Tent & RV camping: $15, 10 Full hookup, Open Apr-Sep, Reservations not accepted, Elev: 1519ft/463m, Tel: 507-227-0495, Nearest town: Magnolia. GPS: 43.645862, -96.081861

142 • E1 | Marilyn DeBates Memorial Park

Total sites: 5, RV sites: 5, Elec sites: 5, Central water, No toilets, No showers, RV dump, Tent & RV camping: $15, Elev: 1621ft/494m, Nearest town: Jasper. GPS: 43.849017, -96.393901

143 • E1 | Olson City Park CG

Total sites: 68, RV sites: 63, Elec sites: 63, Central water, Flush toilet, Free showers, RV dump, Tents: $22/RVs: $28-33, Open Apr-Oct, Reservations accepted, Elev: 1585ft/483m, Tel: 507-329-0760, Nearest town: Worthington. GPS: 43.607551, -95.634851

144 • E1 | Rock River City Park

Total sites: 16, RV sites: 16, Elec sites: 16, Water at site, Flush toilet, Free showers, RV dump, Tents: $15/RVs: $20-25, 8 Full hookup, Reservations not accepted, Elev: 1555ft/474m, Tel: 507-442-7891, Nearest town: Edgerton. GPS: 43.871461, -96.140378

145 • E2 | Blue Earth City CG (Faribault Co Fairgrounds)

Total sites: 14, RV sites: 14, Elec sites: 14, Water at site, Flush toilet, Free showers, RV dump, Tent & RV camping: $25, Free 1st 2 nights, Generator hours: 0700-2200, Open May-Sep, Reservations not accepted, Elev: 1076ft/328m, Tel: 507-600-0130, Nearest town: Blue Earth. GPS: 43.651984, -94.102044

146 • E2 | Everett Park

Total sites: 30, RV sites: 30, Central water, Flush toilet, Free showers, RV dump, Tent & RV camping: $25, Open May-Sep, Reservations not accepted, Elev: 1241ft/378m, Tel: 507-230-0152, Nearest town: Sherburn. GPS: 43.676052, -94.668765

147 • E2 | Island Park

Total sites: 10, RV sites: 10, Elec sites: 10, Central water, No toilets, No showers, No RV dump, Tent & RV camping: $10, 30A only, Reservations not accepted, Elev: 1332ft/406m, Tel: 507-831-6129, Nearest town: Windom. GPS: 43.858888, -95.119089

148 • E2 | Island View City CG

Total sites: 18, RV sites: 18, Elec sites: 18, Water at site, Flush toilet, Free showers, RV dump, Tent & RV camping: $20, 18 Full hookup, Open May-Sep, Reservations not accepted, Elev: 1266ft/

386m, Tel: 507-427-2999, Nearest town: Mountain Lake. GPS: 43.944082, -94.938589

149 • E2 | Tiell Park

Total sites: 23, RV sites: 21, Elec sites: 21, Water at site, Flush toilet, Free showers, RV dump, Tents: $15/RVs: $25, 21 Full hookup, Open May-Oct, Reservations not accepted, Elev: 1070ft/326m, Tel: 507-375-3241, Nearest town: St. James. GPS: 43.974077, -94.640325

150 • E2 | Truman City Park

Total sites: 4, RV sites: 4, Elec sites: 4, Central water, Flush toilet, No showers, RV dump, Tent & RV camping: $15, Reservations not accepted, Elev: 1119ft/341m, Tel: 507-776-7951, Nearest town: Truman. GPS: 43.824992, -94.432323

151 • E2 | Voss Park City

Total sites: 110, RV sites: 110, Elec sites: 110, Central water, Flush toilet, Free showers, No RV dump, Tents: $15/RVs: $20, Open May-Sep, Elev: 1168ft/356m, Tel: 507-317-5701, Nearest town: Butterfield. GPS: 43.963492, -94.803381

152 • E3 | Houston Nature Center Trailhead CG

Total sites: 9, RV sites: 0, Central water, Flush toilet, Free showers, No RV dump, Tents only: $20, Walk-to sites, Open Apr-Oct, Elev: 673ft/205m, Tel: 507-896-4668, Nearest town: Houston. GPS: 43.765798, -91.571904

153 • E3 | North End City Park

Total sites: 10, RV sites: 7, Elec sites: 7, Water at site, Flush toilet, Pay showers, No RV dump, Tent & RV camping: Fee unk, 7 Full hookup, Reservations accepted, Elev: 715ft/218m, Tel: 507-864-7949, Nearest town: Rushford. GPS: 43.815997, -91.753647

154 • E3 | North Park - City

Total sites: 10, RV sites: 6, Elec sites: 6, Central water, Vault/pit toilet, No showers, No RV dump, Tents: $10/RVs: $15, Reservations not accepted, Elev: 1350ft/411m, Tel: 507-886-8122, Nearest town: Harmony. GPS: 43.557714, -92.007097

155 • E3 | Peterson City RV Park

Total sites: 10, RV sites: 10, Elec sites: 10, Water at site, RV dump, No tents/RVs: $30, Reservations accepted, Elev: 755ft/230m, Tel: 507-875-2222, Nearest town: Peterson. GPS: 43.783921, -91.834369

156 • E3 | Pine Lawn City Park

Total sites: 4, RV sites: 4, Elec sites: 4, Central water, Flush toilet, Tents: $5/RVs: $10, Reservations not accepted, Elev: 1309ft/399m, Tel: 507-754-5280, Nearest town: Grand Meadow. GPS: 43.710851, -92.539988

157 • E3 | Riverview City CG

Total sites: 103, RV sites: 43, Elec sites: 43, Water available, Flush toilet, Free showers, RV dump, Tents: $20/RVs: $30, Open all year, Reservations not accepted, Elev: 852ft/260m, Tel: 507-467-3722, Nearest town: Lanesboro. GPS: 43.716427, -91.979794

158 • E3 | Sylvan City Park

Total sites: 25, RV sites: 19, Elec sites: 19, Water available, Flush toilet, Pay showers, RV dump, Tents: $20/RVs: $30, Open all year, Reservations not accepted, Elev: 830ft/253m, Tel: 507-467-3722, Nearest town: Lanesboro. GPS: 43.717328, -91.973806

159 • E3 | Trollskogen City Park

Total sites: 10, RV sites: 6, Elec sites: 6, Flush toilet, Tent & RV camping: Fee unk, Reservations not accepted, Elev: 1266ft/386m, Tel: 507-498-5221, Nearest town: Spring Grove. GPS: 43.557341, -91.643881

Mississippi

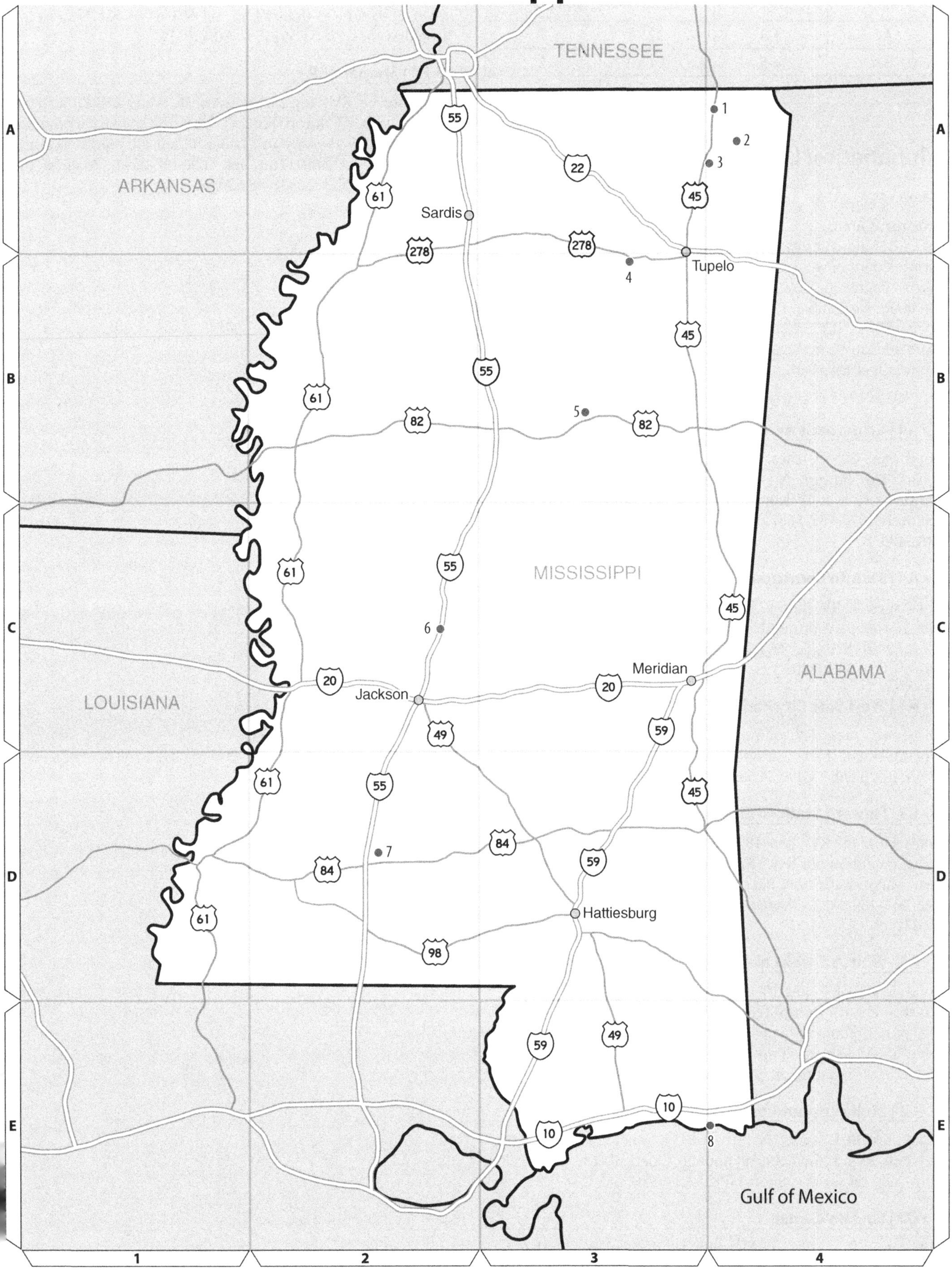
TENNESSEE
ARKANSAS
LOUISIANA
MISSISSIPPI
ALABAMA
Gulf of Mexico
Sardis
Tupelo
Jackson
Meridian
Hattiesburg
1
2
3
4
5
6
7
8
55
22
45
61
278
82
20
49
59
84
98
10
A
B
C
D
E
1
2
3
4

Map	ID	Map	ID
A4	1-3	D2	7
B3	4-5	E4	8
C2	6		

Alphabetical List of Camping Areas

1 • A4 | Crossroads Arena

Total sites: 20, RV sites: 15, Elec sites: 20, Water available, No toilets, No showers, No RV dump, Tent & RV camping: $20, Dump station at Welcome Center, Open all year, Elev: 453ft/138m, Tel: 877-987-8687, Nearest town: Corinth. GPS: 34.909911, -88.548638

2 • A4 | Jacinto Courthouse

Total sites: 2, RV sites: 2, Elec sites: 2, Water at site, No toilets, No showers, RV dump, No tents/RVs: Fee unk, Open all year, Elev: 594ft/181m, Tel: 662-286-8662, Nearest town: Jacinto. GPS: 34.765104, -88.408805

3 • A4 | West Side City Park

Dispersed sites, RV dump, Tent & RV camping: Fee unk, Unconfirmed, Elev: 502ft/153m, Tel: 662-728-4132, Nearest town: Booneville. GPS: 34.665512, -88.571287

4 • B3 | Howard Stafford City Park

Total sites: 18, RV sites: 18, Elec sites: 18, Water at site, Flush toilet, Free showers, Tents: $7/RVs: $18, 15 Full hookup, Open all year, Max Length: 55ft, Reservations accepted, Elev: 456ft/139m, Tel: 662-489-1882, Nearest town: Pontotoc. GPS: 34.235550, -89.021260

5 • B3 | White's Creek Lake Park

Total sites: 10, RV sites: 10, Elec sites: 10, Water at site, Flush toilet, No showers, RV dump, Tent & RV camping: $15, No campfires, Call posted phone # - a policeman will stop by to collect fee, Max Length: 45ft, Reservations accepted, Elev: 419ft/128m, Tel: 662-258-2291, Nearest town: Eupora. GPS: 33.557665, -89.274915

6 • C2 | Multipurpose Complex RV Park

Total sites: 39, RV sites: 39, Elec sites: 39, Water at site, RV dump, No tents/RVs: $25-30, 39 Full hookup, Open all year, Elev: 259ft/79m, Nearest town: Canton. GPS: 32.589998, -90.077837

7 • D2 | Lincoln Center

Total sites: 39, RV sites: 39, Elec sites: 39, Water at site, Flush toilet, Free showers, RV dump, No tents/RVs: $20-25, 39 Full hookup, Open all year, Elev: 489ft/149m, Tel: 601-823-9064, Nearest town: Brookhaven. GPS: 31.597559, -90.408119

8 • E4 | Shepard SP

Total sites: 58, RV sites: 28, Elec sites: 28, Water at site, Flush toilet, Free showers, RV dump, Tents: $15/RVs: $22, State park operated/maintained by the city of Gauier, Open all year, Reservations accepted, Elev: 36ft/11m, Tel: 228-497-2244, Nearest town: Gautier. GPS: 30.372233, -88.630565

Missouri

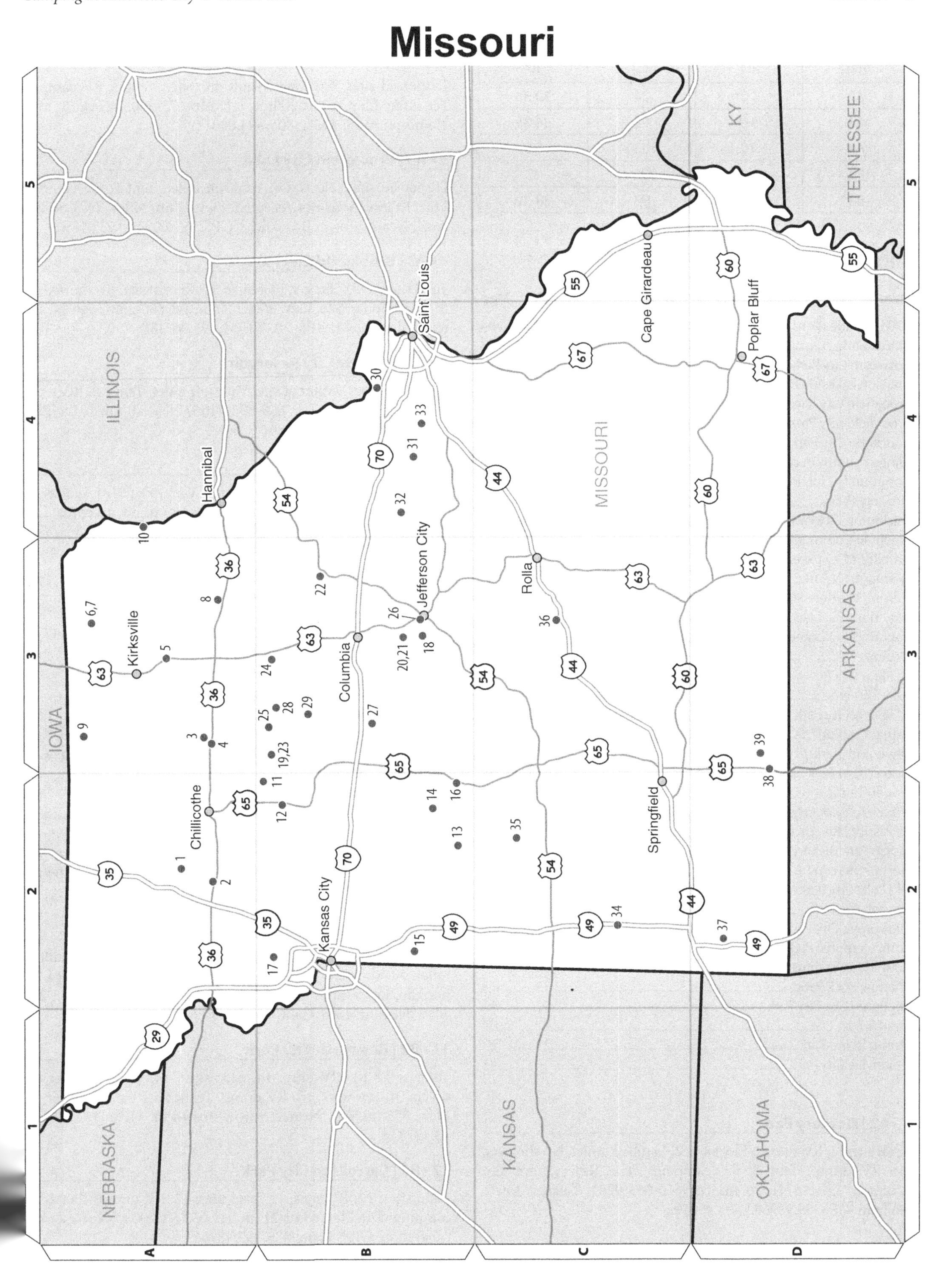
ILLINOIS
IOWA
NEBRASKA
KANSAS
OKLAHOMA
ARKANSAS
TENNESSEE
KY
MISSOURI
Saint Louis
Hannibal
Kirksville
Chillicothe
Kansas City
Columbia
Jefferson City
Rolla
Springfield
Cape Girardeau
Poplar Bluff
A
B
C
D
1
2
3
4
5

Map	ID	Map	ID
A2	1-2	B4	30-33
A3	3-9	C2	34-35
A4	10	C3	36
B2	11-17	D2	37
B3	18-29	D3	38-39

Alphabetical List of Camping Areas

1 • A2 | Dockery Park

Total sites: 2, RV sites: 2, Elec sites: 2, Vault/pit toilet, No showers, No RV dump, Tent & RV camping: Free, Reservations not accepted, Elev: 871ft/265m, Tel: 660-663-9231, Nearest town: Gallatin. GPS: 39.919682, -93.954192

2 • A2 | Hamilton City Lake

Dispersed sites, No water, Vault/pit toilet, Tent & RV camping: Fee unk, Elev: 919ft/280m, Tel: 816-675-2205, Nearest town: Hamilton. GPS: 39.745805, -94.040119

3 • A3 | Brookfield City Lake

Dispersed sites, No water, Vault/pit toilet, Tent & RV camping: Free, Reservations not accepted, Elev: 816ft/249m, Tel: 660-258-5644, Nearest town: Brookfield. GPS: 39.800345, -93.018929

4 • A3 | Brookfield City Park

Total sites: 9, RV sites: 9, Elec sites: 9, Water at site, RV dump, Tent & RV camping: $20, Elev: 800ft/244m, Tel: 660-258-5644, Nearest town: Brookfield. GPS: 39.761564, -93.063188

5 • A3 | La Plata City Reservoir

Dispersed sites, Water at site, Vault/pit toilet, Tents: $7/RVs: $15, Elev: 891ft/272m, Tel: 660-332-7166, Nearest town: La Plata. GPS: 40.018909, -92.466862

6 • A3 | Lake Showme

Total sites: 8, RV sites: 8, No water, Vault/pit toilet, Tent & RV camping: Fee unk, Open all year, Reservations not accepted, Elev: 794ft/242m, Tel: 660-465-7285, Nearest town: Memphis. GPS: 40.438458, -92.216252

7 • A3 | Old Lake City Park

Total sites: 5, RV sites: 5, No water, Vault/pit toilet, No tents/RVs: Free, Elev: 728ft/222m, Nearest town: Memphis. GPS: 40.447956, -92.205123

8 • A3 | Shelbina Lake City Park

Total sites: 85, RV sites: 76, Elec sites: 76, Central water, Flush toilet, Free showers, RV dump, Tents: $10/RVs: $15-19, Elev: 738ft/225m, Tel: 573-588-4755, Nearest town: Shelbina. GPS: 39.720684, -92.040923

9 • A3 | Unionville City Park

Total sites: 45, RV sites: 45, Elec sites: 45, Central water, RV dump, Tent & RV camping: $20, Open Apr-Oct, Elev: 1076ft/328m, Tel: 660-947-2438, Nearest town: Unionville. GPS: 40.480007, -93.010557

10 • A4 | Mississippi Riverfront Park

Total sites: 23, RV sites: 23, Elec sites: 23, Water at site, Vault/pit toilet, No showers, RV dump, Tent & RV camping: $20, 14 Full hookup, Reservations accepted, Elev: 486ft/148m, Tel: 573-288-4413, Nearest town: Canton. GPS: 40.137895, -91.515537

11 • B2 | Bosworth City Park

Total sites: 14, RV sites: 14, Elec sites: 14, Central water, No toilets, No showers, No RV dump, Tents: $5/RVs: $10, Near RR, Elev: 755ft/230m, Nearest town: Bosworth. GPS: 39.472674, -93.327533

12 • B2 | Carrollton City Park

Total sites: 12, RV sites: 12, Elec sites: 12, RV dump, Tent & RV camping: $20, Elev: 695ft/212m, Tel: 660-542-0040, Nearest town: Carrollton. GPS: 39.364835, -93.488669

13 • B2 | Clinton Community Center

Dispersed sites, Central water, Flush toilet, Free showers, Tents only: Free, For bikers on Katy Trail, Elev: 793ft/242m, Tel: 660-885-2181, Nearest town: Clinton. GPS: 38.380335, -93.756225

14 • B2 | Farrington City Park

Total sites: 10, RV sites: 5, Elec sites: 5, Water at site, Flush toilet, Free showers, RV dump, Tents: $10/RVs: $20, Some Full hookup, Near Katy Trail, Elev: 869ft/265m, Tel: 660-647-3130, Nearest town: Windsor. GPS: 38.528335, -93.511942

15 • B2 | Freeman Community Club RV Park

Total sites: 8, RV sites: 8, Elec sites: 8, Water at site, No toilets, No showers, RV dump, Tent & RV camping: $15, 8 Full hookup, Reservations not accepted, Elev: 837ft/255m, Tel: 816-509-5095, Nearest town: Freeman. GPS: 38.616786, -94.494834

16 • B2 | Lincoln City Park

Total sites: 3, RV sites: 3, Elec sites: 3, Central water, No toilets, No showers, No RV dump, No tents/RVs: $10, Elev: 978ft/298m, Nearest town: Lincoln. GPS: 38.391773, -93.325429

17 • B2 | Smith's Fork CG

Total sites: 79, RV sites: 79, Elec sites: 79, Water at site, Flush toilet, Free showers, Tent & RV camping: $30, 79 Full hookup, 7th night free, Stay limit: 30 days, Open Apr-Oct, Reservations accepted, Elev: 820ft/250m, Tel: 816-532-1028, Nearest town: Smithville. GPS: 39.396011, -94.560112

18 • B3 | Binder Park

Total sites: 17, RV sites: 17, Elec sites: 17, Water at site, Flush toilet, Free showers, RV dump, Tent & RV camping: $22, 17 Full hookup, Water at every other site - will need diverter, Open all year, Elev: 655ft/200m, Tel: 573-634-6482, Nearest town: Jefferson City. GPS: 38.590067, -92.303615

19 • B3 | Herring Memorial Park

Total sites: 6, RV sites: 6, Elec sites: 6, Central water, Flush toilet, No showers, RV dump, Tent & RV camping: Free, Open all year, Elev: 784ft/239m, Tel: 660-548-3028, Nearest town: Brunswick. GPS: 39.429419, -93.133595

20 • B3 | Katy Trail - Ballfield Park

Dispersed sites, Central water, Tents only: Free, For bikers on Katy Trail, Elev: 558ft/170m, Nearest town: Hartsburg. GPS: 38.691458, -92.312072

21 • B3 | Katy Trail - Volunteer Park

Dispersed sites, Central water, Flush toilet, Tents only: Free, For bikers on Katy Trail, Toilets 50 yards at trailhead, Elev: 567ft/173m, Nearest town: Hartsburg. GPS: 38.695002, -92.309972

22 • B3 | Lakeview City Park

Total sites: 13, RV sites: 13, Elec sites: 11, No toilets, No showers, RV dump, Tents: $5/RVs: $10, $8 for local residents, Elev: 810ft/247m, Tel: 573-581-2100, Nearest town: Mexico. GPS: 39.153266, -91.894719

23 • B3 | Lewis and Clark City Campsite

Total sites: 3, RV sites: 3, Elec sites: 3, No water, Vault/pit toilet, Tent & RV camping: Free, Elev: 656ft/200m, Tel: 660-548-3028, Nearest town: Brunswick. GPS: 39.422236, -93.131821

24 • B3 | Lionel Thompson City CG

Total sites: 24, RV sites: 24, Elec sites: 24, Water at site, Flush toilet, Free showers, RV dump, Tents: $10/RVs: $30, 24 Full hookup, Dispersed tent area available Apr-Oct, Open all year, Elev: 876ft/267m, Tel: 660-998-0143, Nearest town: Moberly. GPS: 39.421938, -92.467269

25 • B3 | Maxwell Taylor City Park

Total sites: 3, RV sites: 3, Elec sites: 1, No RV dump, Tent & RV camping: Donation, Elev: 709ft/216m, Tel: 660-288-3745, Nearest town: Keytesville. GPS: 39.437830, -92.938660

26 • B3 | North Jefferson RA - Noren Access

Total sites: 3, No water, Vault/pit toilet, Tents only: $5, For bikers on Katy Trail, Reservations not accepted, Elev: 552ft/168m, Nearest town: N. Jefferson. GPS: 38.589556, -92.178292

27 • B3 | Pilot Grove City Park

Dispersed sites, Tents only: Free, Check in w/ police, Reservations not accepted, Elev: 863ft/263m, Nearest town: Pilot Grove. GPS: 38.872358, -92.916509

28 • B3 | Potts Memorial Park

Total sites: 10, RV sites: 10, Elec sites: 10, Central water, Flush toilet, Free showers, Tents: $10/RVs: $20, Elev: 702ft/214m, Tel: 660-388-5114, Nearest town: Salisbury. GPS: 39.402247, -92.801236

29 • B3 | Stump Island Park

Total sites: 17, RV sites: 17, Elec sites: 12, Central water, Flush toilet, Free showers, RV dump, Tents: $10/RVs: $20, 20 amp only, Open Apr-Nov, Elev: 636ft/194m, Tel: 660-338-2377, Nearest town: Glasgow. GPS: 39.218484, -92.848234

30 • B4 | 370 Lakeside Park

Total sites: 60, RV sites: 50, Elec sites: 50, Water available, Flush toilet, Free showers, RV dump, Tents: $30/RVs: $45-50, Stay limit: 14-60 days, Reservations accepted, Elev: 435ft/133m, Tel: 636-387-5253, Nearest town: St Peters. GPS: 38.819914, -90.575357

31 • B4 | Community Club Park

Dispersed sites, Central water, Flush toilet, Free showers, Tents only: $5, For bikers on Katy Trail, Permit required, Elev: 488ft/149m, Tel: 636-433-5554, Nearest town: Marthasville. GPS: 38.626459, -91.060373

32 • B4 | Hermann RV Park

Total sites: 51, RV sites: 51, Elec sites: 51, Water at site, Flush toilet, Free showers, RV dump, Tents: $15/RVs: $20-30, 43 Full hookup, Reservations accepted, Elev: 545ft/166m, Tel: 573-486-5400, Nearest town: Hermann. GPS: 38.698513, -91.440136

33 • B4 | Klondike CP

Total sites: 43, RV sites: 0, Central water, Flush toilet, Free showers,

Tents only: $7-10, Also cabins, Next to Katy Trail, Reservations accepted, Elev: 587ft/179m, Tel: 636-949-7535, Nearest town: Augusta. GPS: 38.582960, -90.833430

34 • C2 | Lamar City Park

Total sites: 25, RV sites: 25, Central water, RV dump, No tents/RVs: $10, 1st 2 nights free, 3-4 20A outlets, Near RR, Stay limit: 7 days, Reservations not accepted, Elev: 938ft/286m, Tel: 417-682-5851, Nearest town: Lamar. GPS: 37.485779, -94.282979

35 • C2 | Osceola RV Park

Total sites: 48, RV sites: 48, Elec sites: 48, Water at site, Flush toilet, Free showers, RV dump, Tents: $14/RVs: $18, 32 Full hookup, $1 senior discount, 7th night free, Open all year, Reservations accepted, Elev: 758ft/231m, Tel: 417-646-8675, Nearest town: Osceola. GPS: 38.052013, -93.698372

36 • C3 | Roubidoux Springs City CG

Total sites: 26, RV sites: 26, Elec sites: 26, Water at site, Flush toilet, Free showers, RV dump, Tent & RV camping: $20, Some Full hookup, Pay at City Hall, Open all year, Reservations accepted, Elev: 781ft/238m, Tel: 573-774-6171, Nearest town: Waynesville. GPS: 37.829174, -92.206655

37 • D2 | Morse Park Hickory Creek RV Park

Total sites: 6, RV sites: 6, Elec sites: 6, Water at site, RV dump, No tents/RVs: $25, Elev: 997ft/304m, Tel: 417-451-8090, Nearest town: Neosho. GPS: 36.882011, -94.371318

38 • D3 | Branson Lakeside RV Park

Total sites: 135, RV sites: 135, Elec sites: 135, Water at site, Flush toilet, Free showers, RV dump, Tent & RV camping: $36-55, 135 Full hookup, $26 in winter, Open all year, Reservations accepted, Elev: 712ft/217m, Tel: 417-334-2915, Nearest town: Branson. GPS: 36.635353, -93.218197

39 • D3 | Shadow Rock Park

Total sites: 25, RV sites: 15, Elec sites: 15, Water at site, Flush toilet, Free showers, RV dump, Tents: $12/RVs: $14-18, 8 Full hookup, Reservations accepted, Elev: 686ft/209m, Tel: 417-546-2876, Nearest town: Forsyth. GPS: 36.683554, -93.103993

Montana

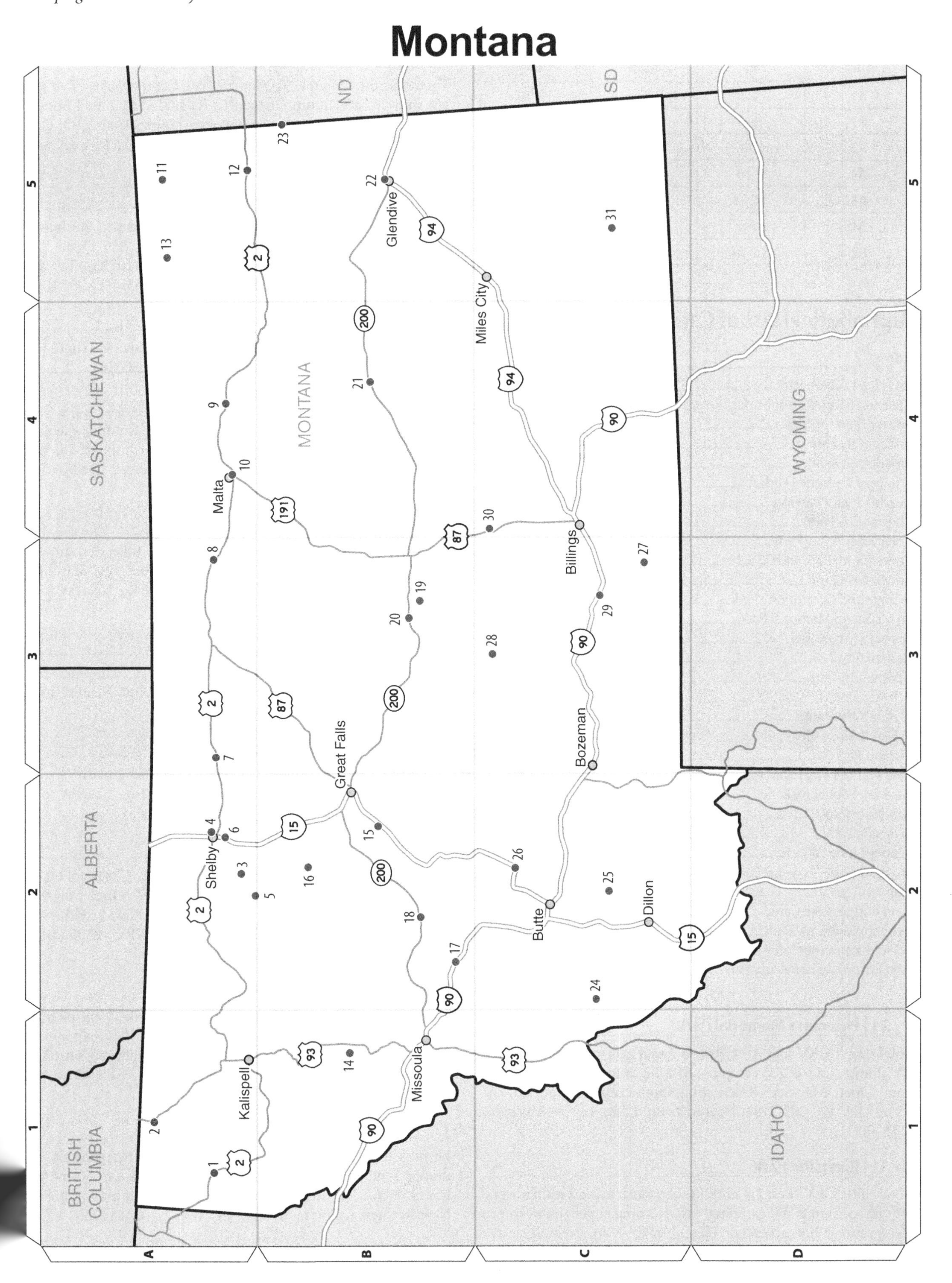
ND
SD
SASKATCHEWAN
ALBERTA
BRITISH COLUMBIA
WYOMING
IDAHO
MONTANA
Glendive
Miles City
Malta
Billings
Great Falls
Shelby
Bozeman
Butte
Dillon
Missoula
Kalispell
A
B
C
D
1
2
3
4
5

Map	ID	Map	ID
A1	1-2	B3	19-20
A2	3-6	B4	21
A3	7-8	B5	22-23
A4	9-10	C2	24-26
A5	11-13	C3	27-29
B1	14	C4	30
B2	15-18	C5	31

Alphabetical List of Camping Areas

Name	ID	Map
American Legion Park	24	C2
Atkinson ParkAtkinson Park	15	B2
Bolster Dam City CG	11	A5
Bridger City Park	27	C3
Broadus City Park	31	C5
Bruegger Centenial Park	12	A5
Charlo City RV Parking	14	B1
Chester City Park	7	A3
Chief Joseph City Park	28	C3
ChoteauCity Park and CG	16	B2
Cowbelles Corral	30	C4
Drummond Community Park	17	B2
Ed McGivern Memorial Park	19	B3
Fireman's Memorial Park	1	A1
Harlem City Park	8	A3
Hooper City Park	18	B2
Itch-Kep-Pe City Park	29	C3
JayCee West Park	22	B5
Jimmy Kariotis City Park	21	B4
Kiwanis Park	20	B3
Lake Frances City Park CG	3	A2
Lake Shel-oole City Park	4	A2
Milk River Park	9	A4
Riverside Park	2	A1
Scobey Lions CG	13	A5
Sharbano Park	23	B5
Trafton City Park	10	A4
Twin Bridges Bike Camp	25	C2
Veterans Memorial Park	26	C2
William Jones Memorial Park	5	A2
Williamson Memorial City Park	6	A2

1 • A1 | Fireman's Memorial Park

Total sites: 15, RV sites: 15, Central water, Flush toilet, No showers, RV dump, Tent & RV camping: $10, $2 dump fee, Stay limit: 5 days, Open May-Sep, Reservations not accepted, Elev: 2077ft/633m, Tel: 406-293-2731, Nearest town: Libby. GPS: 48.391696, -115.563313

2 • A1 | Riverside Park

Total sites: 5, RV sites: 2, Central water, Flush toilet, Free showers, RV dump, Tent & RV camping: $10, Nothing larger than van/pu, Reservations not accepted, Elev: 2569ft/783m, Nearest town: Eureka. GPS: 48.877786, -115.053341

3 • A2 | Lake Frances City Park CG

Total sites: 50, RV sites: 50, Elec sites: 50, Central water, No toilets, No showers, RV dump, Tents: $12/RVs: $25-40, 2 Full hookup, RV sites $20-$25 Oct-Apr, Generator hours: 0700-2200, Open all year, Elev: 3819ft/1164m, Tel: 406-279-3361, Nearest town: Valier. GPS: 48.300615, -112.260319

4 • A2 | Lake Shel-oole City Park

Total sites: 42, RV sites: 27, Elec sites: 27, Water at site, Flush toilet, Free showers, RV dump, Tent & RV camping: $25, Open May-Sep, Reservations not accepted, Elev: 3324ft/1013m, Tel: 406-434-5222, Nearest town: Shelby. GPS: 48.522505, -111.853913

5 • A2 | William Jones Memorial Park

Dispersed sites, Tent & RV camping: Free, Elev: 4121ft/1256m, Nearest town: Dupuyer. GPS: 48.191769, -112.503361

6 • A2 | Williamson Memorial City Park

Total sites: 25, RV sites: 25, Elec sites: Unk, Central water, No toilets, No showers, RV dump, Tent & RV camping: $8, Elev: 3114ft/949m, Tel: 406-434-5222, Nearest town: Shelby. GPS: 48.424561, -111.875472

7 • A3 | Chester City Park

Total sites: 8, RV sites: 4, Central water, Flush toilet, No showers, No RV dump, No tents/RVs: Donation, Near RR, Stay limit: 3 days, Elev: 3130ft/954m, Tel: 406 759-5635, Nearest town: Chester. GPS: 48.511178, -110.969907

8 • A3 | Harlem City Park

Dispersed sites, Vault/pit toilet, Tent & RV camping: Free, Reservations not accepted, Elev: 2368ft/722m, Nearest town: Harlem. GPS: 48.532262, -108.785863

9 • A4 | Milk River Park

Dispersed sites, No water, Vault/pit toilet, No tents/RVs: Free, Reservations not accepted, Elev: 2136ft/651m, Nearest town: Hinsdale. GPS: 48.397092, -107.083566

10 • A4 | Trafton City Park

Total sites: 15, RV sites: 15, Central water, Flush toilet, No showers, No RV dump, Tent & RV camping: $5, Open May-Nov Max Length: 40ft, Reservations not accepted, Elev: 2234ft/681m Tel: 406-654-1251, Nearest town: Malta. GPS: 48.364215, -107.870545

11 • A5 | Bolster Dam City CG

Total sites: 18, RV sites: 9, Elec sites: 9, Water at site, Vault/pit toilet No showers, No RV dump, Tents: Free/RVs: $10, Open all year Max Length: 45ft, Reservations not accepted, Elev: 2076ft/633m Tel: 406-765-1700, Nearest town: Plentywood. GPS: 48.785472 -104.553866

12 • A5 | Bruegger Centenial Park

Dispersed sites, Central water, Flush toilet, No showers, RV dump, Tent & RV camping: Free, Stay limit: 5 days, Generator hours: 0600-2100, Reservations not accepted, Elev: 1923ft/586m Nearest town: Culbertson. GPS: 48.146853, -104.512755

13 • A5 | Scobey Lions CG

Total sites: 10, RV sites: 10, Elec sites: 10, Central water, No toilets, No showers, RV dump, Tent & RV camping: Fee unk, Open May-Sep, Reservations not accepted, Elev: 2457ft/749m, Tel: 701-770-4993, Nearest town: Scobey. GPS: 48.793249, -105.419961

14 • B1 | Charlo City RV Parking

Dispersed sites, No water, No toilets, No tents/RVs: Fee unk, Unconfirmed, Reservations not accepted, Elev: 2939ft/896m, Nearest town: Charlo. GPS: 47.437407, -114.172199

15 • B2 | Atkinson ParkAtkinson Park

Total sites: 3, RV dump, No tents/RVs: Donation, Highway noise, Elev: 3409ft/1039m, Nearest town: Cascade. GPS: 47.276334, -111.703177

16 • B2 | ChoteauCity Park and CG

Total sites: 5, RV sites: 5, Central water, Flush toilet, No showers, RV dump, Tent & RV camping: $10, Open all year, Reservations not accepted, Elev: 3819ft/1164m, Tel: 406-466-2510, Nearest town: Choteau. GPS: 47.811566, -112.179204

17 • B2 | Drummond Community Park

Total sites: 10, RV sites: 10, Elec sites: 3, Water at site, Flush toilet, No RV dump, Tents: $10/RVs: $25, Call to have electric box unlocked, No dump station in town, Stay limit: 7 days, Open May-Oct, Reservations not accepted, Elev: 3944ft/1202m, Tel: 406-288-3231, Nearest town: Drummond. GPS: 46.661339, -113.150809

18 • B2 | Hooper City Park

Total sites: 28, RV sites: 28, Elec sites: 10, Central water, Flush toilet, Free showers, Tents: $10/RVs: $15-25, Open Apr-Sep, Reservations not accepted, Elev: 4550ft/1387m, Tel: 406-362-4949, Nearest town: Lincoln. GPS: 46.954832, -112.671318

19 • B3 | Ed McGivern Memorial Park

Total sites: 10, RV sites: 10, Vault/pit toilet, Tent & RV camping: Fee unk, Elev: 4399ft/1341m, Nearest town: Lewiston. GPS: 46.980291, -109.286366

20 • B3 | Kiwanis Park

Total sites: 18, RV sites: 14, Central water, Flush toilet, No showers, No RV dump, Tent & RV camping: Donation, Right beside runway, Reservations not accepted, Elev: 4108ft/1252m, Nearest town: Lewistown. GPS: 47.055186, -109.460483

21 • B4 | Jimmy Kariotis City Park

Total sites: 5, RV sites: 1, Central water, Vault/pit toilet, Tent & RV camping: Free, Stay limit: 2 days, Open all year, Max Length: 30ft, Reservations not accepted, Elev: 2592ft/790m, Tel: 406-557-2692, Nearest town: Jordan. GPS: 47.318195, -106.910456

22 • B5 | JayCee West Park

Total sites: 4, RV sites: 4, No water, No toilets, No tents/RVs: Free, Must be self-contained, Reservations not accepted, Elev: 2050ft/625m, Tel: 406-377-5601, Nearest town: West Glendive. GPS: 47.108259, -104.723876

23 • B5 | Sharbano Park

Total sites: 3, RV sites: 3, Elec sites: 1, Flush toilet, Free showers, RV dump, No tents/RVs: $15, 1 Full hookup, Stay limit: 7 days, Elev: 1906ft/581m, Tel: 406-742-5616, Nearest town: Fairview. GPS: 47.857404, -104.043335

24 • C2 | American Legion Park

Total sites: 15, RV sites: 15, Central water, Vault/pit toilet, No showers, No RV dump, Tent & RV camping: Donation, Open all year, Reservations not accepted, Elev: 6052ft/1845m, Nearest town: Wisdom. GPS: 45.618819, -113.458833

25 • C2 | Twin Bridges Bike Camp

Dispersed sites, Central water, Free showers, Tents only: Donation, Reservations not accepted, Elev: 4634ft/1412m, Nearest town: Twin Bridges. GPS: 45.544894, -112.334208

26 • C2 | Veterans Memorial Park

Total sites: 3, RV sites: 3, Central water, No toilets, No showers, RV dump, No tents/RVs: $5, Stay limit: 1 day, Elev: 4908ft/1496m, Nearest town: Boulder. GPS: 46.238874, -112.117679

27 • C3 | Bridger City Park

Total sites: 6, RV sites: 6, Elec sites: 6, Water at site, No toilets, No showers, RV dump, Tents: $10/RVs: $20, 6 Full hookup, Stay limit: 10 days, Open May-Sep, Reservations not accepted, Elev: 3652ft/1113m, Nearest town: Bridger. GPS: 45.296204, -108.910683

28 • C3 | Chief Joseph City Park

Total sites: 20, RV sites: 20, Elec sites: 20, Central water, No toilets, No showers, No RV dump, Tent & RV camping: $20, Open Apr-Sep, Reservations not accepted, Elev: 4183ft/1275m, Tel: 406-632-5523, Nearest town: Harlowton. GPS: 46.434821, -109.837801

29 • C3 | Itch-Kep-Pe City Park

Total sites: 30, RV sites: 30, Central water, Vault/pit toilet, No showers, No RV dump, Tent & RV camping: Free, Stay limit: 14 days, Open Apr-Oct, Reservations not accepted, Elev: 3570ft/1088m, Tel: 406-322-5313, Nearest town: Columbus. GPS: 45.627698, -109.250097

30 • C4 | Cowbelles Corral

Total sites: 34, RV sites: 35, Central water, Vault/pit toilet, No showers, No RV dump, Tent & RV camping: Donation, Open all year, Max Length: 40ft, Reservations not accepted, Elev: 3179ft/969m, Tel: 406-323-1966, Nearest town: Roundup. GPS: 46.439697, -108.531738

31 • C5 | Broadus City Park

Total sites: 6, RV sites: 6, Central water, Flush toilet, Tent & RV camping: Free, Reservations not accepted, Elev: 3034ft/925m, Nearest town: Broadus. GPS: 45.439303, -105.409654

Nebraska

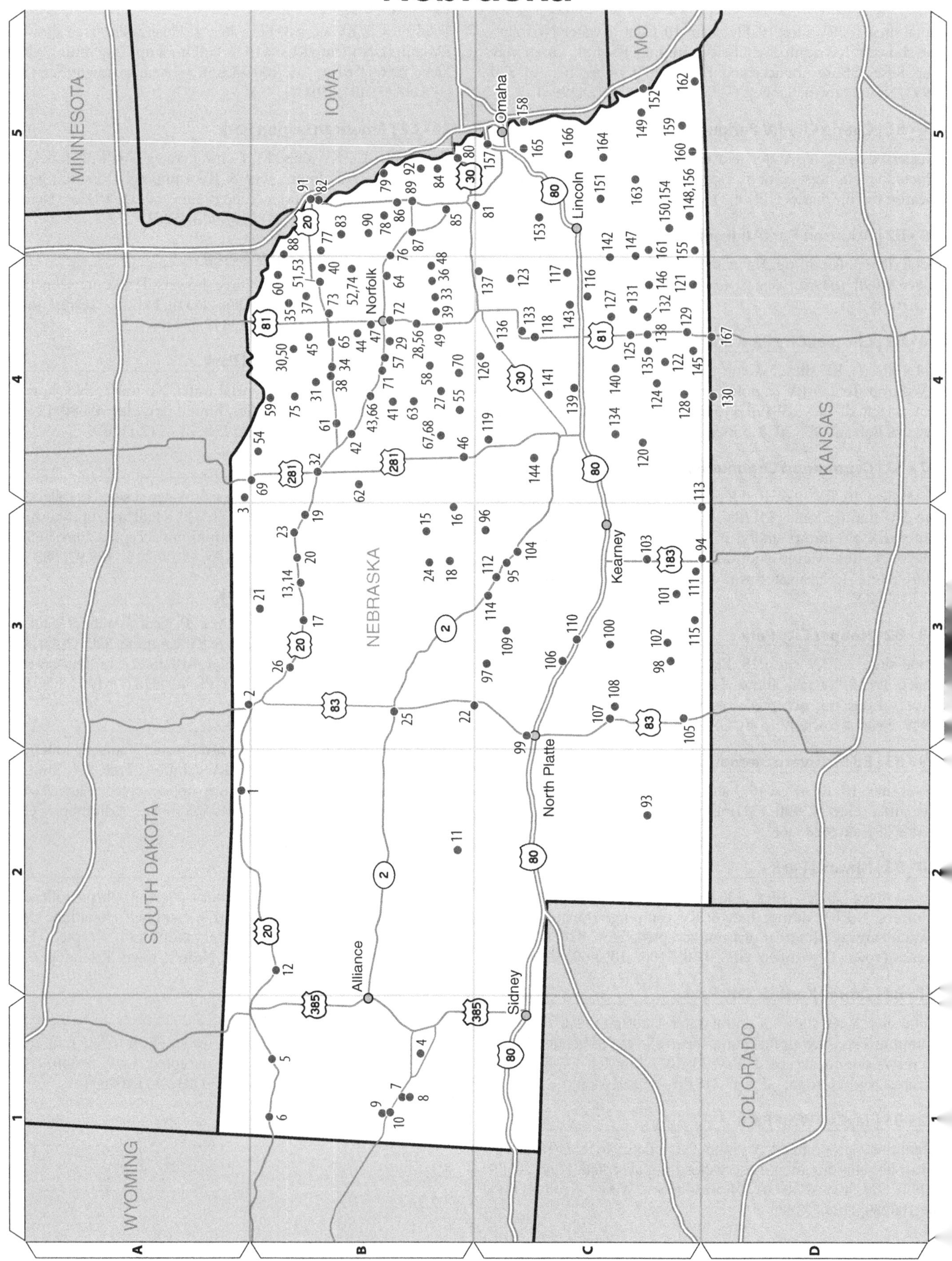

NEBRASKA
MINNESOTA
IOWA
MO
SOUTH DAKOTA
WYOMING
COLORADO
KANSAS
Omaha
Lincoln
Norfolk
Kearney
North Platte
Alliance
Sidney
A
B
C
D
1
2
3
4
5

Map	ID	Map	ID
A2	1	B5	77-92
A3	2	C2	93
A4	3	C3	94-115
B1	4-10	C4	116-146
B2	11-12	C5	147-166
B3	13-26	D4	167
B4	27-76		

Alphabetical List of Camping Areas

Name	ID	Map
Albion City RV Park	27	B4
Allen Municipal CG	77	B5
Alma City RV Park	94	C3
American Legion Memorial City Park	147	C5
Ansley City Park	95	C3
Arbor City Park	148	C5
Arcadia Garden Club Park	96	C3
Arnold Lake RA	97	C3
Arthur Park	11	B2
Auburn Recreation Complex	149	C5
Bancroft Municipal Park	78	B5
Barnes City Park	28	B4
Bassett City Park	13	B3
Bassett RA	14	B3
Battle Creek Municipal Park	29	B4
Bayard City Park	4	B1
Beatrice Riverside Park	150	C5
Beaver Crossing Municipal	116	C4
Beck Memorial Park	79	B5
Bennett City Park	151	C5
Bloomfield City Park	30	B4
Blue Valley CG	117	C4
Bob Hardy RV Park	80	B5
Brownville Riverside Park	152	C5
Bruce City Park	31	B4
Buckley City Park	118	C4
Burwell City Park	15	B3
Bussell City Park	16	B3
Butte City Park	3	A4
Cambridge City RV Park	98	C3
Carney City Park	32	B4
Centennial City Park	33	B4
Ceresco City Park	153	C5
Chautauqua Municipal Park	154	C5
Chester Municipal Park	167	D4
Chilvers Park	34	B4
Christiansen Field	81	B5
City Camper Court	35	B4
Clarkson City Park	36	B4
Cody City Park	99	C3
Cody City Park	1	A2
Coleridge Village Park	37	B4
Cottonwood Cove Park	82	B5
Cottonwood Park	119	C4
Country Club	38	B4
Crawford City Park	5	B1
Creston City Park	39	B4
Crystal Lake	120	C4
Crystal Springs Lake	121	C4
Davenport City Park	122	C4
David City Park	123	C4
Diller City Park	155	C5
Dixon City Park	40	B4
East City Park	17	B3
Edgar City Camp Facility	124	C4
Elgin City Park	41	B4
Emerson City Park	83	B5
Eustis City Park	100	C3
Ewing City Park	42	B4
Feits Memorial Park	156	C5
Fred Penn Park	43	B4
Geneva City Park	125	C4
Genoa City Park	126	C4
George Mitchell Park	101	C3
Gilbert City Park	127	C4
Gilman Park	44	B4
Gladstone City Park	45	B4
Glenn Cunningham Lake	157	C5
Golden Acres RV Park	18	B3
Greeley City Park	46	B4
Hadar City RV Parking	47	B4
Harbine Park	128	C4
Harrison City Park	6	B1
Haworth City Park	158	C5
Hebron Riverside Park	129	C4
Herman City Park	84	B5
Holbrook City Park	102	C3
Holdrege City RV Park	103	C3
Hooper Memorial Park	85	B5
Howells Community Park	48	B4
Humboldt Lake City Park	159	C5
Humphrey City Park	49	B4
Island Park City CG	86	B5
John D. Sims Memorial Park	104	C3
Karrer Park	105	C3
Knox Co Fairgrounds	50	B4
Lafayette Park City CG	106	C3
Laurel City Park	51	B4
Lincoln Park West	130	C4
Lions Camper Park	52	B4
Lions Club Park	53	B4
Lynch City Park	54	B4
Maywood City Park	107	C3
Mel's Landing City Park	55	B4
Memorial City Park	56	B4
Mill Park	108	C3
MIll Race Park	19	B3
Mill Stone Wayside Park	57	B4
Milligan RV Park	131	C4
Morgan Municipal Park	109	C3
Muny City Park	110	C3
Neligh Park	87	B5
Newcastle CG	88	B5
Newman Grove City Park	58	B4
Niobrara City Park	59	B4
Oakland City Park	89	B5
Obert City Park	60	B4

1 • A2 | Cody City Park

Total sites: 7, RV sites: 7, Elec sites: 7, Central water, Flush toilet, Free showers, RV dump, Tents: $10/RVs: $20, Open May-Oct, Reservations not accepted, Elev: 3104ft/946m, Tel: 402-823-4118, Nearest town: Cody. GPS: 42.935386, -101.244755

2 • A3 | Valentine City Park

Total sites: 32, RV sites: 12, Central water, Flush toilet, Free showers, RV dump, Tent & RV camping: $5, Fee for dumping, Open all year, Reservations not accepted, Elev: 2483ft/757m, Tel: 402-376-2323, Nearest town: Valentine. GPS: 42.886106, -100.548834

3 • A4 | Butte City Park

Total sites: 2, RV sites: 2, Elec sites: 2, Water available, Vault/pit toilet, No showers, No RV dump, Tent & RV camping: $5, Open all year, Elev: 1790ft/546m, Tel: 402-775-2426, Nearest town: Butte. GPS: 42.910911, -98.841634

4 • B1 | Bayard City Park

Total sites: 3, RV sites: 3, Elec sites: 3, Water at site, No tents/RVs: $10, 1st 2 nights free, Elev: 3836ft/1169m, Tel: 308-586-1121, Nearest town: Bayard. GPS: 41.762278, -103.322019

5 • B1 | Crawford City Park

Total sites: 10, RV sites: 10, Elec sites: 4, Central water, Flush toilet, No showers, RV dump, Tents: $10/RVs: $20, Near RR, 3-day limit, all 4 sites share 1 electric pole, Stay limit: 14 days, Open all year, Elev: 3674ft/1120m, Tel: 308-665-1300, Nearest town: Crawford. GPS: 42.686614, -103.417491

6 • B1 | Harrison City Park

Total sites: 2, RV sites: 2, Elec sites: 2, Central water, Flush toilet, No showers, No RV dump, Tent & RV camping: Donation, Max Length: 40ft, Reservations not accepted, Elev: 4884ft/1489m, Nearest town: Harrison. GPS: 42.689752, -103.885327

7 • B1 | Riverside Park City CG

Total sites: 93, RV sites: 43, Elec sites: 43, Water at site, Flush toilet, Free showers, RV dump, Tents: $10/RVs: $10-25, Some Full hookup, Stay limit: 14 days, Open May-Sep, Reservations accepted, Elev: 3878ft/1182m, Tel: Info: 308-632-6342/Res: 308-631-2619, Nearest town: Scotts Bluff. GPS: 41.853767, -103.681814

8 • B1 | Robidoux RV Park

Total sites: 100, RV sites: 42, Elec sites: 42, Water at site, Flush toilet, Free showers, RV dump, Tents: $13/RVs: $29-35, 37 Full hookup, Open all year, Reservations accepted, Elev: 3980ft/1213m, Tel: 308-436-2046, Nearest town: Gering. GPS: 41.812777, -103.676647

9 • B1 | Scenic Knolls City Golf Course and CG

Total sites: 6, RV sites: 6, Elec sites: 6, Water at site, Flush toilet, Free showers, No RV dump, No tents/RVs: $15, Elev: 4064ft/1239m, Tel: 308-623-2468, Nearest town: Mitchell. GPS: 41.977731, 103.819005

10 • B1 | Zeigler City Park

Total sites: 4, RV sites: 4, Elec sites: 4, Central water, No toilet, No showers, No RV dump, No tents/RVs: $5, Open all year, Elev

3947ft/1203m, Tel: 308-623-1616, Nearest town: Mitchell. GPS: 41.938558, -103.805836

11 • B2 | Arthur Park

Total sites: 8, RV sites: 8, Central water, Vault/pit toilet, No RV dump, Tent & RV camping: Free, 8 Full hookup, Reservations not accepted, Elev: 3648ft/1112m, Nearest town: Arthur. GPS: 41.570649, -101.690549

12 • B2 | Sunset City RV Park

Total sites: 10, RV sites: 10, Elec sites: 10, Water at site, No toilets, No showers, RV dump, Tent & RV camping: $25, 10 Full hookup, Elev: 3824ft/1166m, Tel: 308-638-7275, Nearest town: Hay Springs. GPS: 42.680337, -102.692347

13 • B3 | Bassett City Park

Total sites: 17, RV sites: 17, Elec sites: 17, Central water, Flush toilet, Free showers, RV dump, No tents/RVs: Donation, Additional 50 sites at adjacent fairgrounds, Reservations not accepted, Elev: 2329ft/710m, Tel: 402-684-3338, Nearest town: Bassett. GPS: 42.577838, -99.539862

14 • B3 | Bassett RA

Dispersed sites, No water, Tent & RV camping: Free, Reservations not accepted, Elev: 2330ft/710m, Tel: 402-684-3338, Nearest town: Bassett. GPS: 42.575873, -99.546716

15 • B3 | Burwell City Park

Total sites: 12, RV sites: 8, Elec sites: 8, Central water, Vault/pit toilet, No showers, No RV dump, Tent & RV camping: $5, No water in winter, Open all year, Elev: 2156ft/657m, Tel: 308-346-4509, Nearest town: Burwell. GPS: 41.788931, -99.132992

16 • B3 | Bussell City Park

Total sites: 30, RV sites: 8, Elec sites: 8, Water at site, Flush toilet, Free showers, RV dump, Tent & RV camping: $10, No water in winter, Stay limit: 5 days, Open all year, Reservations not accepted, Elev: 2050ft/625m, Tel: 308-728-5791, Nearest town: Ord. GPS: 41.606468, -98.938009

17 • B3 | East City Park

Total sites: 30, RV sites: 30, Elec sites: 30, Water at site, No toilets, No showers, RV dump, Tents: $7/RVs: $10, Open May-Oct, Max Length: 30ft, Elev: 2510ft/765m, Tel: 402-387-2494, Nearest town: Ainsworth. GPS: 42.548001, -99.845423

18 • B3 | Golden Acres RV Park

Total sites: 8, RV sites: 8, Elec sites: 8, Water at site, Flush toilet, Free showers, RV dump, Tents: $5/RVs: $14, Shower at pool in summer, Elev: 2326ft/709m, Tel: 308-527-4200, Nearest town: Sargent. GPS: 41.638258, -99.372342

19 • B3 | MIll Race Park

Total sites: 28, RV sites: 16, Elec sites: 16, Central water, Vault/pit toilet, No showers, No RV dump, Tents: $7/RVs: $15, Open all year, Reservations not accepted, Elev: 2089ft/637m, Tel: 402-684-2921, Nearest town: Atkinson. GPS: 42.537597, -98.999354

20 • B3 | Spring Valley Wayside Park

Dispersed sites, Central water, Vault/pit toilet, Tents only: Fee unk, Elev: 2264ft/690m, Nearest town: Newport. GPS: 42.593984, -99.341571

21 • B3 | Springview RA

Total sites: 4, RV sites: 4, Elec sites: 4, Water at site, Flush toilet, Free showers, RV dump, Tents: $10/RVs: $15, Reservations accepted, Elev: 2448ft/746m, Tel: 402-497-2901, Nearest town: Springview. GPS: 42.827206, -99.743658

22 • B3 | Stapleton Village Park

Total sites: 4, RV sites: 4, Elec sites: 4, No toilets, No showers, No RV dump, Tent & RV camping: $15, Bathhouse closed in winter, Open all year, Elev: 2897ft/883m, Nearest town: Stapleton. GPS: 41.480564, -100.514566

23 • B3 | Stuart Municipal Park

Total sites: 40, RV sites: 20, Elec sites: 20, Water at site, Flush toilet, Free showers, RV dump, Tent & RV camping: $10, Open Mar-Nov, Reservations not accepted, Elev: 2182ft/665m, Tel: 402-924-3647, Nearest town: Stuart. GPS: 42.606435, -99.139841

24 • B3 | Taylor Tourist Park

Total sites: 6, RV sites: 6, Elec sites: 6, Water at site, Flush toilet, Free showers, RV dump, No tents/RVs: $12, 6 Full hookup, Open Apr-Nov, Elev: 2284ft/696m, Tel: 308-942-6199, Nearest town: Taylor. GPS: 41.770515, -99.382481

25 • B3 | Thedford City Park

Total sites: 4, RV sites: 4, Elec sites: 4, Central water, No toilets, No showers, No RV dump, Tent & RV camping: Donation, Near RR, Open all year, Elev: 2877ft/877m, Nearest town: Thedford. GPS: 41.977775, -100.582104

26 • B3 | Village Park

Total sites: 2, RV sites: 2, Elec sites: 2, Water at site, Flush toilet, No showers, RV dump, No tents/RVs: Donation, Open May-Sep, Elev: 2700ft/823m, Tel: 402-967-3054, Nearest town: Wood Lake. GPS: 42.637518, -100.237661

27 • B4 | Albion City RV Park

Total sites: 26, RV sites: 26, Elec sites: 26, Water at site, Flush toilet, Free showers, RV dump, Tents: $10/RVs: $15, 26 Full hookup, Reservations not accepted, Elev: 1827ft/557m, Tel: 402-395-2428, Nearest town: Albion. GPS: 41.681768, -98.008560

28 • B4 | Barnes City Park

Total sites: 3, RV sites: 3, Elec sites: 3, Water at site, Flush toilet, Free showers, No RV dump, No tents/RVs: $12, 3 Full hookup, No pets, Stay limit: 14 days, Reservations not accepted, Elev: 1653ft/504m, Nearest town: Madison. GPS: 41.822315, -97.456575

29 • B4 | Battle Creek Municipal Park

Total sites: 1, RV sites: 1, Elec sites: 1, Central water, Flush toilet, No showers, RV dump, No tents/RVs: Donation, Stay limit: 3 days, Open May-Oct, Reservations not accepted, Elev: 1604ft/489m, Tel: 402-675-2165, Nearest town: Battle Creek. GPS: 41.992854, -97.600043

30 • B4 | Bloomfield City Park

Total sites: 6, RV sites: 6, Elec sites: 6, Water at site, Flush toilet,

Free showers, RV dump, Tent & RV camping: $5-10, Open all year, Elev: 1703ft/519m, Tel: 402-373-4396, Nearest town: Bloomfield. GPS: 42.593762, -97.647998

31 • B4 | Bruce City Park

Total sites: 7, RV sites: 7, Elec sites: 7, Water at site, Flush toilet, Free showers, RV dump, Tents: Free/RVs: $10-15, 4 Full hookup, Open Apr-Oct, Reservations not accepted, Elev: 1647ft/502m, Tel: 402-358-3557, Nearest town: Creighton. GPS: 42.463386, -97.912348

32 • B4 | Carney City Park

Total sites: 22, RV sites: 18, Elec sites: 18, Water at site, Flush toilet, Free showers, RV dump, Tent & RV camping: Donation, 15-amps, Open Apr-Sep, Reservations not accepted, Elev: 1972ft/601m, Tel: 402-336-3640, Nearest town: O'Neill. GPS: 42.451001, -98.644819

33 • B4 | Centennial City Park

Total sites: 14, RV sites: 14, Elec sites: 14, Water at site, Flush toilet, Free showers, RV dump, Tent & RV camping: $10, Open Apr-Oct, Elev: 1594ft/486m, Tel: 402-487-3303, Nearest town: Leigh. GPS: 41.701739, -97.246489

34 • B4 | Chilvers Park

Total sites: 4, RV sites: 4, Elec sites: 4, Water at site, No toilets, No showers, No RV dump, Tent & RV camping: Donation, Suggested donation - $10, Stay limit: 3 days, Open all year, Reservations not accepted, Elev: 1700ft/518m, Tel: 402-582-4928, Nearest town: Plainview. GPS: 42.351628, -97.790696

35 • B4 | City Camper Court

Total sites: 21, RV sites: 6, Elec sites: 6, Water at site, No toilets, No showers, RV dump, No tents/RVs: Donation, Open Apr-Oct, Elev: 1371ft/418m, Tel: 402-254-6353, Nearest town: Hartington. GPS: 42.624988, -97.265003

36 • B4 | Clarkson City Park

Total sites: 40, RV sites: 20, Elec sites: 20, Water at site, Flush toilet, Free showers, RV dump, Tent & RV camping: $15, Open May-Sep, Elev: 1483ft/452m, Tel: 402-892-3100, Nearest town: Clarkson. GPS: 41.727452, -97.116868

37 • B4 | Coleridge Village Park

Total sites: 4, RV sites: 4, Elec sites: 4, Water at site, No toilets, No showers, RV dump, Tent & RV camping: Free, Donation appreciated, Open all year, Elev: 1544ft/471m, Tel: 402-283-4464, Nearest town: Coleridge. GPS: 42.509454, -97.203997

38 • B4 | Country Club

Total sites: 4, RV sites: 4, Elec sites: 4, No toilets, No showers, No RV dump, No tents/RVs: $10, Elev: 1752ft/534m, Tel: 402-582-3445, Nearest town: Plainview. GPS: 42.363986, -97.862997

39 • B4 | Creston City Park

Total sites: Unk, No toilets, No showers, RV dump, Tent & RV camping: Fee unk, Unconfirmed, Elev: 1614ft/492m, Nearest town: Creston. GPS: 41.709279, -97.360777

40 • B4 | Dixon City Park

Dispersed sites, No toilets, No showers, No RV dump, Tent & RV camping: Fee unk, Unconfirmed, Elev: 1444ft/440m, Nearest town: Dixon. GPS: 42.416028, -96.996902

41 • B4 | Elgin City Park

Total sites: 23, RV sites: 8, Elec sites: 8, Water at site, Flush toilet, Free showers, RV dump, Tent & RV camping: $15, Open May-Oct, Elev: 1936ft/590m, Tel: 402-843-5822, Nearest town: Elgin. GPS: 41.986957, -98.076673

42 • B4 | Ewing City Park

Total sites: 15, RV sites: 6, Elec sites: 6, Water at site, No toilets, No showers, RV dump, Tent & RV camping: $11, Open all year, Elev: 1867ft/569m, Tel: 402-626-7718, Nearest town: Ewing. GPS: 42.255508, -98.340078

43 • B4 | Fred Penn Park

Dispersed sites, Central water, Flush toilet, No showers, No RV dump, Tents only: $5, Open Apr-Oct, Reservations not accepted, Elev: 1729ft/527m, Tel: 402-887-4066, Nearest town: Neligh. GPS: 42.124987, -98.037673

44 • B4 | Gilman Park

Total sites: 4, RV sites: 4, Elec sites: 4, Water at site, Flush toilet, Free showers, No RV dump, Tent & RV camping: $10, 5-day limit, Open May-Oct, Elev: 1588ft/484m, Tel: 402-329-4873, Nearest town: Pierce. GPS: 42.200826, -97.519471

45 • B4 | Gladstone City Park

Total sites: 13, RV sites: 8, Elec sites: 8, Water at site, No toilets, No showers, RV dump, No tents/RVs: $10, Open Apr-Sep, Max Length: 25ft, Elev: 1759ft/536m, Tel: 402-586-2311, Nearest town: Wausa. GPS: 42.503321, -97.542904

46 • B4 | Greeley City Park

Total sites: 10, RV sites: 10, Elec sites: 10, Water at site, No toilets, No showers, No RV dump, Tent & RV camping: Free, Stay limit 3 days, Open May-Sep, Elev: 2014ft/614m, Tel: 308-428-4010 Nearest town: Greeley Center. GPS: 41.551247, -98.537541

47 • B4 | Hadar City RV Parking

Total sites: 4, RV sites: 4, Elec sites: 4, Water available, Flush toilet Free showers, No RV dump, Tent & RV camping: $12, Open al year, Reservations not accepted, Elev: 1552ft/473m, Nearest town Hadar. GPS: 42.107440, -97.452446

48 • B4 | Howells Community Park

Total sites: 10, RV sites: 10, Elec sites: 10, Central water, Flus toilet, No showers, RV dump, Tent & RV camping: $15, 4 Fu hookup near horseshoe pits, Elev: 1460ft/445m, Tel: 402-986 1666, Nearest town: Howells. GPS: 41.728972, -97.004089

49 • B4 | Humphrey City Park

Total sites: 2, RV sites: 2, Elec sites: 2, Tent & RV camping: Fe unk, Unconfirmed, Reservations not accepted, Elev: 1685ft/514m Tel: 402-923-9000, Nearest town: Humphrey. GPS: 41.686635, 97.489506

50 • B4 | Knox Co Fairgrounds

Total sites: 30, RV sites: 30, Elec sites: 30, Water at site, Flush toilet, Free showers, No RV dump, No tents/RVs: $15, Elev: 1709ft/521m, Tel: 402-373-4396, Nearest town: Bloomfield. GPS: 42.597952, -97.636038

51 • B4 | Laurel City Park

Total sites: 7, RV sites: 7, Elec sites: 7, Water at site, Flush toilet, Free showers, RV dump, Tent & RV camping: $5, No water in winter, Open all year, Elev: 1466ft/447m, Tel: 402-256-3112, Nearest town: Laurel. GPS: 42.426741, -97.088041

52 • B4 | Lions Camper Park

Total sites: 18, RV sites: 6, Elec sites: 6, Water at site, No toilets, No showers, RV dump, Tent & RV camping: $8, Open Apr-Oct, Reservations not accepted, Elev: 1424ft/434m, Tel: 402-375-3369, Nearest town: Wayne. GPS: 42.236032, -96.987862

53 • B4 | Lions Club Park

Total sites: 5, RV sites: 0, Central water, Flush toilet, Free showers, No RV dump, Tents only: Donation, Open Apr-Oct, Elev: 1480ft/451m, Tel: 402-256-3112, Nearest town: Laurel. GPS: 42.424713, -97.094797

54 • B4 | Lynch City Park

Total sites: 16, RV sites: 8, Elec sites: 8, Water at site, Flush toilet, Free showers, RV dump, Tents: $4/RVs: $10, Open Mar-Nov, Elev: 1404ft/428m, Tel: 402-569-3050, Nearest town: Lynch. GPS: 42.827693, -98.466671

55 • B4 | Mel's Landing City Park

Total sites: 13, RV sites: 3, Central water, Vault/pit toilet, No showers, No RV dump, Tents: Free/RVs: $5, No water in winter, Open all year, Reservations not accepted, Elev: 1778ft/542m, Tel: 308-358-0240, Nearest town: Cedar Rapids. GPS: 41.563073, -98.147048

56 • B4 | Memorial City Park

Total sites: 10, RV sites: 6, Elec sites: 6, Water at site, Flush toilet, Free showers, RV dump, Tents: $5/RVs: $12, 6 Full hookup, No pets, Stay limit: 14 days, Open May-Oct, Reservations not accepted, Elev: 1581ft/482m, Tel: 402-454-2675, Nearest town: Madison. GPS: 41.834299, -97.455312

57 • B4 | Mill Stone Wayside Park

Total sites: 4, RV sites: 4, Elec sites: 4, Central water, Vault/pit toilet, No showers, No RV dump, Tent & RV camping: Donation, 15-amp only, Open all year, Elev: 1618ft/493m, Tel: 402-634-2225, Nearest town: Meadow Grove. GPS: 42.032185, -97.728496

58 • B4 | Newman Grove City Park

Total sites: 10, RV sites: 10, Elec sites: 10, Water at site, No toilets, No showers, RV dump, Tent & RV camping: $10, 10 Full hookup, Open Apr-Oct, Elev: 1716ft/523m, Tel: 402-447-6444, Nearest town: Newman Grove. GPS: 41.751377, -97.776034

59 • B4 | Niobrara City Park

Total sites: 3, RV sites: 3, Elec sites: 3, No toilets, No showers, No RV dump, Tent & RV camping: Fee unk, Unconfirmed, Elev: 1234ft/376m, Tel: 402-857-3565, Nearest town: Niobrara. GPS: 42.753388, -98.037021

60 • B4 | Obert City Park

Total sites: 4, RV sites: 2, Central water, Vault/pit toilet, No showers, No RV dump, Tent & RV camping: Fee unk, Open all year, Elev: 1342ft/409m, Tel: 402-692-3105, Nearest town: Obert. GPS: 42.688294, -97.027902

61 • B4 | Orchard City Park

Total sites: 4, RV sites: 2, Elec sites: 2, Water at site, Flush toilet, Free showers, RV dump, Tent & RV camping: Donation, 5 nights free, Reservations not accepted, Elev: 1952ft/595m, Nearest town: Orchard. GPS: 42.335059, -98.244935

62 • B4 | Perkins Memorial Park

Total sites: 2, RV sites: 2, Elec sites: 2, Central water, Flush toilet, No showers, No RV dump, No tents/RVs: Free, Elev: 2126ft/648m, Nearest town: Chambers. GPS: 42.203249, -98.741787

63 • B4 | Petersburg City Park

Total sites: 8, RV sites: 8, Elec sites: 8, Water at site, No toilets, No showers, RV dump, Tent & RV camping: $15, 8 Full hookup, Open all year, Elev: 1900ft/579m, Tel: 402-386-5551, Nearest town: Petersburg. GPS: 41.856097, -98.082898

64 • B4 | Pilger Park

Total sites: 5, RV sites: 5, Elec sites: 5, Vault/pit toilet, Tent & RV camping: Fee unk, Open all year, Elev: 1408ft/429m, Tel: 402-396-3563, Nearest town: Pilger. GPS: 42.010197, -97.057985

65 • B4 | Poolside Park

Total sites: 5, RV sites: 5, Elec sites: 5, RV dump, No tents/RVs: Free, Stay limit: 7 days, Elev: 1660ft/506m, Nearest town: Osmond. GPS: 42.357223, -97.599918

66 • B4 | Riverside Park

Total sites: 36, RV sites: 26, Elec sites: 14, Water at site, Flush toilet, Free showers, RV dump, Tents: $5/RVs: $13, Open Apr-Sep, Reservations not accepted, Elev: 1732ft/528m, Tel: 402-887-4066, Nearest town: Neligh. GPS: 42.122213, -98.024489

67 • B4 | Spalding City Park

Total sites: 4, RV sites: 4, Elec sites: 4, Water at site, No toilets, No showers, RV dump, Tent & RV camping: Donation, Open all year, Elev: 1893ft/577m, Tel: 308-497-2416, Nearest town: Spalding. GPS: 41.684929, -98.361488

68 • B4 | Spalding Dam Site

Total sites: 19, RV sites: 4, Elec sites: 4, Water at site, Vault/pit toilet, No showers, RV dump, Tent & RV camping: Donation, 2-day limit, Open all year, Elev: 1883ft/574m, Tel: 308-497-2416, Nearest town: Spalding. GPS: 41.680877, -98.366062

69 • B4 | Spencer Park Fairgrounds

Total sites: 14, RV sites: 8, Elec sites: 8, Water at site, Flush toilet, Free showers, RV dump, Tents: $3/RVs: $8, Elev: 1696ft/517m, Tel: 402-589-1038, Nearest town: Spencer. GPS: 42.875865, -98.705955

70 • B4 | St. Edward City Park

Total sites: 3, RV sites: 3, Elec sites: 3, Water at site, No toilets, No showers, RV dump, No tents/RVs: $6, Open all year, Elev: 1673ft/510m, Tel: 402-678-2212, Nearest town: St Edward. GPS: 41.572797, -97.864647

71 • B4 | Sunrise City Park

Total sites: 4, RV sites: 4, Elec sites: 4, Water at site, No toilets, No showers, RV dump, No tents/RVs: Donation, Open Apr-Oct, Elev: 1673ft/510m, Tel: 402-368-2232, Nearest town: Tilden. GPS: 42.046657, -97.826592

72 • B4 | Ta-Ha-Zouka Park

Total sites: 23, RV sites: 13, Elec sites: 13, Central water, Flush toilet, Free showers, RV dump, Tents: $12/RVs: $12-18, In off-season showers and restrooms are not open and campers may park outside of the campground along the road and plug into the power pedestals - $12, Stay limit: 7 days, Open Apr-Oct, Reservations not accepted, Elev: 1516ft/462m, Tel: 402-844-2180, Nearest town: Norfolk. GPS: 42.005240, -97.424140

73 • B4 | Veterans Memorial City Park

Total sites: 6, RV sites: 6, Elec sites: 6, Water at site, Flush toilet, Free showers, RV dump, Tent & RV camping: Donation, Elev: 1667ft/508m, Tel: 402-337-0567, Nearest town: Randolph. GPS: 42.376904, -97.355061

74 • B4 | Victor City Park

Total sites: 12, RV sites: 12, Elec sites: 12, Central water, Flush toilet, No showers, RV dump, Tent & RV camping: $7, Open all year, Elev: 1453ft/443m, Tel: 402-375-1300, Nearest town: Wayne. GPS: 42.225979, -97.018587

75 • B4 | Wildwood Acres Park

Total sites: 27, RV sites: 27, Elec sites: 27, Central water, Flush toilet, Free showers, No RV dump, Tent & RV camping: $9-11, Open Apr-Nov, Elev: 1384ft/422m, Tel: 402-668-2621, Nearest town: Verdigre. GPS: 42.592125, -98.029028

76 • B4 | Wisner River Park

Total sites: 50, RV sites: 21, Elec sites: 21, Water at site, Flush toilet, Free showers, RV dump, Tents: Free/RVs: $15, Open all year, Reservations not accepted, Elev: 1368ft/417m, Tel: 402-529-6616, Nearest town: Wisner. GPS: 41.980486, -96.914536

77 • B5 | Allen Municipal CG

Total sites: 4, RV sites: 4, Elec sites: 4, Water at site, Flush toilet, Free showers, RV dump, No tents/RVs: Donation, 4 Full hookup, Elev: 1506ft/459m, Tel: 402-635-2444, Nearest town: Allen. GPS: 42.412305, -96.847784

78 • B5 | Bancroft Municipal Park

Total sites: 5, RV sites: 3, Elec sites: 3, Central water, No toilets, No showers, RV dump, Tent & RV camping: $6, Open May-Oct, Elev: 1355ft/413m, Tel: 402-648-3332, Nearest town: Bancroft. GPS: 42.007211, -96.575088

79 • B5 | Beck Memorial Park

Total sites: 40, RV sites: 28, Elec sites: 28, Water available, Flush toilet, Free showers, RV dump, Tents: $11/RVs: $20, Open Apr-Oct, Elev: 1034ft/315m, Tel: 402-349-5360, Nearest tow Decatur. GPS: 42.004347, -96.245159

80 • B5 | Bob Hardy RV Park

Total sites: 15, RV sites: 8, Elec sites: 8, Central water, No toilets, N showers, RV dump, Tents: $13/RVs: $18, Stay limit: 5 days, Ope Apr-Oct, Reservations not accepted, Elev: 1070ft/326m, Tel: 40 426-4191, Nearest town: Blair. GPS: 41.546460, -96.141660

81 • B5 | Christiansen Field

Total sites: 45, RV sites: 45, Elec sites: 45, Water at site, Flush toile Free showers, RV dump, Tent & RV camping: $15, Open all yea Elev: 1202ft/366m, Tel: 402-727-2630, Nearest town: Fremon GPS: 41.444823, -96.523715

82 • B5 | Cottonwood Cove Park

Total sites: 19, RV sites: 13, Elec sites: 13, Water at site, Flush toile Free showers, RV dump, Tent & RV camping: $22, Open Ma Oct, Elev: 1099ft/335m, Tel: 402-987-3448, Nearest town: Dako City. GPS: 42.412146, -96.413836

83 • B5 | Emerson City Park

Total sites: 7, RV sites: 7, Elec sites: 7, Water at site, Flush toile No tents/RVs: $8, 7 Full hookup, Reservations not accepte Elev: 1461ft/445m, Nearest town: Emerson. GPS: 42.282768, 96.727923

84 • B5 | Herman City Park

Total sites: 3, RV sites: 3, Elec sites: 3, No toilets, No showers, N RV dump, Tent & RV camping: Fee unk, Unconfirmed, Ele 1037ft/316m, Tel: 402-456-7500, Nearest town: Herman. GP 41.672104, -96.217995

85 • B5 | Hooper Memorial Park

Total sites: 3, RV sites: 3, Elec sites: 3, Water at site, No toilet No showers, No RV dump, Tent & RV camping: Donatio Unconfirmed, Stay limit: 1 day, Open all year, Elev: 1230ft/375n Tel: 402-654-3649, Nearest town: Hooper. GPS: 41.615947, 96.547436

86 • B5 | Island Park City CG

Total sites: 18, RV sites: 16, Elec sites: 16, Water at site, Flush toile Free showers, RV dump, Tent & RV camping: $13, Open Apr-Oc Reservations not accepted, Elev: 1263ft/385m, Tel: 402-687-248 Nearest town: Lyons. GPS: 41.936229, -96.481109

87 • B5 | Neligh Park

Total sites: 17, RV sites: 17, Elec sites: 17, Central water, Flus toilet, Free showers, RV dump, Tent & RV camping: $15, $2 dum fee, Max Length: 30ft, Reservations not accepted, Elev: 1296f 395m, Nearest town: West Point. GPS: 41.841678, -96.718624

88 • B5 | Newcastle CG

Total sites: 8, RV sites: 3, Elec sites: 3, Central water, No toilet No showers, No RV dump, Tent & RV camping: Fee unk, Ope all year, Elev: 1270ft/387m, Tel: 402-692-3192, Nearest tow Newcastle. GPS: 42.650054, -96.868741

89 • B5 | Oakland City Park

Total sites: 13, RV sites: 13, Elec sites: 13, Water at site, Flush toile

Free showers, RV dump, Tent & RV camping: $15, Open Apr-Oct, Reservations not accepted, Elev: 1240ft/378m, Tel: 402-685-5822, Nearest town: Oakland. GPS: 41.830697, -96.475039

90 • B5 | Pender City Park

Total sites: 6, RV sites: 6, Elec sites: 6, Central water, No toilets, No showers, RV dump, No tents/RVs: $5, Elev: 1329ft/405m, Nearest town: Pender. GPS: 42.113961, -96.712919

91 • B5 | Scenic Park City CG

Total sites: 141, RV sites: 135, Elec sites: 135, Water at site, Flush toilet, Free showers, RV dump, Tents: $25/RVs: $25-34, Open Apr-Oct, Reservations accepted, Elev: 1060ft/323m, Tel: 402-494-7531, Nearest town: South Sioux City. GPS: 42.485264, -96.402465

92 • B5 | Tekamah Memorial Park

Total sites: 8, RV sites: 8, Elec sites: 8, Water at site, No toilets, No showers, RV dump, Tent & RV camping: $5, Open Apr-Oct, Elev: 1041ft/317m, Tel: 402-374-2521, Nearest town: Tekamah. GPS: 41.786169, -96.218841

93 • C2 | Wauneta RV Park

Total sites: 32, RV sites: 32, Elec sites: 32, Water at site, No toilets, No showers, RV dump, No tents/RVs: $10-20, Elev: 2976ft/907m, Tel: 308-394-5390, Nearest town: Wauneta. GPS: 40.412713, -101.370067

94 • C3 | Alma City RV Park

Total sites: 38, RV sites: 38, Elec sites: 38, Water at site, Flush toilet, Free showers, RV dump, Tent & RV camping: $20, 38 Full hookup, Open Apr-Oct, Reservations not accepted, Elev: 1995ft/608m, Tel: 308-928-3102, Nearest town: Alma. GPS: 40.095694, -99.360071

95 • C3 | Ansley City Park

Total sites: 10, RV sites: 6, Elec sites: 6, Central water, No toilets, No showers, No RV dump, Tent & RV camping: Fee unk, Open May-Sep, Elev: 2310ft/704m, Tel: 308-935-1467, Nearest town: Ansley. GPS: 41.289959, -99.388894

96 • C3 | Arcadia Garden Club Park

Total sites: 10, RV sites: 6, Elec sites: 6, Central water, Vault/pit toilet, No showers, RV dump, Tent & RV camping: $20, Open all year, Elev: 2162ft/659m, Tel: 308-789-6552, Nearest town: Arcadia. GPS: 41.422622, -99.129996

97 • C3 | Arnold Lake RA

Total sites: 80, RV sites: 80, Elec sites: 20, Water at site, No toilets, No showers, RV dump, Tents: $6/RVs: $15, Open all year, Reservations not accepted, Elev: 2710ft/826m, Tel: 308-848-2228, Nearest town: Arnold. GPS: 41.412712, -100.196068

98 • C3 | Cambridge City RV Park

Total sites: 11, RV sites: 11, Elec sites: 11, Water at site, Flush toilet, Free showers, RV dump, Tent & RV camping: Donation, Near RR, Elev: 2293ft/699m, Tel: 308-697-3711, Nearest town: Cambridge. GPS: 40.282721, -100.159779

99 • C3 | Cody City Park

Total sites: 40, RV sites: 40, Central water, Flush toilet, No showers, Tent & RV camping: $5, Stay limit: 7 days, Open May-Oct, Reservations not accepted, Elev: 2805ft/855m, Tel: 308-535-6706, Nearest town: North Platte. GPS: 41.150671, -100.758158

100 • C3 | Eustis City Park

Total sites: 2, RV sites: 2, Elec sites: 2, Central water, No toilets, No showers, RV dump, No tents/RVs: Free, 20 amp, Elev: 2631ft/802m, Tel: 308-486-3661, Nearest town: Eustis. GPS: 40.659909, -100.026419

101 • C3 | George Mitchell Park

Total sites: 10, RV sites: 10, Elec sites: 10, Water at site, Vault/pit toilet, No showers, RV dump, Tent & RV camping: $8, 1st night free, Open all year, Elev: 2087ft/636m, Tel: 308-824-3511, Nearest town: Oxford. GPS: 40.247041, -99.636704

102 • C3 | Holbrook City Park

Total sites: 5, RV sites: 5, Elec sites: 5, Central water, Vault/pit toilet, No showers, No RV dump, Tent & RV camping: Fee unk, Location uncertain, Open all year, Elev: 2215ft/675m, Tel: 308-493-5915, Nearest town: Holbrook. GPS: 40.304448, -100.010212

103 • C3 | Holdrege City RV Park

Total sites: 7, RV sites: 7, Elec sites: 7, Water at site, Flush toilet, Free showers, RV dump, Tent & RV camping: $10, Near RR, Open all year, Max Length: 40ft, Reservations not accepted, Elev: 2330ft/710m, Tel: 308-995-8681, Nearest town: Holdrege. GPS: 40.434672, -99.369179

104 • C3 | John D. Sims Memorial Park

Dispersed sites, Tent & RV camping: Fee unk, Near RR, Elev: 2254ft/687m, Nearest town: Mason City. GPS: 41.223879, -99.296891

105 • C3 | Karrer Park

Total sites: 7, RV sites: 7, Elec sites: 7, Central water, Flush toilet, Free showers, RV dump, Tent & RV camping: Donation, Stay limit: 3 days, Open all year, Max Length: 30ft, Elev: 2520ft/768m, Tel: 308-345-2022, Nearest town: McCook. GPS: 40.197507, -100.602895

106 • C3 | Lafayette Park City CG

Total sites: 42, RV sites: 30, Elec sites: 30, Water at site, Flush toilet, Free showers, RV dump, Tents: $15/RVs: $25, Open Apr-Oct, Reservations accepted, Elev: 2615ft/797m, Tel: 308-537-2299, Nearest town: Gothenburg. GPS: 40.944092, -100.165527

107 • C3 | Maywood City Park

Total sites: 6, RV sites: 3, Elec sites: 3, Water at site, No toilets, No showers, RV dump, Tent & RV camping: $5, 1st night free, Open Apr-Oct, Elev: 2674ft/815m, Tel: 308-362-4299, Nearest town: Maywood. GPS: 40.654956, -100.619327

108 • C3 | Mill Park

Total sites: 9, RV sites: 9, Elec sites: 9, Water at site, No toilets, No showers, RV dump, No tents/RVs: $5, 1st 3 nights free, Reservations not accepted, Elev: 2585ft/788m, Tel: 308-367-4122, Nearest town: Curtis. GPS: 40.625731, -100.523817

109 • C3 | Morgan Municipal Park

Total sites: 30, RV sites: 6, Elec sites: 6, Central water, Flush toilet, Free showers, No RV dump, Tent & RV camping: $5, Open all year, Elev: 2562ft/781m, Tel: 308-836-2262, Nearest town: Callaway. GPS: 41.292403, -99.922612

110 • C3 | Muny City Park

Total sites: 30, RV sites: 18, Elec sites: 18, Water at site, Flush toilet, Free showers, RV dump, Tent & RV camping: $10, Near RR, Open all year, Elev: 2507ft/764m, Tel: 308-784-3907, Nearest town: Cozad. GPS: 40.866442, -99.997958

111 • C3 | Orleans City Park

Total sites: 8, RV sites: 8, Elec sites: 8, Water at site, No toilets, No showers, RV dump, Tent & RV camping: $15, Open all year, Reservations not accepted, Elev: 2064ft/629m, Tel: 308-473-4185, Nearest town: Orleans. GPS: 40.133511, -99.453194

112 • C3 | Sorensen Village Park

Total sites: 5, RV sites: 1, Elec sites: 1, Central water, No toilets, No showers, No RV dump, Tent & RV camping: $10, Unconfirmed, Stay limit: 3 days, Open all year, Elev: 2382ft/726m, Tel: 308-935-1569, Nearest town: Berwyn. GPS: 41.349909, -99.500455

113 • C3 | Southpark Municipal CG

Total sites: 5, RV sites: 5, Elec sites: 5, Water at site, No toilets, No showers, RV dump, Tent & RV camping: $15, 6 Full hookup, Open all year, Max Length: 40ft, Elev: 1870ft/570m, Tel: 308-425-6295, Nearest town: Franklin. GPS: 40.092183, -98.952772

114 • C3 | Tomahawk Municipal Park

Total sites: 15, RV sites: 15, Elec sites: 15, Water at site, Flush toilet, Free showers, RV dump, Tent & RV camping: $20, 15 Full hookup, Open all year, Elev: 2497ft/761m, Tel: 308-872-2003, Nearest town: Broken Bow. GPS: 41.404106, -99.648751

115 • C3 | Westside City Park

Total sites: 4, RV sites: 4, Elec sites: 4, Water at site, No toilets, No showers, RV dump, Tents: $6/RVs: $15, Open all year, Reservations not accepted, Elev: 2195ft/669m, Tel: 308-268-2145, Nearest town: Beaver City. GPS: 40.135295, -99.833339

116 • C4 | Beaver Crossing Municipal

Total sites: 6, RV sites: 6, Elec sites: 6, Water at site, Flush toilet, Tent & RV camping: Donation, Open Apr-Nov, Elev: 1476ft/450m, Tel: 402-532-3925, Nearest town: Beaver Crossing. GPS: 40.777260, -97.276610

117 • C4 | Blue Valley CG

Total sites: 16, RV sites: 16, Elec sites: 16, Central water, Vault/pit toilet, No showers, RV dump, Tents: $7/RVs: $15, $10 for seniors, Open Apr-Oct, Reservations not accepted, Elev: 1444ft/440m, Tel: 402-643-4000, Nearest town: Seward. GPS: 40.901387, -97.096283

118 • C4 | Buckley City Park

Total sites: 12, RV sites: 12, Elec sites: 12, Central water, Flush toilet, RV dump, Tent & RV camping: Donation, Open all year, Reservations not accepted, Elev: 1634ft/498m, Tel: 402-764-2561, Nearest town: Stromsburg. GPS: 41.106456, -97.600863

119 • C4 | Cottonwood Park

Total sites: 5, RV sites: 5, Elec sites: 5, Central water, Flush toilet, Free showers, No RV dump, Tent & RV camping: $15, Open Apr-Nov, Elev: 1850ft/564m, Tel: 308-246-5278, Nearest town: Wolbach. GPS: 41.397089, -98.398475

120 • C4 | Crystal Lake

Total sites: 62, RV sites: 62, Elec sites: 12, Central water, Vault/pit toilet, No showers, No RV dump, Tents: $7/RVs: $13, Stay limit: 14 days, Generator hours: 0600-2200, Reservations not accepted, Elev: 1821ft/555m, Tel: 308-385-6210, Nearest town: Ayr. GPS: 40.455566, -98.440186

121 • C4 | Crystal Springs Lake

Total sites: 60, RV sites: 60, Elec sites: 60, Water at site, Flush toilet, Free showers, RV dump, Tent & RV camping: $10, No water in winter, Stay limit: 14 days, Open all year, Reservations not accepted, Elev: 1312ft/400m, Tel: 402-729-2148, Nearest town: Fairbury. GPS: 40.130182, -97.205987

122 • C4 | Davenport City Park

Total sites: 2, RV sites: 2, Elec sites: 2, Water at site, No toilets, No showers, RV dump, No tents/RVs: $5, Open all year, Elev: 1670ft/509m, Tel: 402-364-2292, Nearest town: Davenport. GPS: 40.311684, -97.809802

123 • C4 | David City Park

Total sites: 12, RV sites: 12, Elec sites: 12, Water at site, No toilets, No showers, RV dump, Tent & RV camping: $10, Open Apr-Oct, Elev: 1614ft/492m, Tel: 402-367-3135, Nearest town: David City. GPS: 41.244427, -97.124234

124 • C4 | Edgar City Camp Facility

Total sites: 4, RV sites: 4, Elec sites: 4, No toilets, No showers, RV dump, No tents/RVs: Donation, Elev: 1725ft/526m, Tel: 402-224-5145, Nearest town: Edgar. GPS: 40.362158, -97.969287

125 • C4 | Geneva City Park

Dispersed sites, Central water, Flush toilet, Tents only: Free, Unconfirmed, Stay limit: 1 day, Reservations not accepted, Elev: 1634ft/498m, Nearest town: Geneva. GPS: 40.523079, -97.593268

126 • C4 | Genoa City Park

Total sites: 10, RV sites: 4, Elec sites: 4, Water at site, Flush toilet Free showers, RV dump, Tent & RV camping: $10, First nigh free, Open all year, Elev: 1565ft/477m, Tel: 402-993-2330, Neares town: Genoa. GPS: 41.442554, -97.737233

127 • C4 | Gilbert City Park

Total sites: 2, RV sites: 2, Elec sites: 2, Central water, No toilets No showers, RV dump, No tents/RVs: $10, Open all year, Ma Length: 33ft, Elev: 1609ft/490m, Tel: 402-266-3051, Nearest town Exeter. GPS: 40.638576, -97.449893

128 • C4 | Harbine Park

Total sites: 5, RV sites: 5, Elec sites: 5, Water at site, No toilets, N showers, RV dump, Tent & RV camping: $10, 5 Full hookup, 3 day limit, Open all year, Reservations not accepted, Elev: 1696ft

517m, Tel: 402-225-4401, Nearest town: Nelson. GPS: 40.196481, -98.068853

129 • C4 | Hebron Riverside Park

Total sites: 16, RV sites: 16, Elec sites: 16, Water at site, Flush toilet, Free showers, RV dump, Tents: $5/RVs: $15, Open Apr-Nov, Elev: 1473ft/449m, Tel: 402-768-6322, Nearest town: Hebron. GPS: 40.163661, -97.582728

130 • C4 | Lincoln Park West

Total sites: 20, RV sites: 20, Elec sites: 20, Water at site, No toilets, No showers, RV dump, Tent & RV camping: Donation, $5/day after 2 weeks, Open all year, Reservations not accepted, Elev: 1594ft/486m, Tel: 402-879-4713, Nearest town: Superior. GPS: 40.020599, -98.083205

131 • C4 | Milligan RV Park

Total sites: 6, RV sites: 6, Elec sites: 6, Water at site, No toilets, No showers, RV dump, Tent & RV camping: $5, Open Apr-Sep, Elev: 1604ft/489m, Tel: 402-629-4446, Nearest town: Milligan. GPS: 40.499854, -97.391489

132 • C4 | Ohiowa RV Park

Total sites: 9, RV sites: 6, Elec sites: 6, Water at site, No toilets, No showers, No RV dump, Tent & RV camping: $7, Open Apr-Oct, Elev: 1608ft/490m, Tel: 402-295-2350, Nearest town: Ohiowa. GPS: 40.410536, -97.452821

133 • C4 | Osceola City Park

Total sites: 2, RV sites: 2, Elec sites: 2, Central water, No toilets, No showers, No RV dump, No tents/RVs: Free, Stay limit: 3 days, Max Length: 35ft, Elev: 1660ft/506m, Tel: 402-747-3411, Nearest town: Osceola. GPS: 41.183336, -97.547489

134 • C4 | Prairie Ridge Ballfields

Dispersed sites, No toilets, Tent & RV camping: Free, Parking lot, Elev: 1909ft/582m, Tel: 402-461-2324, Nearest town: Hastings. GPS: 40.625497, -98.377245

135 • C4 | Shickley City Park

Total sites: 6, RV sites: 3, Central water, No toilets, No showers, No RV dump, Tent & RV camping: $5, Open all year, Elev: 1663ft/507m, Tel: 402-627-2055, Nearest town: Shickley. GPS: 40.416056, -97.723242

136 • C4 | Silver Creek City Park

Total sites: 4, RV sites: 4, Elec sites: 4, Central water, No toilets, No showers, No RV dump, Tent & RV camping: Fee unk, 15-amp only, Open May-Oct, Elev: 1550ft/472m, Tel: 308-773-2348, Nearest town: Silver Creek. GPS: 41.313737, -97.662477

137 • C4 | South Park City CG

Total sites: 45, RV sites: 35, Elec sites: 35, Water at site, Flush toilet, Pay showers, RV dump, Tents: $10/RVs: $15-20, 6 Full hookup, Open Apr-Oct, Reservations not accepted, Elev: 1365ft/416m, Tel: 402-352-3101, Nearest town: Schuyler. GPS: 41.434723, -97.059778

138 • C4 | Strang City Park

Total sites: 3, RV sites: 3, Elec sites: 3, Central water, No toilets, No showers, No RV dump, Tent & RV camping: Free, Elev: 1637ft/499m, Tel: 402-759-4910, Nearest town: Strang. GPS: 40.413065, -97.586818

139 • C4 | Streeter Municipal Park

Total sites: 20, RV sites: 18, Elec sites: 18, Central water, No toilets, No showers, RV dump, Tent & RV camping: Donation, Stay limit: 3 days, Open May-Oct, Max Length: 27ft, Reservations not accepted, Elev: 1775ft/541m, Tel: 402-694-6992, Nearest town: Aurora. GPS: 40.873634, -98.003056

140 • C4 | Sutton City Park

Total sites: 17, RV sites: 17, Elec sites: 17, Water at site, Flush toilet, RV dump, No tents/RVs: $5-10, 14 Full hookup, Pay at City Hall, Near RR, Generator hours: 0600-2200, Elev: 1676ft/511m, Tel: 402-773-4225, Nearest town: Sutton. GPS: 40.613132, -97.855339

141 • C4 | Tooley City Park

Total sites: 5, RV sites: 0, No water, No toilets, Tents only: Fee unk, Open all year, Elev: 1749ft/533m, Tel: 308-986-2522, Nearest town: Marquette. GPS: 41.030808, -98.057303

142 • C4 | Tuxedo City Park

Total sites: 20, RV sites: 20, Elec sites: 20, Water at site, Flush toilet, Free showers, RV dump, Tents: Free/RVs: $10, Open Apr-Oct, Reservations not accepted, Elev: 1358ft/414m, Tel: 402-826-4314, Nearest town: Crete. GPS: 40.631136, -96.971275

143 • C4 | Utica City Park

Total sites: 6, RV sites: 6, Elec sites: 6, Water at site, No toilets, No showers, RV dump, Tent & RV camping: $10, Elev: 1594ft/486m, Tel: 402-534-4237, Nearest town: Utica. GPS: 40.890722, -97.348408

144 • C4 | Village Park

Total sites: 4, RV sites: 4, Elec sites: 4, Central water, Flush toilet, No showers, RV dump, Tent & RV camping: $10, Open May-Sep, Elev: 1877ft/572m, Nearest town: Dannebrog. GPS: 41.117271, -98.545077

145 • C4 | Washington Park

Total sites: 10, RV sites: 10, Elec sites: 10, Water at site, Flush toilet, Free showers, RV dump, Tent & RV camping: Donation, Open all year, Elev: 1549ft/472m, Tel: 402-365-4260, Nearest town: Deshler. GPS: 40.136195, -97.721259

146 • C4 | Western Village Park

Total sites: 6, RV sites: 6, Elec sites: 2, Water at site, No toilets, No showers, RV dump, No tents/RVs: Donation, Open all year, Elev: 1499ft/457m, Tel: 402-433-2861, Nearest town: Western. GPS: 40.392934, -97.196986

147 • C5 | American Legion Memorial City Park

Total sites: 43, RV sites: 43, Elec sites: 43, Water at site, Flush toilet, Free showers, RV dump, Tents: $5/RVs: $18, Open all year, Elev: 1312ft/400m, Tel: 402-821-3233, Nearest town: Wilber. GPS: 40.472448, -96.961369

148 • C5 | Arbor City Park

Total sites: 6, RV sites: 6, Elec sites: 6, Water at site, No toilets, No showers, RV dump, Tent & RV camping: $18, Open Apr-Oct, Elev: 1250ft/381m, Tel: 402-645-3377, Nearest town: Wymore. GPS: 40.129149, -96.665492

149 • C5 | Auburn Recreation Complex

Total sites: 12, RV sites: 12, Elec sites: 12, Central water, No toilets, No showers, RV dump, Tent & RV camping: $10, Elev: 925ft/282m, Tel: 402-274-3420, Nearest town: Auburn. GPS: 40.401672, -95.847307

150 • C5 | Beatrice Riverside Park

Total sites: 13, RV sites: 8, Elec sites: 8, Water at site, Flush toilet, Free showers, RV dump, Tent & RV camping: $18, 8 Full hookup, Open Apr-Oct, Reservations not accepted, Elev: 1263ft/385m, Tel: 402-228-5248, Nearest town: Beatrice. GPS: 40.273640, -96.768910

151 • C5 | Bennett City Park

Dispersed sites, Central water, Vault/pit toilet, No showers, Tent & RV camping: Fee unk, 3 day limit, Open May-Sep, Reservations not accepted, Elev: 1299ft/396m, Nearest town: Bennett. GPS: 40.680635, -96.505606

152 • C5 | Brownville Riverside Park

Total sites: 12, RV sites: 6, Central water, Vault/pit toilet, No showers, No RV dump, Tent & RV camping: Fee unk, Elev: 904ft/276m, Tel: 402-883-2575, Nearest town: Brownville. GPS: 40.393021, -95.650921

153 • C5 | Ceresco City Park

Total sites: 2, RV sites: 2, Central water, Flush toilet, No tents/RVs: Free, Notify police, No water in winter, Open all year, Elev: 1193ft/364m, Tel: 402-665-2391, Nearest town: Cerersco. GPS: 41.057140, -96.642064

154 • C5 | Chautauqua Municipal Park

Total sites: 20, RV sites: 20, Elec sites: 20, Water at site, Flush toilet, Free showers, RV dump, Tent & RV camping: $18, 20 Full hookup, Elev: 1250ft/381m, Tel: 402-228-5248, Nearest town: Beatrice. GPS: 40.252988, -96.739005

155 • C5 | Diller City Park

Total sites: 15, RV sites: 15, Elec sites: 15, Water at site, Flush toilet, No showers, RV dump, Tent & RV camping: $13-15, Full hookup sites, Open all year, Elev: 1362ft/415m, Tel: 402-793-5330, Nearest town: Diller. GPS: 40.110367, -96.935037

156 • C5 | Feits Memorial Park

Total sites: 15, RV sites: 5, Central water, Vault/pit toilet, No showers, No RV dump, Tent & RV camping: Free, Stay limit: 3 days, Open all year, Elev: 1220ft/372m, Tel: 402-645-3539, Nearest town: Blue Springs. GPS: 40.139704, -96.655062

157 • C5 | Glenn Cunningham Lake

Total sites: 58, RV sites: 58, Elec sites: 41, Water at site, Flush toilet, Free showers, RV dump, Tents: $12/RVs: $12-17, Open Apr-Oct, Reservations accepted, Elev: 1135ft/346m, Tel: 402-444-5920, Nearest town: Omaha. GPS: 41.344555, -96.044924

158 • C5 | Haworth City Park

Total sites: 128, RV sites: 107, Elec sites: 107, Water at site, RV dump, Tents: $20/RVs: $20-25, Open all year, Reservations accepted, Elev: 965ft/294m, Tel: 402-933-3717, Nearest town: Bellevue. GPS: 41.134766, -95.883301

159 • C5 | Humboldt Lake City Park

Total sites: 11, RV sites: 11, Elec sites: 11, Central water, Flush toilet, Free showers, RV dump, Tent & RV camping: $15, Open all year, Reservations not accepted, Elev: 983ft/300m, Tel: 402-862-2171, Nearest town: Humboldt. GPS: 40.160594, -95.949888

160 • C5 | Pawnerosa City Pond and Campsite

Total sites: 15, RV sites: 8, Elec sites: 8, Water at site, No toilets, No showers, No RV dump, Tent & RV camping: $8, No water/rest rooms Nov-Mar, Reservations accepted, Elev: 1145ft/349m, Tel: 402-852-2781, Nearest town: Pawnee City. GPS: 40.104985, -96.162975

161 • C5 | Peterson Park

Total sites: 4, RV sites: 4, Elec sites: 4, Flush toilet, No showers, No RV dump, Tent & RV camping: $15, Reservations not accepted, Elev: 1296ft/395m, Nearest town: DeWitt. GPS: 40.394496, -96.926351

162 • C5 | Stanton Lake City Park

Total sites: 13, RV sites: 13, Elec sites: 13, Water at site, Flush toilet, Free showers, RV dump, Tents: $5/RVs: $15, No water in winter, Reservations accepted, Elev: 988ft/301m, Tel: 402-245-2851, Nearest town: Falls City. GPS: 40.069755, -95.612907

163 • C5 | Sterling Village Park

Total sites: 2, RV sites: 2, No water, Vault/pit toilet, No tents/RVs: $10, Unconfirmed, Open Apr-Oct, Elev: 1191ft/363m, Tel: 402-866-4545, Nearest town: Sterling. GPS: 40.460875, -96.373589

164 • C5 | Syracuse South Park

Total sites: 5, RV sites: 5, Water at site, No toilets, No showers, RV dump, No tents/RVs: $10-16, Open May-Oct, Elev: 1042ft/318m, Tel: 402-269-2601, Nearest town: Syracuse. GPS: 40.654469, -96.186793

165 • C5 | Walnut Creek RA

Total sites: 44, RV sites: 44, Elec sites: 44, Water at site, Flush toilet No showers, RV dump, Tent & RV camping: $16, Reservations not accepted, Elev: 1086ft/331m, Tel: 402-679-9889, Nearest town: Papillon. GPS: 41.135111, -96.076745

166 • C5 | Weeping Water City Park

Total sites: 18, RV sites: 18, Elec sites: 18, Flush toilet, Fre showers, Tents: $7/RVs: $15, Generator hours: 0600-2200, Elev 1099ft/335m, Tel: 402-267-5152, Nearest town: Weeping Water GPS: 40.870508, -96.148176

167 • D4 | Chester Municipal Park

Total sites: 2, RV sites: 2, Elec sites: 2, Water at site, No toilets, No showers, No RV dump, No tents/RVs: Free, Stay limit: 14 days Open Apr-Sep, Elev: 1644ft/501m, Tel: 402-324-5755, Nearest town: Chester. GPS: 40.015871, -97.619899

Nevada

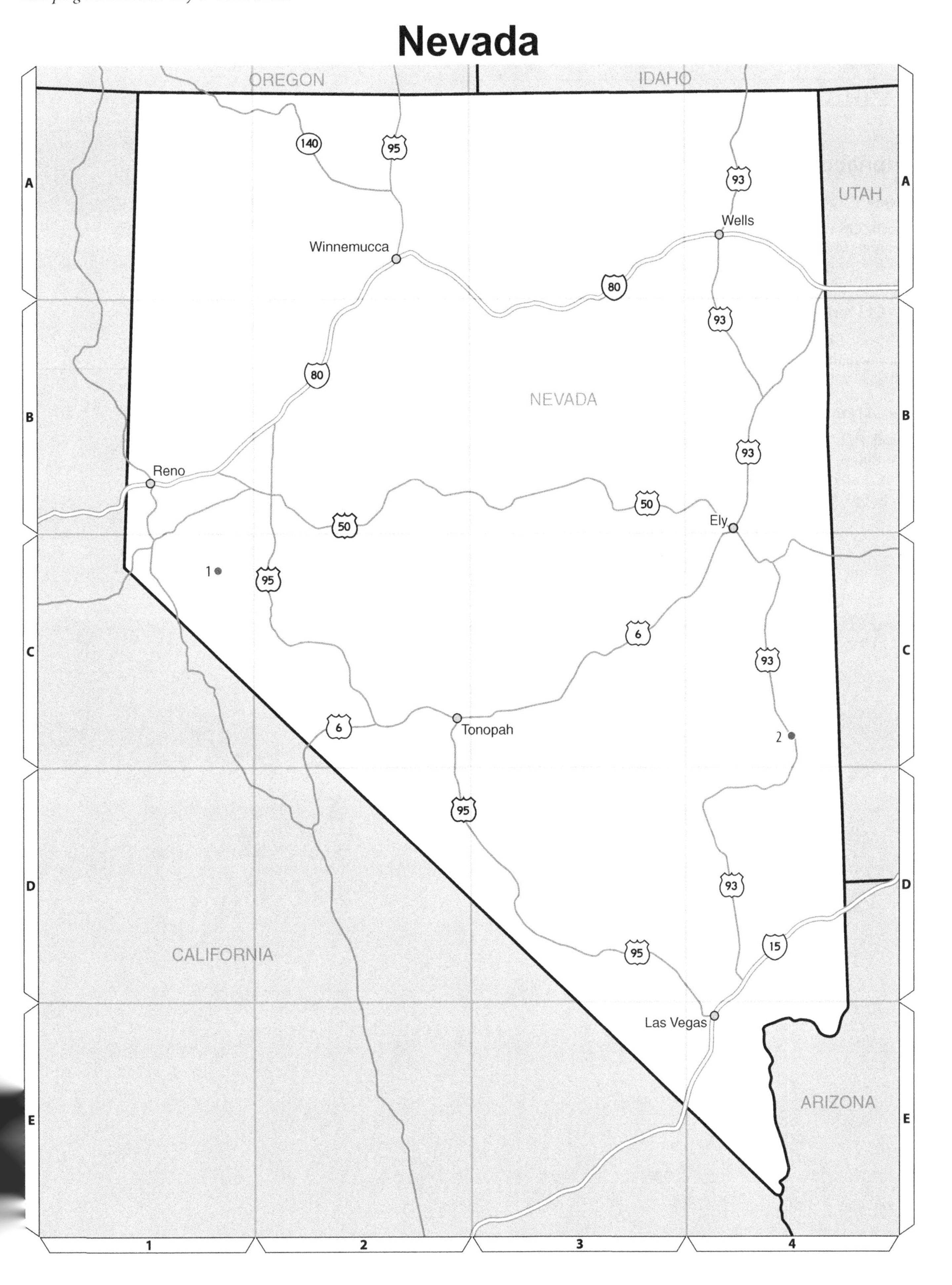
OREGON
IDAHO
UTAH
NEVADA
CALIFORNIA
ARIZONA
Winnemucca
Wells
Reno
Ely
Tonopah
Las Vegas
140
95
93
80
50
6
15
1
2
A
B
C
D
E
1
2
3
4

Map	ID	Map	ID
C1	1	C4	2

Alphabetical List of Camping Areas

Name	ID	Map
Pioche City RV Park	2	C4
Yerington City Park	1	C1

1 • C1 | Yerington City Park

Dispersed sites, No water, No toilets, Tent & RV camping: Free, Elev: 4403ft/1342m, Tel: 775-463-7733, Nearest town: Yerington. GPS: 38.989602, -119.181892

2 • C4 | Pioche City RV Park

Total sites: 10, RV sites: 10, Water at site, No toilets, No showers, RV dump, No tents/RVs: Donation, Stay limit: 7 days, Open all year, Reservations not accepted, Elev: 5924ft/1806m, Tel: 775-962-1585, Nearest town: Pioche. GPS: 37.937922, -114.451679

New Hampshire

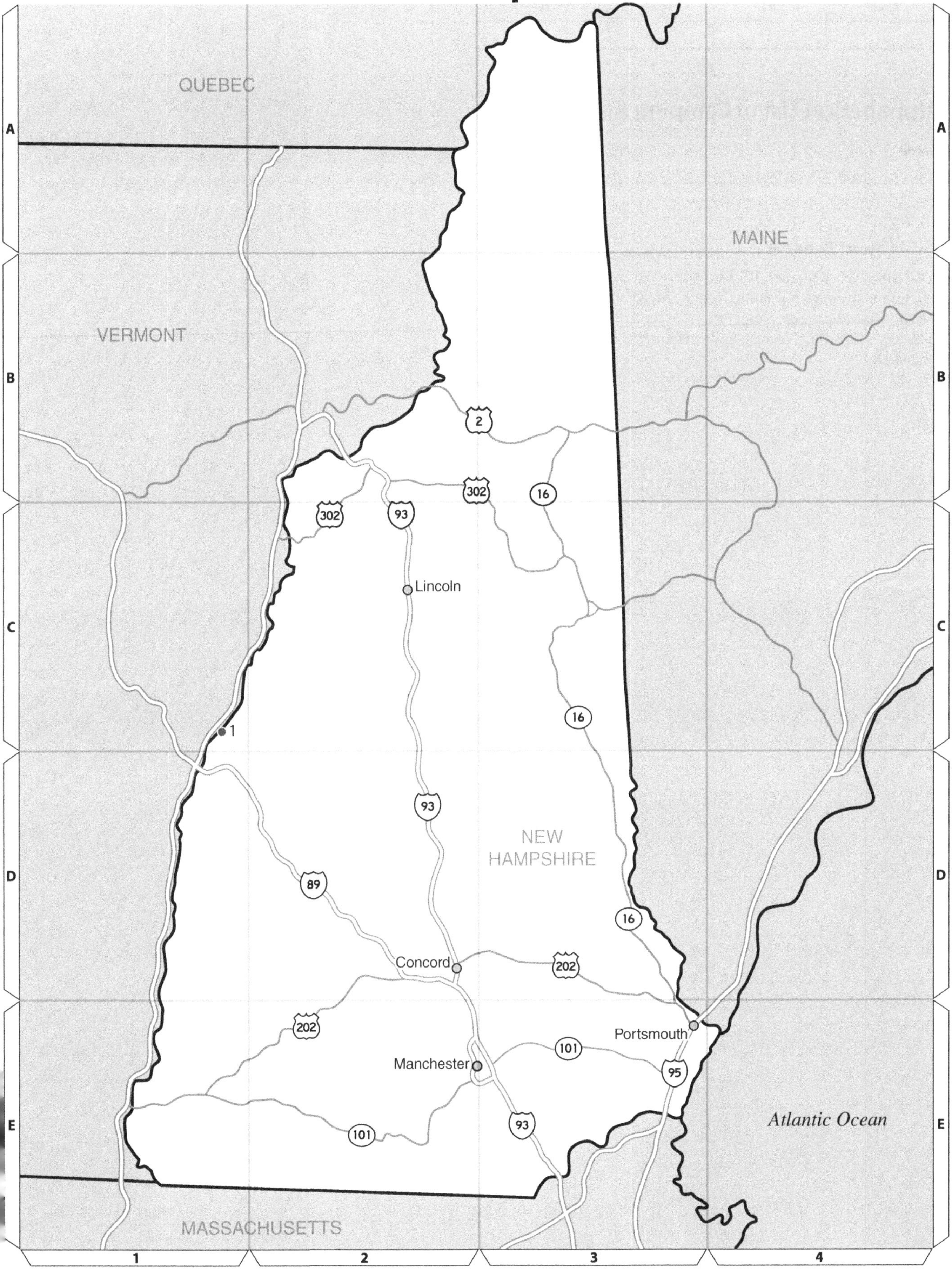

QUEBEC

VERMONT

MAINE

NEW HAMPSHIRE

MASSACHUSETTS

Atlantic Ocean

Lincoln

Concord

Manchester

Portsmouth

1

2 302 302 16 93 93 16 89 16 202 202 101 95 101 93

A B C D E

1 2 3 4

Map	ID	Map	ID
C1	1		

Alphabetical List of Camping Areas

1 • C1 | Storrs Pond RA

Total sites: 29, RV sites: 17, Elec sites: 17, Central water, Flush toilet, Free showers, RV dump, Tents: $32/RVs: $45-50, Stay limit: 7 days, Open May-Sep, Reservations accepted, Elev: 476ft/145m, Tel: 603-643-2134, Nearest town: Hanover. GPS: 43.723982, -72.264026

New Jersey

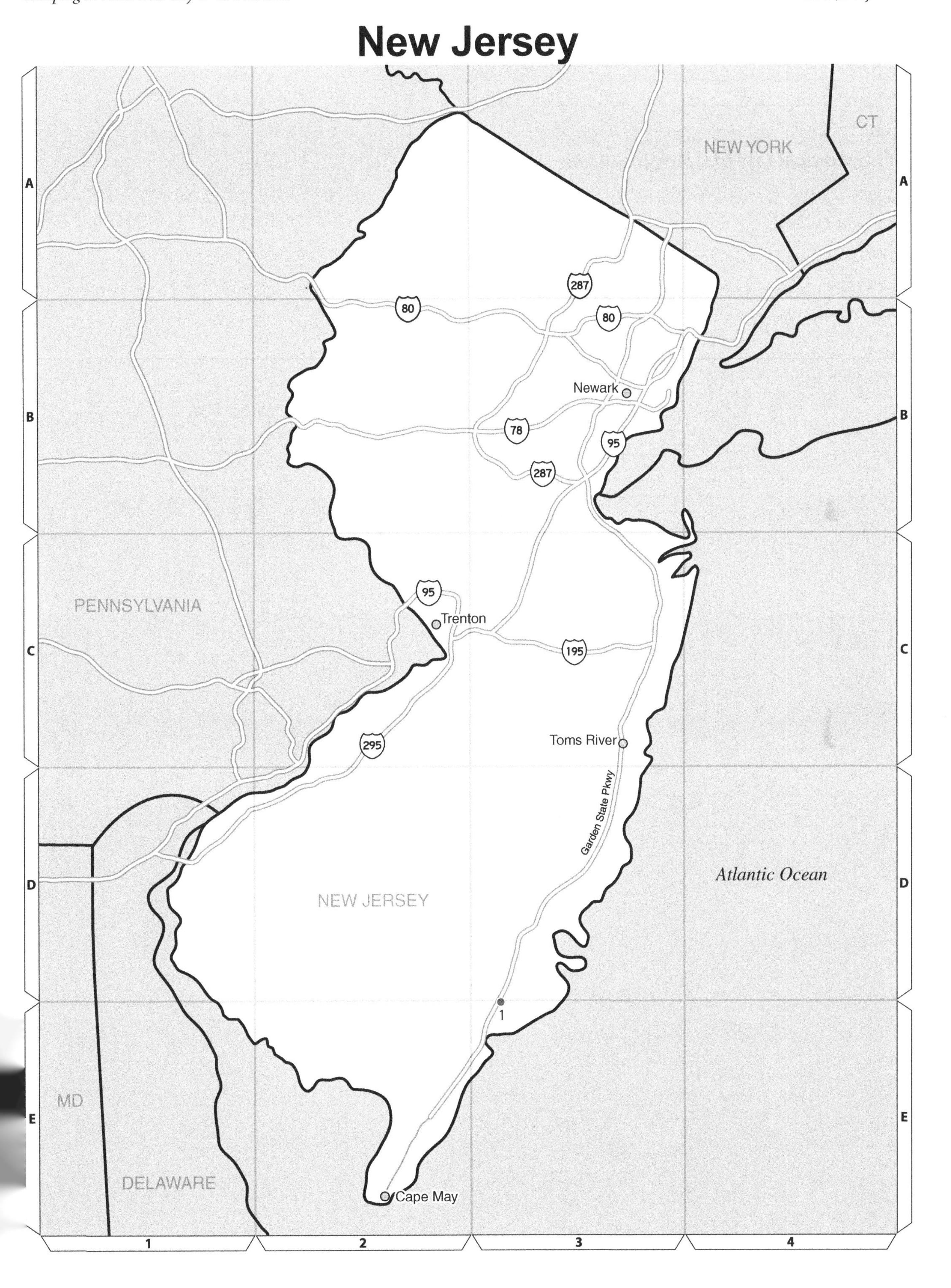

NEW YORK
CT
PENNSYLVANIA
NEW JERSEY
MD
DELAWARE
Atlantic Ocean
Newark
Trenton
Toms River
Cape May
Garden State Pkwy
287
80
78
95
195
295
1
A
B
C
D
E
2
3
4

Map	ID	Map	ID
E3	1		

Alphabetical List of Camping Areas

1 • E3 | Birch Grove City Park

Total sites: 50, Water at site, Flush toilet, Free showers, RV dump, Tents: $25/RVs: $30-35, Full hookup sites, No pets in tents, Open Apr-Sep, Reservations accepted, Elev: 26ft/8m, Tel: 609-641-3778, Nearest town: Northfield. GPS: 39.376229, -74.566576

New Mexico

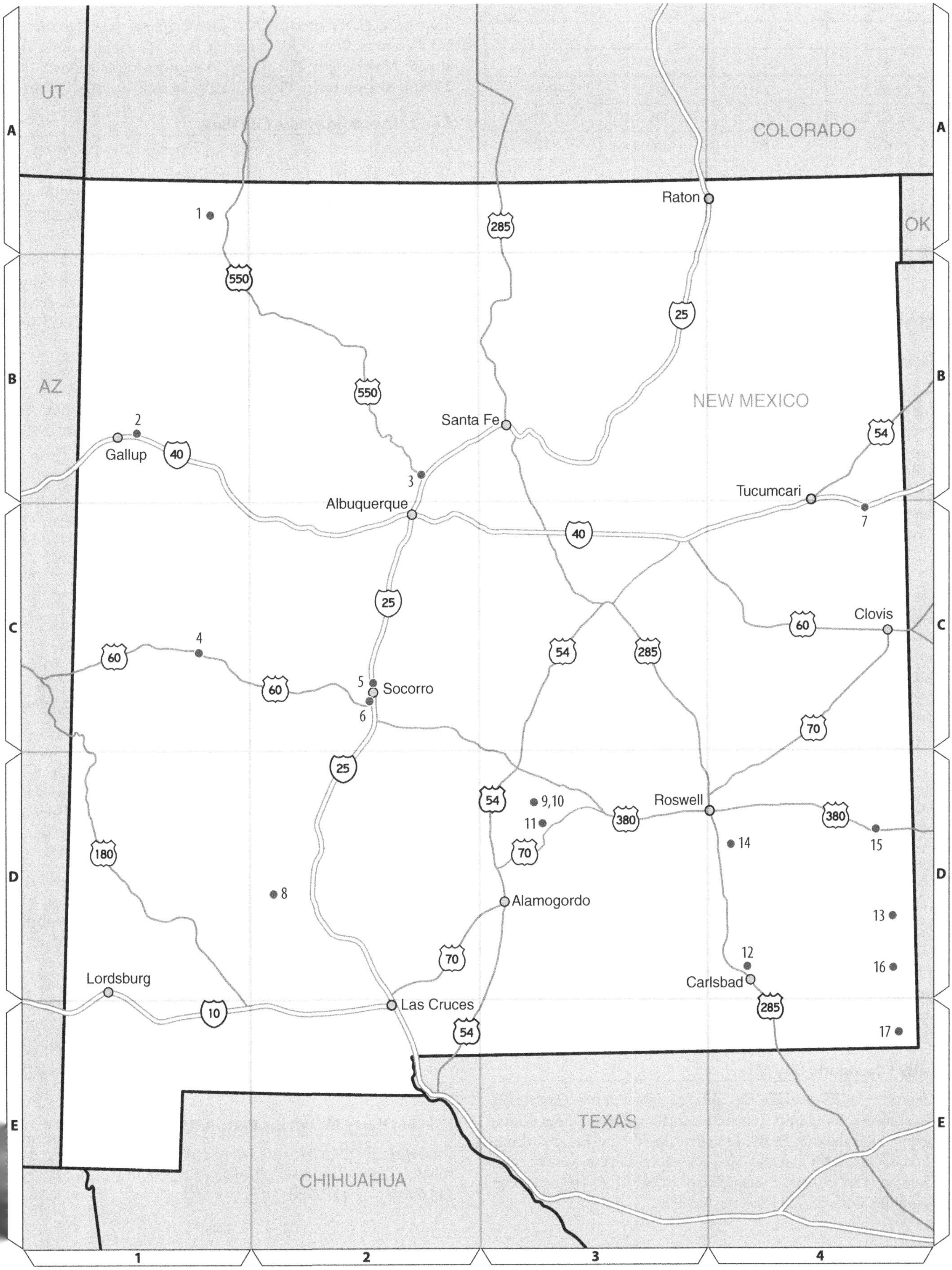

UT
COLORADO
OK
AZ
NEW MEXICO
TEXAS
CHIHUAHUA
A
B
C
D
E
1
2
3
4
Raton
Santa Fe
Gallup
Albuquerque
Tucumcari
Clovis
Socorro
Roswell
Alamogordo
Lordsburg
Las Cruces
Carlsbad
1
2
3
4
5
6
7
8
9,10
11
12
13
14
15
16
17
550
285
25
40
54
60
70
380
180
10

Map	ID	Map	ID
A1	1	C4	7
B1	2	D2	8
B2	3	D3	9-11
C1	4	D4	12-16
C2	5-6	E4	17

Abbreviations for Agencies

CID Carlsbad Irrigation District

Alphabetical List of Camping Areas

Name	ID	Map
Avalon Reservoir Dispersed – CID	12	D4
Blue Hole/Apple Orchard Dispersed	9	D3
Bonito Lake - Westside	10	D3
Coronado City CG	3	B2
Escondida Lake City Park	5	C2
Grindstone Lake City Park	11	D3
Harry McAdams Park - City	13	D4
Hillsboro City RV Park	8	D2
Jackson City Park	4	C1
Jal City Park	17	E4
Lake Farmington Camping	1	A1
Lake Van	14	D4
Randolph Rampy Park	15	D4
Red Rock City Park	2	B1
Rodeo and Sports Complex	6	C2
San Jon Municipal Park	7	C4
Stephens Park	16	D4

1 • A1 | Lake Farmington Camping

Total sites: 21, RV sites: 5, No water, Vault/pit toilet, No showers, No RV dump, Tent & RV camping: $5, Stay limit: 14 days, Generator hours: 0600-2200, Reservations accepted, Elev: 5700ft/1737m, Tel: 505-599-1197, Nearest town: Flora Vista. GPS: 36.797439, -108.099183

2 • B1 | Red Rock City Park

Total sites: 25, RV sites: 25, Water available, Flush toilet, Free showers, RV dump, Tent & RV camping: $20, Open all year, Reservations required, Elev: 6691ft/2039m, Tel: 505-722-3839, Nearest town: Gallup. GPS: 35.541430, -108.609520

3 • B2 | Coronado City CG

Total sites: 31, RV sites: 23, Elec sites: 23, Water at site, Flush toilet, Pay showers, RV dump, Tents: $14-18/RVs: $20-30, Fees double during ABQ Balloon Fiesta, Tent area closed Nov-Feb, Stay limit: 14 days, Generator hours: 0700-2200, Open all year, Reservations accepted, Elev: 5076ft/1547m, Tel: 505-980-8256, Nearest town: Bernalillo. GPS: 35.324341, -106.559239

4 • C1 | Jackson City Park

Total sites: 20, RV sites: 20, No water, Vault/pit toilet, No showers, No RV dump, Tent & RV camping: Free, Stay limit: 3 days, Open all year, Max Length: 25ft, Reservations not accepted, Elev: 7795ft/2376m, Nearest town: Pietown. GPS: 34.298759, -108.131391

5 • C2 | Escondida Lake City Park

Total sites: 19, RV sites: 19, Elec sites: 16, Water at site, RV dump, Tents: $6/RVs: $10-18, 16 Full hookup, Stay limit: 7 days, Open all year, Reservations not accepted, Elev: 4613ft/1406m, Tel: 575-835-0589, Nearest town: Socorro. GPS: 34.123678, -106.889641

6 • C2 | Rodeo and Sports Complex

Total sites: 50, RV sites: 50, Elec sites: 50, Water at site, RV dump, No tents/RVs: $30, 50 Full hookup, Horse stalls: $15, Reservations accepted, Elev: 4830ft/1472m, Tel: 575-838-7517, Nearest town: Socorro. GPS: 34.034045, -106.913891

7 • C4 | San Jon Municipal Park

Total sites: 10, RV sites: 10, Flush toilet, Tent & RV camping: Free, Open all year, Max Length: 38ft, Elev: 4034ft/1230m, Nearest town: San Jon. GPS: 35.107286, -103.331701

8 • D2 | Hillsboro City RV Park

Total sites: 20, RV sites: 14, Elec sites: 14, Water at site, Vault/pit toilet, No showers, RV dump, Tents: $6/RVs: $6-16, 11 Full hookup, Open all year, Reservations accepted, Elev: 5266ft/1605m, Tel: 575-895-5703, Nearest town: Hillsboro. GPS: 32.921080, -107.569558

9 • D3 | Blue Hole/Apple Orchard Dispersed

Dispersed sites, No water, Vault/pit toilet, Tent & RV camping: $11, Reservations not accepted, Elev: 7483ft/2281m, Tel: 575-336-4157, Nearest town: Angus. GPS: 33.454032, -105.752554

10 • D3 | Bonito Lake - Westside

Dispersed sites, Water available, Vault/pit toilet, Tent & RV camping: $14, Open all year, Reservations not accepted, Elev: 7421ft/2262m, Nearest town: Ruidoso. GPS: 33.456303, -105.743505

11 • D3 | Grindstone Lake City Park

Total sites: 28, RV sites: 6, Elec sites: 0, Central water, Flush toilet Free showers, Tents: $10/RVs: $20, No open fires, Stay limit: 7 days, Generator hours: 0700-0900/1800-2000, Max Length: 15'-26ft, Reservations not accepted, Elev: 6941ft/2116m, Tel: 575-257-5030, Nearest town: Ruidoso. GPS: 33.324559, -105.683792

12 • D4 | Avalon Reservoir Dispersed – CID

Dispersed sites, No toilets, Tent & RV camping: Free, Open all year, Reservations not accepted, Elev: 3173ft/967m, Tel: 505-885-3203, Nearest town: Carlsbad. GPS: 32.493081, -104.247742

13 • D4 | Harry McAdams Park - City

Total sites: 20, RV sites: 20, No tents/RVs: $18, Open all year, Elev: 3694ft/1126m, Tel: 505-392-5845, Nearest town: Hobbs. GPS: 32.769743, -103.207746

14 • D4 | Lake Van

Total sites: 30, RV sites: 30, Elec sites: 15, Water at site, Flush toilet, RV dump, Tent & RV camping: $15, Elev: 3448ft/1051m, Tel: 575-734-5482, Nearest town: Dexter. GPS: 33.194882, -104.359557

15 • D4 | Randolph Rampy Park

Total sites: 5, RV sites: 5, Elec sites: 5, Water at site, No toilets, No showers, RV dump, No tents/RVs: Free, Stay limit: 3 days, Open all year, Reservations not accepted, Elev: 4001ft/1220m, Tel: 575-398-4633, Nearest town: Tatum. GPS: 33.258939, -103.311799

16 • D4 | Stephens Park

Total sites: 9, RV sites: 9, Elec sites: 5, Water at site, No toilets, No showers, No RV dump, No tents/RVs: Free, 3 days free, Reservations not accepted, Elev: 3521ft/1073m, Tel: 575-441-0190, Nearest town: Eunice. GPS: 32.464503, -103.228372

17 • E4 | Jal City Park

Total sites: 5, RV sites: 5, Elec sites: 5, Water available, Flush toilet, Free showers, RV dump, Tent & RV camping: Free, Stay limit: 3 days, Reservations not accepted, Elev: 3018ft/920m, Tel: 575-395-2620, Nearest town: Jal. GPS: 32.101259, -103.191322

New York

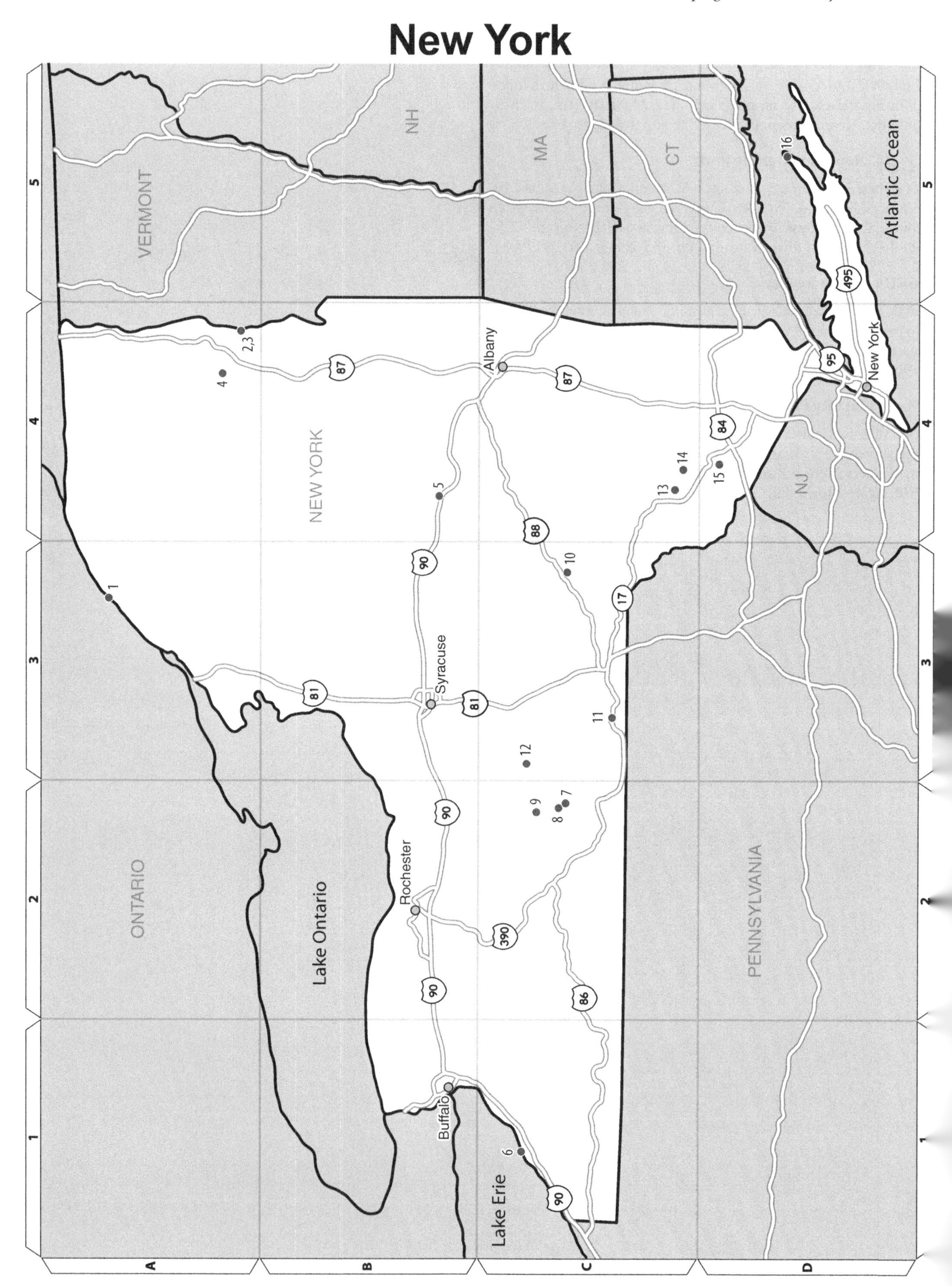
VERMONT
NH
MA
CT
Atlantic Ocean
NEW YORK
ONTARIO
Lake Ontario
Lake Erie
PENNSYLVANIA
NJ
Albany
Syracuse
Rochester
Buffalo
New York
87
90
81
88
17
84
95
495
390
86
1
2,3
4
5
6
7
8
9
10
11
12
13
14
15
16
A
B
C
D
1
2
3
4
5

Map	ID	Map	ID
A3	1	C3	10-12
A4	2-4	C4	13-14
B4	5	D4	15
C1	6	D5	16
C2	7-9		

Alphabetical List of Camping Areas

1 • A3 | Lisbon Beach CG

Total sites: 108, RV sites: 93, Elec sites: 93, Water at site, Flush toilet, Free showers, RV dump, Tents: Fee unk/RVs: $40, 57 Full hookup, Open May-Sep, Elev: 260ft/79m, Tel: 315-393-5374, Nearest town: Ogdensburg. GPS: 44.771292, -75.369992

2 • A4 | Bulwagga Bay Town CG

Total sites: 150, RV sites: 150, Elec sites: 100, Water at site, Flush toilet, Pay showers, RV dump, Tents: $31/RVs: $41-51, Also cabins, Lots of seasonal sites, Open May-Oct, Elev: 114ft/35m, Tel: 518-546-7500, Nearest town: Port Henry. GPS: 44.035802, -73.458265

3 • A4 | Champ RV Park Village CG

Total sites: 100, RV sites: 100, Elec sites: 100, Water at site, Flush toilet, Pay showers, RV dump, Tents: $30/RVs: $40-50, Lower fees after Labor Day, Open May-Oct, Elev: 107ft/33m, Tel: 518-546-7123, Nearest town: Port Henry. GPS: 44.050798, -73.454483

4 • A4 | Chapel Pond Dispersed

Dispersed sites, No water, Vault/pit toilet, Tents only: Free, Reservations not accepted, Elev: 1286ft/392m, Nearest town: Keene. GPS: 44.149718, -73.767931

5 • B4 | St Johnsville Campsite and Marina City Park

Total sites: 40, RV sites: 40, Elec sites: 40, Water at site, Flush toilet, Free showers, RV dump, Tent & RV camping: $35, Near RR, Elev: 318ft/97m, Tel: 518-568-7406, Nearest town: St Johnsville. GPS: 42.995070, -74.678410

6 • C1 | Sheridan Bay Park

Total sites: 13, RV sites: 13, Elec sites: 13, Water at site, RV dump, Tent & RV camping: Fee unk, Elev: 607ft/185m, Tel: 716-366-5831, Nearest town: Silver Creek. GPS: 42.519139, -79.268833

7 • C2 | Havana Glen Park

Total sites: 24, RV sites: 14, Elec sites: 14, Water at site, Flush toilet, Free showers, RV dump, Tents: $22/RVs: $30, Full hookup sites, Elev: 492ft/150m, Tel: 607-535-9476, Nearest town: Montour Falls. GPS: 42.336261, -76.831123

8 • C2 | Montour Marina and CG

Total sites: 115, RV sites: 115, Elec sites: 115, Central water, Flush toilet, Free showers, RV dump, Tent & RV camping: $41-46, Elev: 456ft/139m, Tel: 607-535-9397, Nearest town: Montour Falls. GPS: 42.354014, -76.852443

9 • C2 | Smith Memorial Park

Total sites: 72, RV sites: 72, Elec sites: 13, Central water, Flush toilet, Free showers, RV dump, Tents: $35-40/RVs: $50-55, 27 transient sites, Generator hours: 0900-2200, Open May-Oct, Reservations accepted, Elev: 532ft/162m, Tel: 607-546-9911, Nearest town: Hector. GPS: 42.491547, -76.885823

10 • C3 | East Sidney Dam RA

Total sites: 75, RV sites: 75, Flush toilet, Free showers, RV dump, Tents: $20/RVs: $25, Senior discount, Open May-Sep, Reservations accepted, Elev: 1201ft/366m, Tel: 607-829-6433, Nearest town: Sidney. GPS: 42.326955, -75.223021

11 • C3 | Hickories Park

Total sites: 95, RV sites: 65, Elec sites: 65, Water at site, Flush toilet, Free showers, RV dump, Tents: $17/RVs: $25-30, Some Full hookup, Near RR, Reservations not accepted, Elev: 810ft/247m, Tel: 607-687-0123, Nearest town: Owego. GPS: 42.090668, -76.222007

12 • C3 | Meyers Park

Total sites: 19, RV sites: 19, Elec sites: 19, Water at site, Flush toilet, Free showers, RV dump, Tent & RV camping: $34, Local residents: $2 discount, Reservations accepted, Elev: 394ft/120m, Tel: 607-533-7388, Nearest town: Lansing. GPS: 42.538569, -76.545592

13 • C4 | Morningside Park

Total sites: 139, RV sites: 139, Elec sites: 90, Water at site, Flush toilet, Free showers, RV dump, Tent & RV camping: $35, Some Full hookup sites, local residents: $20, Open May-Oct, Elev: 1408ft/429m, Tel: 914-434-5877, Nearest town: South Fallsburg. GPS: 41.750687, -74.649685

14 • C4 | Mountaindale Park

Total sites: 110, RV sites: 110, Elec sites: 70, Central water, Flush toilet, Free showers, RV dump, Tent & RV camping: $35, All seasonal, Stay limit: 7 days, Open May-Oct, Elev: 1102ft/336m, Tel: 914-434-7337, Nearest town: Mountain Dale. GPS: 41.700412, -74.517146

15 • D4 | Korn's CG - City

Total sites: 95, RV sites: 95, Elec sites: 95, Water at site, RV dump, Tent & RV camping: $50, Dump fee $25, Open May-Oct, Elev:

548ft/167m, Tel: 845-386-3433, Nearest town: Wallkill. GPS: 41.510705, -74.472043

16 • D5 | McCann CG

Total sites: 40, RV sites: 40, Elec sites: 40, Water at site, Flush toilet, Free showers, RV dump, Tents: $35/RVs: $50, Generator hours: 0800-2200, Open May-Oct, Elev: 16ft/5m, Tel: 631-477-0043, Nearest town: Greenport. GPS: 41.106797, -72.373033

North Carolina

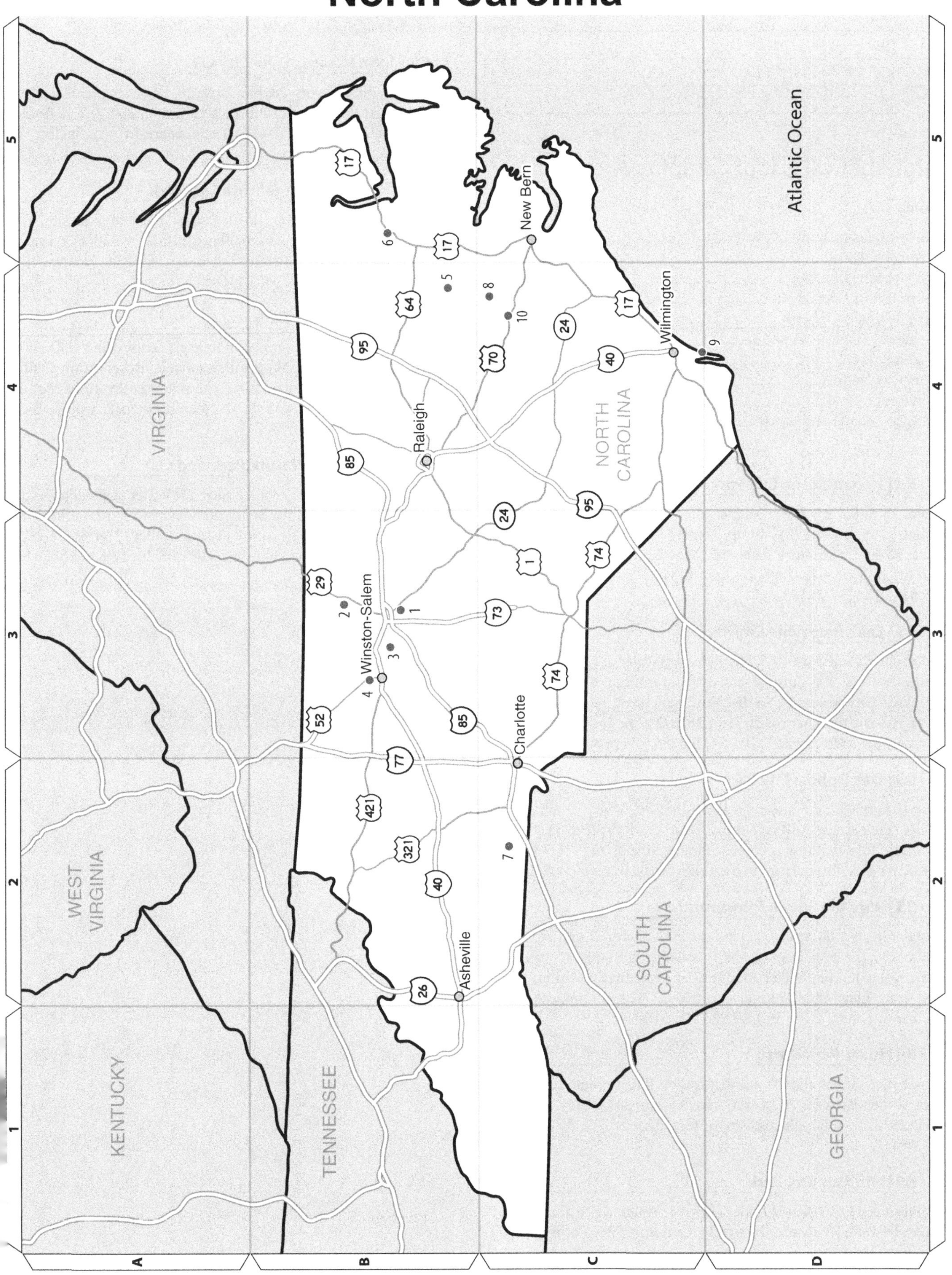

Map	ID	Map	ID
B3	1-4	C2	7
B4	5	C4	8-10
B5	6		

Alphabetical List of Camping Areas

1 • B3 | Hagan-Stone City Park

Total sites: 86, RV sites: 70, Elec sites: 70, Water available, Flush toilet, Free showers, RV dump, Tents: $15/RVs: $25, Group sites: $60, $2 senior/military discount, Max Length: 45ft, Elev: 814ft/248m, Tel: 336-641-2090, Nearest town: Pleasant Garden. GPS: 35.953707, -79.738588

2 • B3 | Lake Reidsville City Park

Total sites: 46, RV sites: 46, Elec sites: 46, Water at site, Flush toilet, Free showers, RV dump, Tent & RV camping: $28-30, 28 Full hookup, City residents: $5 discount, Stay limit: 14 days, Open all year, Reservations accepted, Elev: 761ft/232m, Tel: 336-349-4738, Nearest town: Reidsville. GPS: 36.293885, -79.683022

3 • B3 | Oak Hollow City Park

Total sites: 103, RV sites: 90, Elec sites: 90, Water at site, Flush toilet, Free showers, RV dump, Tents: $30/RVs: $30-35, 90 Full hookup, Reservations accepted, Elev: 824ft/251m, Tel: 336-883-3492, Nearest town: High Point. GPS: 36.011022, -80.008357

4 • B3 | Winston Salem Fairgrounds

Total sites: 50, RV sites: 37, Elec sites: 37, Water at site, No tents/RVs: $30, 37 Full hookup, Not available mid-Sep to mid-Oct during Dixie Fair, Water may not be available in winter, Open all year, Elev: 981ft/299m, Tel: 336-727-2236, Nearest town: Winston-Salem. GPS: 36.127769, -80.251509

5 • B4 | River Park North

Total sites: 5, RV sites: 0, Central water, Flush toilet, Tents only: $10, Open all year, Reservations not accepted, Elev: 15ft/5m, Tel: 252-329-4560, Nearest town: Greenville. GPS: 35.627265, -77.360577

6 • B5 | Windsor City Park

Total sites: 11, RV sites: 11, Elec sites: 11, Water at site, Flush toilet, Free showers, RV dump, Tent & RV camping: $20, $15/night after 14 days, Open all year, Elev: 49ft/15m, Tel: 252-794-2331, Nearest town: Windsor. GPS: 35.985585, -76.939945

7 • C2 | John H. Moss Lake City CG

Total sites: 28, RV sites: 28, Elec sites: 28, Water at site, Flush toilet, Free showers, RV dump, Tent & RV camping: $20, 28 Full hookup, Elev: 725ft/221m, Tel: 704-482-7926, Nearest town: Shelby. GPS: 35.276005, -81.458305

8 • C4 | Contentnea Creekside City Park

Total sites: 25, RV sites: 10, Elec sites: 10, Water at site, Flush toilet, Free showers, RV dump, Tents: $10/RVs: $20, Reservations not accepted, Elev: 20ft/6m, Tel: 252-524-5168, Nearest town: Grifton. GPS: 35.367237, -77.436861

9 • C4 | Freeman City Park

Dispersed sites, No water, No toilets, Tents only: $30, Beach camping, Weekly/annual permits available, Reservation required Apr-Sep, Stay limit: 14 days, Open all year, Reservations required, Elev: 6ft/2m, Tel: 910-458-4614, Nearest town: Carolina Beach. GPS: 34.065241, -77.879507

10 • C4 | Neuseway Nature Park and CG

Total sites: 23, RV sites: 23, Elec sites: 23, Water at site, Flush toilet, Free showers, RV dump, Tents: $10/RVs: $20, 32 Full hookup, Open all year, Reservations not accepted, Elev: 30ft/9m, Tel: 252-939-3367, Nearest town: Kinston. GPS: 35.261178, -77.587319

North Dakota

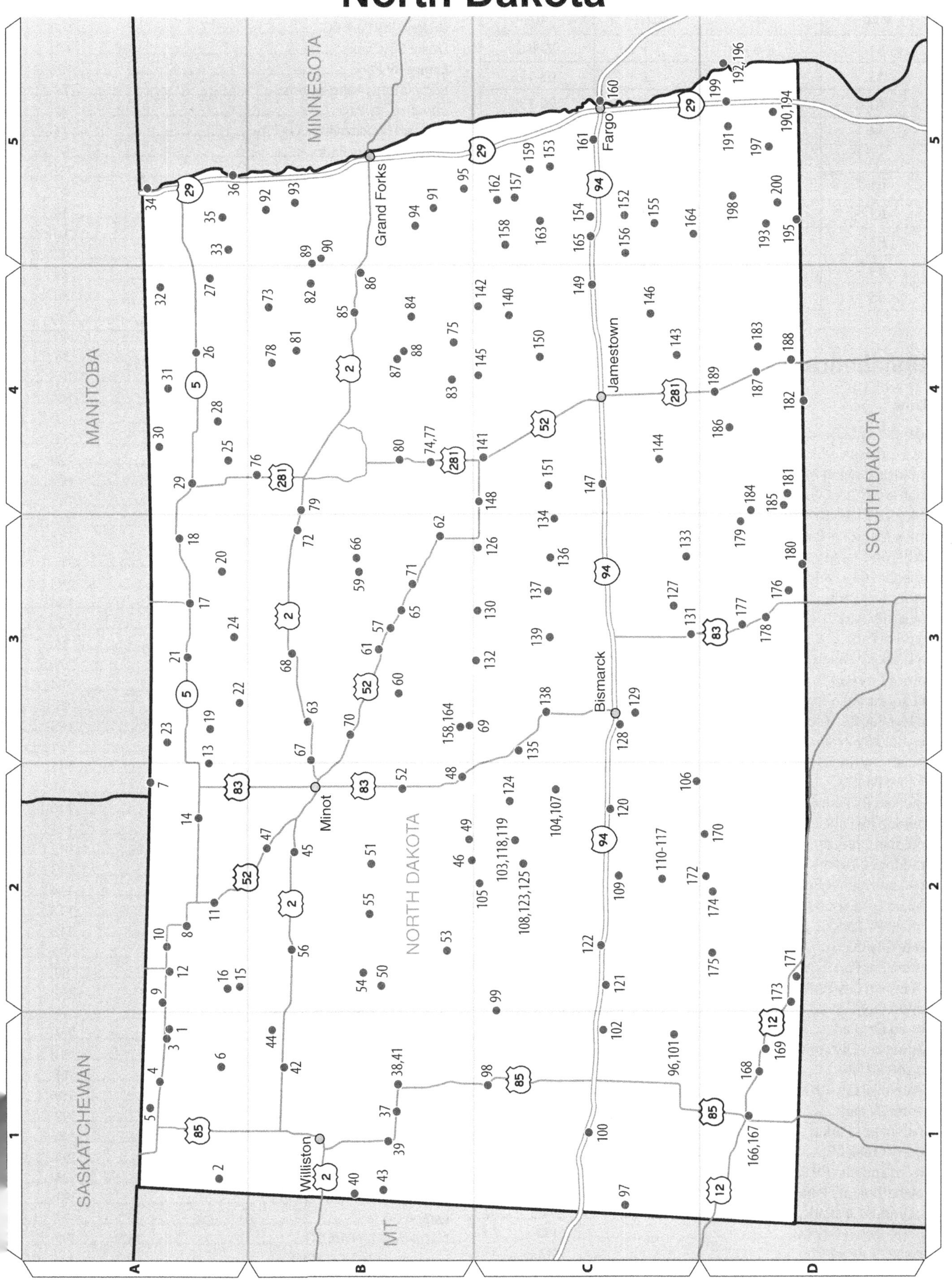

Map	ID	Map	ID
A1	1-6	C1	96-102
A2	7-16	C2	103-125
A3	17-24	C3	126-139
A4	25-32	C4	140-151
A5	33-36	C5	152-165
B1	37-44	D1	166-169
B2	45-56	D2	170-175
B3	57-72	D3	176-180
B4	73-88	D4	181-189
B5	89-95	D5	190-200

Alphabetical List of Camping Areas

Name	ID	Map
Adams City CG	73	B4
Alice City Park	152	C5
American Legion Memorial Park	190	D5
Anamoose City CG	57	B3
Antelope Creek RV Park	103	C2
Antler Memorial Park	7	A2
Archie and Jesse Campbell Memorial Park	74	B4
Arnegard City Park CG	37	B1
Arthur City Park	153	C5
Ashley RV Park	181	D4
B and M Park	96	C1
Ball Park RV Park	104	C2
Barney City Park	191	D5
Baukol-Noonan Trout Pond	1	A1
Beaver Bay RA - City	105	C2
Berthold RV Park	45	B2
Beulah Bay RA	46	B2
Binford Park CG	75	B4
Bowbells RV Park	8	A2
Bowdon RV Park	126	C3
Bowman Lions Park CG	166	D1
Braddock City Park CG	127	C3
Brekken-Holmes RA	58	B3
Buffalo Lake Sportsmen CG	59	B3
Buffalo RV Park	154	C5
Butte City CG	60	B3
Butte View Park	167	D1
C A Brown City Park	140	C4
Cando City CG	76	B4
Carpio City Park	47	B2
Carrington City Park	141	C4
Carson RV Site	170	D2
Centennial City Park	106	C2
Center RV Park	107	C2
Chahinkapa Park	192	D5
Cherry Creek CG	38	B1
City of Enderlin RV Park	155	C5
Coleharbor City Park	48	B2
Columbus City Park	9	A2
Cooperstown City CG	142	C4
Crystal City Park CG	33	A5
Dacotah Centennial Park	128	C3
Dickey City Park CG	143	C4
Drake City Park	61	B3
Eagles RV Park	108	C2
Eddy County Fairgrounds	77	B4
Edmore City Park	78	B4
Egeland Sportsman's CG - City	25	A4
Fessenden City Park	62	B3
Fingal City CG	156	C5
Fireman's Memorial Park	79	B4
First Responders City Park	39	B1
Flaxton Water Tower Park	10	A2
Forbes City Park	182	D4
Fordville City Park	89	B5
Fordville Dam RA	90	B5
Forman Lions CG	193	D5
Fort Buford SHS	40	B1
Fort Daer City Park	34	A5
Fullerton City Park	183	D4
Gackle RV Park	144	C4
Galesburg City CG	157	C5
Gascoyne Lake City CG	168	D1
General Sibley City Park	129	C3
Glen Ullin Memorial Park - City	109	C2
Glenfield City Park	145	C4
Golva City CG	97	C1
Goodrich City Park CG	130	C3
Granville City Park	63	B3
Grassy Butte Community Park	98	C1
Green Lake RA	184	D4
Grenora City Park	2	A1
Hager City Park	35	A5
Hague City Park	176	D3
Hankinson City Park	194	D5
Hatton Park Board CG	91	B5
Havana City Park	195	D5
Haynes City Park CG	171	D2
Hazelton City Park CG	131	C3
Hazen Bay RA	49	B2
Heart Butte Res - Crappie Creek - BOR	110	C2
Heart Butte Res - Downstream RA - BOR	111	C2
Heart Butte Res - Hawebesi - BOR	112	C2
Heart Butte Res - Koehlers Point - BOR	113	C2
Heart Butte Res - Rattlesnake Point - BOR	114	C2
Heart Butte Res - Rimrock - BOR	115	C2
Heart Butte Res - Schatz's Point - BOR	116	C2
Heart Butte Res - Schelle's Point - BOR	117	C2
Hendrickson City Park	80	B4
Hope City Park	158	C5
Hoskins Lake Recreation Park	185	D4
Hunter City Park CG	159	C5
John Moses Memorial Park	118	C
Kenmare City CG	11	A
Kidder RA	196	D
Killdeer City Park	99	C
Kulm City CG	186	D
Lake Holmes	64	B
Langdon City Park CG	26	A
Lawton Centennial Park CG	81	B
Legion CG	27	A
Leistikow City Park CG	92	B
Lewis and Clark City RV Park	119	C

1 • A1 | Baukol-Noonan Trout Pond

Total sites: 8, RV sites: 8, Elec sites: 4, Central water, Tent & RV camping: Fee unk, Elev: 1998ft/609m, Tel: 701-925-3000, Nearest town: Noonan. GPS: 48.871954, -102.950005

2 • A1 | Grenora City Park

Total sites: 20, RV sites: 20, Elec sites: 20, Water at site, Tent & RV camping: Fee unk, No transient spaces, Elev: 2123ft/647m, Nearest town: Grenora. GPS: 48.619298, -103.941467

3 • A1 | Noonan Lions CG

Total sites: 7, RV sites: 7, Elec sites: 7, Water at site, RV dump, Tent & RV camping: $10, 7 Full hookup, Elev: 1992ft/607m, Tel: 701-925-3000, Nearest town: Noonan. GPS: 48.886559, -103.007679

4 • A1 | Pioneer Village

Total sites: 30, RV sites: 30, Elec sites: 30, Water at site, Flush toilet, Free showers, RV dump, Tent & RV camping: $10, Reservations not accepted, Elev: 1952ft/595m, Tel: 810-923-8465, Nearest town: Crosby. GPS: 48.908915, -103.301078

5 • A1 | Rud Anderson City Park

Total sites: 4, RV sites: 4, Elec sites: 2, No water, No toilets, No showers, No RV dump, Tent & RV camping: Free, 1 shared elec box, Camp on any vacant lot in town, Reservations not accepted, Elev: 2070ft/631m, Tel: 701-965-5500, Nearest town: Ambrose. GPS: 48.952638, -103.482282

6 • A1 | Wildrose City Park CG

Total sites: 6, RV sites: 6, Elec sites: 6, Central water, RV dump, Tent & RV camping: $20, Elev: 2247ft/685m, Tel: 701-539-2172, Nearest town: Wildrose. GPS: 48.630736, -103.186203

7 • A2 | Antler Memorial Park

Dispersed sites, Vault/pit toilet, No showers, RV dump, Tent & RV camping: Free, Open May-Nov, Elev: 1526ft/465m, Tel: 701-267-3370, Nearest town: Antler. GPS: 48.991720, -101.278158

8 • A2 | Bowbells RV Park

Total sites: 3, RV sites: 3, Elec sites: 3, Water at site, Flush toilet, Free showers, RV dump, Tent & RV camping: $20, 3 Full hookup, Open May-Sep, Reservations not accepted, Elev: 1965ft/599m, Tel: 701-377-2608, Nearest town: Bowbells. GPS: 48.803898, -102.249979

9 • A2 | Columbus City Park

Total sites: 6, RV sites: 6, Elec sites: 3, No RV dump, Tent & RV camping: $10, Elev: 1923ft/586m, Tel: 701-939-5243, Nearest town: Columbus. GPS: 48.904990, -102.775580

10 • A2 | Flaxton Water Tower Park

Total sites: 2, RV sites: 2, Elec sites: 2, No toilets, No showers, No RV dump, No tents/RVs: Free, Elev: 1923ft/586m, Tel: 701-596-3539, Nearest town: Flaxton. GPS: 48.899333, -102.392752

11 • A2 | Kenmare City CG

Total sites: 34, RV sites: 34, Elec sites: 30, Water at site, Flush toilet, Free showers, RV dump, Tents: $5/RVs: $25, 24 Full hookup, Elev: 1942ft/592m, Tel: 701-385-4232, Nearest town: Kenmare. GPS: 48.678422, -102.074584

12 • A2 | Lignite City Park CG

Total sites: 2, RV sites: 2, Elec sites: 2, Central water, Flush toilet, Free showers, RV dump, Tent & RV camping: Free, Elev: 1982ft/604m, Tel: 701-933-2850, Nearest town: Lignite. GPS: 48.876298, -102.563542

13 • A2 | Maxbass City Park CG

Total sites: 3, RV sites: 3, Elec sites: 3, Central water, Vault/pit toilet, Tent & RV camping: Fee unk, Elev: 1501ft/458m, Tel: 701-268-3287, Nearest town: Maxbass. GPS: 48.721242, -101.145491

14 • A2 | Mohall City CGs

Total sites: 20, RV sites: 20, Elec sites: 20, Water at site, Flush toilet, Free showers, RV dump, Tent & RV camping: $12, 10 Full hookup, Elev: 1642ft/500m, Tel: 701-756-6464, Nearest town: Mohall. GPS: 48.760497, -101.516144

15 • A2 | Powers Lake City Park

Total sites: 12, RV sites: 12, Elec sites: 11, Central water, Flush toilet, Free showers, RV dump, Tent & RV camping: Fee unk, Reservations accepted, Elev: 2213ft/675m, Tel: 701-705-5369, Nearest town: Powers Lake. GPS: 48.559006, -102.643285

16 • A2 | Smishek Lake City Park

Total sites: 60, RV sites: 60, Elec sites: 30, Flush toilet, Free showers, Tent & RV camping: Fee unk, Reservations not accepted, Elev: 2241ft/683m, Tel: 701-464-5108, Nearest town: Powers Lake. GPS: 48.612554, -102.666218

17 • A3 | Log House City CG

Total sites: 6, RV sites: 6, Elec sites: 6, Water at site, No toilets, No showers, RV dump, No tents/RVs: Fee unk, 6 Full hookup, Open May-Sep, Elev: 1693ft/516m, Tel: 701-244-5860, Nearest town: Dunseith. GPS: 48.808292, -100.062308

18 • A3 | Neameyer Field CG

Total sites: 8, RV sites: 8, Elec sites: 8, Water at site, Flush toilet, Free showers, RV dump, Tent & RV camping: $15, 8 Full hookup, Open May-Oct, Elev: 1808ft/551m, Tel: 701-477-3610, Nearest town: Rolla. GPS: 48.855929, -99.612701

19 • A3 | Newburg City Park CG

Total sites: 12, RV sites: 12, Elec sites: 12, Central water, Flush toilet, Tent & RV camping: Fee unk, Elev: 1450ft/442m, Tel: 701-272-6253, Nearest town: Newburg. GPS: 48.713901, -100.910251

20 • A3 | Rolette RV Park

Total sites: 8, RV sites: 8, Elec sites: 8, Water at site, No toilets, No showers, RV dump, Tent & RV camping: $12, 8 Full hookup, Reservations accepted, Elev: 1624ft/495m, Tel: 701-246-3511, Nearest town: Rolette. GPS: 48.663883, -99.849412

21 • A3 | Tommy Turtle City Park

Total sites: 16, RV sites: 16, Elec sites: 16, Water at site, Flush toilet, Pay showers, RV dump, No tents/RVs: $12, Elev: 1637ft/499m, Tel: 701-228-3030, Nearest town: Bottineau. GPS: 48.822803, -100.432222

22 • A3 | Upham City Park CG

Total sites: 10, RV sites: 10, Elec sites: 10, Water at site, No toilets, No showers, RV dump, Tents: Fee unk/RVs: $15, 2 Full hookup, Elev: 1447ft/441m, Tel: 701-768-2839, Nearest town: Upham. GPS: 48.578900, -100.729010

23 • A3 | Westhope City Park

Total sites: 5, RV sites: 5, Elec sites: 5, No toilets, No showers, RV dump, Tent & RV camping: Fee unk, Elev: 1493ft/455m, Tel: 701-245-6316, Nearest town: Westhope. GPS: 48.908996, -101.011589

24 • A3 | Willow City CG

Total sites: 2, RV sites: 2, Elec sites: 2, Tent & RV camping: Free, Location approximate, Open May-Oct, Elev: 1472ft/449m, Tel: 701-366-4545, Nearest town: Willow City. GPS: 48.604565, -100.290878

25 • A4 | Egeland Sportsman's CG - City

Total sites: 12, RV sites: 12, Elec sites: 12, Central water, Flush toilet, Free showers, RV dump, Tent & RV camping: Fee unk, Elev: 1523ft/464m, Tel: 701-266-5123, Nearest town: Egeland. GPS: 48.626424, -99.098249

26 • A4 | Langdon City Park CG

Total sites: 13, RV sites: 13, Elec sites: 13, Water at site, Flush toilet, Free showers, RV dump, Tent & RV camping: $6-20, Elev: 1604ft/489m, Tel: 701-256-2155, Nearest town: Langdon. GPS: 48.765236, -98.373247

27 • A4 | Legion CG

Total sites: 4, RV sites: 2, Elec sites: 4, RV dump, Tent & RV camping: Donation, Elev: 1066ft/325m, Tel: 701-993-8723, Nearest town: Mountain. GPS: 48.688208, -97.866271

28 • A4 | Munich Park CG

Total sites: 5, RV sites: 5, Elec sites: 5, Water at site, Flush toilet, Free showers, Tent & RV camping: Fee unk, 5 Full hookup, Elev: 1598ft/487m, Nearest town: Munich. GPS: 48.668804, -98.837494

29 • A4 | Rock Lake City Park

Total sites: 9, RV sites: 9, Elec sites: 1, Central water, Vault/pit toilet, No showers, No RV dump, Tent & RV camping: Fee unk, Elev: 1535ft/468m, Tel: 701-266-5318, Nearest town: Rock Lake. GPS: 48.793663, -99.248079

30 • A4 | Sarles City Park CG

Dispersed sites, Central water, Vault/pit toilet, No showers, No RV dump, Tent & RV camping: Fee unk, Elev: 1585ft/483m, Tel: 701-697-5270, Nearest town: Sarles. GPS: 48.945241, -99.000217

31 • A4 | Wales City Park CG

Total sites: 4, RV sites: 2, Elec sites: 2, Vault/pit toilet, Tent & RV camping: Fee unk, Elev: 1568ft/478m, Tel: 701-283-5337, Nearest town: Wales. GPS: 48.894277, -98.602737

32 • A4 | Walhalla Riverside City Park

Total sites: 52, RV sites: 35, Elec sites: 35, Water at site, Flush toilet, Free showers, RV dump, Tents: $15/RVs: $28, Open May-Sep, Reservations accepted, Elev: 971ft/296m, Tel: 701-549-3289, Nearest town: Walhalla. GPS: 48.919678, -97.914551

33 • A5 | Crystal City Park CG

Dispersed sites, No water, Tent & RV camping: Fee unk, Elev: 899ft/274m, Tel: 701-657-2299, Nearest town: Crystal. GPS: 48.598587, -97.676043

34 • A5 | Fort Daer City Park

Total sites: 12, RV sites: 12, Elec sites: 12, Central water, Flush toilet, Free showers, RV dump, Tents: $10/RVs: $20, 12 Full hookup, Reservations not accepted, Elev: 771ft/235m, Tel: 701-825-6819, Nearest town: Pembina. GPS: 48.965422, -97.240665

35 • A5 | Hager City Park

Dispersed sites, No water, No toilets, Tent & RV camping: Free, Elev: 830ft/253m, Tel: 701-257-6640, Nearest town: St. Thomas. GPS: 48.619176, -97.454462

36 • A5 | Schumacher Park

Total sites: 24, RV sites: 24, Elec sites: 24, Water at site, Flush toilet, Free showers, RV dump, Tents: $20/RVs: $25, Elev: 802ft/244m, Tel: 701-454-6199, Nearest town: Drayton. GPS: 48.566083, -97.182874

37 • B1 | Arnegard City Park CG

Total sites: 7, RV sites: 7, Elec sites: 4, Water at site, Flush toilet, Free showers, RV dump, Tent & RV camping: Fee unk, 4 Full hookup, Elev: 2244ft/684m, Tel: 701-586-3453, Nearest town: Arnegard. GPS: 47.810854, -103.439737

38 • B1 | Cherry Creek CG

Total sites: 30, RV sites: 30, Elec sites: 30, Water at site, Flush toilet, Free showers, RV dump, Tent & RV camping: $30, 30 Full hookup, Elev: 2058ft/627m, Tel: 701-842-2626, Nearest town: Watford City. GPS: 47.800894, -103.267724

39 • B1 | First Responders City Park

Total sites: 6, RV sites: 6, Elec sites: 6, Water at site, No toilets, No showers, RV dump, Tent & RV camping: Fee unk, Dump 2 blocks away, Elev: 2188ft/667m, Tel: 701-572-3060, Nearest town: Alexander. GPS: 47.843234, -103.641604

40 • B1 | Fort Buford SHS

Dispersed sites, Central water, No RV dump, Tent & RV camping: Free, Stay limit: 4 days, Elev: 1903ft/580m, Tel: 701-575-9034, Nearest town: Buford. GPS: 47.985812, -104.001493

41 • B1 | Rough Rider Center Tourist Park

Total sites: 20, RV sites: 12, Elec sites: 12, Central water, Flush toilet, Pay showers, RV dump, Tents: $15/RVs: $15-30, 12 Full hookup, Reservations not accepted, Elev: 2067ft/630m, Tel: 701-570-3677, Nearest town: Watford City. GPS: 47.804961, -103.272351

42 • B1 | South Park

Dispersed sites, Central water, No toilets, No showers, No RV dump, Tent & RV camping: $10, Near RR, Open May-Sep, Elev: 2264ft/690m, Tel: 701-568-2204, Nearest town: Ray. GPS: 48.339179, -103.170993

43 • B1 | Sundheim Park

Dispersed sites, No toilets, Tent & RV camping: Free, Elev: 1857ft/566m, Tel: 701-444-5440, Nearest town: Cartwright. GPS: 47.860659, -103.969352

44 • B1 | Tioga City Park

Total sites: 12, RV sites: 12, Elec sites: 12, Central water, Flush toilet, Free showers, RV dump, Tent & RV camping: Fee unk, Elev: 2238ft/682m, Tel: 701-664-2563, Nearest town: Tioga. GPS: 48.399205, -102.931207

45 • B2 | Berthold RV Park

Total sites: 6, RV sites: 6, Elec sites: 6, Water at site, No toilets, No showers, RV dump, No tents/RVs: $20, 6 Full hookup, Reservations not accepted, Elev: 2073ft/632m, Tel: 701-453-3641, Nearest town: Berthold. GPS: 48.317231, -101.734102

46 • B2 | Beulah Bay RA

Total sites: 117, RV sites: 117, Elec sites: 117, Central water, Flush toilet, Free showers, RV dump, Tents: $10/RVs: $23-27, Also cabins, 24 Full hookup, Open May-Sep, Reservations accepted,

Elev: 1886ft/575m, Tel: 701-873-5852, Nearest town: Beulah. GPS: 47.491371, -101.765527

47 • B2 | Carpio City Park

Total sites: 7, RV sites: 7, Elec sites: 7, Central water, Vault/pit toilet, No showers, No RV dump, Tent & RV camping: $15, Elev: 1690ft/515m, Tel: 701-468-5960, Nearest town: Carpio. GPS: 48.443848, -101.712646

48 • B2 | Coleharbor City Park

Dispersed sites, No water, No toilets, Tent & RV camping: Fee unk, Elev: 1900ft/579m, Tel: 701-442-3454, Nearest town: Coleharbor. GPS: 47.541981, -101.222421

49 • B2 | Hazen Bay RA

Total sites: 135, RV sites: 129, Elec sites: 129, Water at site, Flush toilet, Free showers, RV dump, Tents: $15/RVs: $23-25, 107 Full hookup, Open May-Sep, Reservations accepted, Elev: 1880ft/573m, Tel: 701-487-3474, Nearest town: Hazen. GPS: 47.503636, -101.624443

50 • B2 | Lewis and Clark Reunion Bay

Dispersed sites, No toilets, Tents only: Free, Elev: 1852ft/564m, Tel: 701-627-4812, Nearest town: New Town. GPS: 47.899224, -102.608602

51 • B2 | Makoti Threshers CG

Total sites: 80, RV sites: 80, Elec sites: 80, Central water, Flush toilet, Free showers, Tent & RV camping: Fee unk, Elev: 2083ft/635m, Tel: 701-726-5623, Nearest town: Makoti. GPS: 47.958644, -101.806956

52 • B2 | Max City Camper Park

Total sites: 8, RV sites: 8, Elec sites: 8, Water at site, Tent & RV camping: $15, Reservations not accepted, Elev: 2110ft/643m, Tel: 701-500-1846, Nearest town: Max. GPS: 47.824092, -101.299646

53 • B2 | McKenzie Bay RA

Total sites: 27, RV sites: 27, Elec sites: 22, Central water, Flush toilet, Free showers, RV dump, Tent & RV camping: Fee unk, Open May-Sep, Elev: 1857ft/566m, Tel: 701-759-3366, Nearest town: Mandaree. GPS: 47.598403, -102.364559

54 • B2 | New Town Marina

Total sites: 55, RV sites: 55, Central water, Flush toilet, Free showers, RV dump, Tent & RV camping: Fee unk, Elev: 1847ft/563m, Tel: 701-627-3900, Nearest town: New Town. GPS: 47.982491, -102.530441

55 • B2 | North City Park CG

Total sites: 12, RV sites: 12, Elec sites: 12, Central water, No toilets, No showers, RV dump, Tent & RV camping: Fee unk, Elev: 1989ft/606m, Tel: 701-862-3459, Nearest town: Parshall. GPS: 47.962959, -102.131655

56 • B2 | Stanley City Park

Total sites: 15, RV sites: 12, Elec sites: 12, Central water, Flush toilet, Free showers, RV dump, Tents: $6/RVs: $15, Near RR, Reservations not accepted, Elev: 2251ft/686m, Tel: 701-628-2225, Nearest town: Stanley. GPS: 48.321262, -102.390273

57 • B3 | Anamoose City CG

Total sites: 2, RV sites: 2, Elec sites: 2, Water at site, No tents/RVs: $20, Reservations not accepted, Elev: 1594ft/486m, Tel: 701-465-7208, Nearest town: Anamoose. GPS: 47.880094, -100.237938

58 • B3 | Brekken-Holmes RA

Total sites: 18, RV sites: 18, Elec sites: 18, No water, Vault/pit toilet, No showers, No RV dump, Tents: Free/RVs: $15, Reservations not accepted, Elev: 1821ft/555m, Tel: 701-250-4592, Nearest town: Underwood. GPS: 47.547493, -100.885211

59 • B3 | Buffalo Lake Sportsmen CG

Total sites: 15, RV sites: 9, Elec sites: 9, Central water, Flush toilet, Free showers, No RV dump, Tent & RV camping: Fee unk, Elev: 1522ft/464m, Tel: 701-249-3461, Nearest town: Esmond. GPS: 48.023787, -99.853234

60 • B3 | Butte City CG

Total sites: 3, RV sites: 3, Elec sites: 3, Water at site, RV dump, No tents/RVs: Fee unk, Location approximate, Open all year, Elev: 1724ft/525m, Tel: 701-626-7177, Nearest town: Butte. GPS: 47.840735, -100.665986

61 • B3 | Drake City Park

Total sites: 12, RV sites: 12, Elec sites: 12, Central water, No toilets, No showers, RV dump, Tents: $8/RVs: $10, Open May-Sep, Elev: 1667ft/508m, Nearest town: Drake. GPS: 47.928129, -100.373833

62 • B3 | Fessenden City Park

Total sites: 12, RV sites: 8, Elec sites: 8, Central water, Flush toilet, Free showers, RV dump, Tent & RV camping: $8, Reservations not accepted, Elev: 1608ft/490m, Tel: 701-547-3291, Nearest town: Fessenden. GPS: 47.645632, -99.628566

63 • B3 | Granville City Park

Total sites: 10, RV sites: 10, Elec sites: 10, Water at site, Tent & RV camping: Fee unk, Elev: 1519ft/463m, Nearest town: Granville. GPS: 48.265242, -100.848227

64 • B3 | Lake Holmes

Dispersed sites, No water, Vault/pit toilet, Tent & RV camping Fee unk, Elev: 1814ft/553m, Nearest town: Turtle Lake. GPS 47.538554, -100.875462

65 • B3 | Martin City Park CG

Total sites: 12, RV sites: 12, Elec sites: 12, Central water, No toilets No showers, RV dump, No tents/RVs: $15, Reservations no accepted, Elev: 1618ft/493m, Tel: 701-693-2856, Nearest town Martin. GPS: 47.825046, -100.115124

66 • B3 | Randy Marthe Memorial Park CG

Total sites: 8, RV sites: 3, Elec sites: 3, Central water, Flus toilet, Free showers, No RV dump, Tent & RV camping: $1 Reservations not accepted, Elev: 1624ft/495m, Tel: 701-249-836 Nearest town: Esmond. GPS: 48.037882, -99.767041

67 • B3 | Surrey RV Park

Total sites: 10, RV sites: 10, Elec sites: 10, Water at site, Tent

RV camping: $15, Elev: 1608ft/490m, Tel: 701-852-4154, Nearest town: Surrey. GPS: 48.242345, -101.123578

68 • B3 | Towner City Park CG

Total sites: 4, RV sites: 4, Elec sites: 4, Vault/pit toilet, Tent & RV camping: Free, Elev: 1483ft/452m, Tel: 701-537-5834, Nearest town: Towner. GPS: 48.341221, -100.405911

69 • B3 | Turtle Lake City Park

Total sites: 6, RV sites: 6, Elec sites: 6, Central water, No toilets, No showers, RV dump, Tent & RV camping: Fee unk, Elev: 1870ft/570m, Tel: 701-448-2596, Nearest town: Turtle Lake. GPS: 47.517235, -100.881808

70 • B3 | Velva Pool and CG

Total sites: 22, RV sites: 18, Elec sites: 18, Water at site, Flush toilet, Free showers, RV dump, Tents: $5/RVs: $15, 18 Full hookup, Reservations accepted, Elev: 1516ft/462m, Tel: 701-626-2661, Nearest town: Velva. GPS: 48.059781, -100.939222

71 • B3 | West Side City Park

Total sites: 17, RV sites: 17, Elec sites: 17, Central water, Flush toilet, Free showers, RV dump, Tents: $12/RVs: $15-20, Near RR, Open Apr-Oct, Reservations not accepted, Elev: 1605ft/489m, Tel: 701-341-0313, Nearest town: Harvey. GPS: 47.774119, -99.943072

72 • B3 | York City Park CG

Dispersed sites, Tents only: Fee unk, Beside RR, Elev: 1613ft/492m, Tel: 701-592-3271, Nearest town: York. GPS: 48.312823, -99.573719

73 • B4 | Adams City CG

Total sites: 2, RV sites: 2, Elec sites: 2, Central water, No toilets, No showers, RV dump, Tent & RV camping: Fee unk, Open May-Sep, Elev: 1568ft/478m, Tel: 701-944-2701, Nearest town: Adams. GPS: 48.423183, -98.076739

74 • B4 | Archie and Jesse Campbell Memorial Park

Total sites: 12, RV sites: 12, Elec sites: 12, Water at site, Flush toilet, Free showers, Tent & RV camping: $12, Reservations not accepted, Elev: 1506ft/459m, Tel: 701-947-2461, Nearest town: New Rockford. GPS: 47.686613, -99.127571

75 • B4 | Binford Park CG

Total sites: 6, RV sites: 6, Elec sites: 6, Water at site, Flush toilet, Free showers, RV dump, Tent & RV camping: $25, Elev: 1516ft/462m, Tel: 701-676-2531, Nearest town: Binford. GPS: 47.563268, -98.349811

76 • B4 | Cando City CG

Total sites: 14, RV sites: 14, Elec sites: 14, Water at site, Flush toilet, Free showers, RV dump, Tent & RV camping: $18, 5 Full hookup, Reservations not accepted, Elev: 1463ft/446m, Tel: 701-968-3383, Nearest town: Cando. GPS: 48.493857, -99.201878

77 • B4 | Eddy County Fairgrounds

Total sites: 15, RV sites: 15, Elec sites: 15, Water at site, Flush toilet, Free showers, RV dump, No tents/RVs: $12, 15 Full hookup, Elev: 1529ft/466m, Tel: 701-947-2084, Nearest town: New Rockford. GPS: 47.672879, -99.143318

78 • B4 | Edmore City Park

Total sites: 10, RV sites: 4, Elec sites: 4, Central water, RV dump, Tent & RV camping: Fee unk, Elev: 1516ft/462m, Tel: 701-644-2425, Nearest town: Edmore. GPS: 48.413477, -98.450499

79 • B4 | Fireman's Memorial Park

Dispersed sites, No water, No toilets, Tent & RV camping: Free, Elev: 1503ft/458m, Tel: 701-466-2930, Nearest town: Leeds. GPS: 48.294598, -99.441259

80 • B4 | Hendrickson City Park

Total sites: 6, RV sites: 6, Elec sites: 6, Vault/pit toilet, Tents: $5/RVs: $11, Elev: 1473ft/449m, Tel: 701-996-3576, Nearest town: Sheyenne. GPS: 47.828781, -99.120791

81 • B4 | Lawton Centennial Park CG

Total sites: 5, RV sites: 1, Elec sites: 1, Tent & RV camping: Free, Elev: 1519ft/463m, Tel: 701-655-3641, Nearest town: Lawton. GPS: 48.302397, -98.367417

82 • B4 | Matejeck Dam RA

Dispersed sites, No water, Vault/pit toilet, Tent & RV camping: Fee unk, Elev: 1345ft/410m, Nearest town: Lankin. GPS: 48.227212, -97.925827

83 • B4 | McHenry City Park CG

Dispersed sites, No water, No toilets, Tent & RV camping: Fee unk, Elev: 1506ft/459m, Tel: 701-785-2112, Nearest town: McHenry. GPS: 47.576265, -98.586936

84 • B4 | McVille Dam CG

Total sites: 25, RV sites: 25, Elec sites: 25, Water at site, Tent & RV camping: $20, Elev: 1434ft/437m, Tel: 701-322-5600, Nearest town: McVille. GPS: 47.761808, -98.166095

85 • B4 | Michigan City Park CG

Total sites: 4, RV sites: 4, Elec sites: 4, Central water, Flush toilet, No showers, No RV dump, Tent & RV camping: Donation, Reservations not accepted, Elev: 1516ft/462m, Tel: 701-259-2553, Nearest town: Michigan. GPS: 48.026277, -98.128935

86 • B4 | Niagara Park

Total sites: 4, RV sites: 4, Elec sites: 4, Tent & RV camping: Fee unk, Elev: 1442ft/440m, Tel: 701-397-5833, Nearest town: Niagara. GPS: 47.995528, -97.867079

87 • B4 | Tolna City Park CG

Total sites: 4, RV sites: 4, Elec sites: 4, Vault/pit toilet, Tent & RV camping: $10, Reservations accepted, Elev: 1453ft/443m, Tel: 701-230-0356, Nearest town: Tolna. GPS: 47.825413, -98.437057

88 • B4 | Tolna Dam

Total sites: 10, RV sites: 10, Elec sites: 4, Vault/pit toilet, Tent & RV camping: Donation, Reservations not accepted, Elev: 1378ft/420m, Tel: 701-230-0356, Nearest town: Tolna. GPS: 47.802653, -98.396111

89 • B5 | Fordville City Park

Dispersed sites, No water, No toilets, No tents/RVs: Fee unk, Elev: 1143ft/348m, Nearest town: Fordville. GPS: 48.215654, -97.789214

90 • B5 | Fordville Dam RA

Total sites: 47, RV sites: 23, Elec sites: 23, Water at site, Flush toilet, Free showers, RV dump, Tents: $10/RVs: $20, 19 Full hookup, Elev: 1138ft/347m, Tel: 701-343-2078, Nearest town: Fordville. GPS: 48.175059, -97.761883

91 • B5 | Hatton Park Board CG

Total sites: 4, RV sites: 4, Elec sites: 4, Water at site, No toilets, No showers, RV dump, Tent & RV camping: $15, 4 Full hookup, Reservations not accepted, Elev: 1083ft/330m, Tel: 701-543-3243, Nearest town: Hatton. GPS: 47.642851, -97.455231

92 • B5 | Leistikow City Park CG

Total sites: 63, RV sites: 63, Elec sites: 63, Water at site, Flush toilet, Free showers, RV dump, Tents: $10-15/RVs: $28, 63 Full hookup, Open May-Oct, Reservations accepted, Elev: 833ft/254m, Tel: 701-352-1842, Nearest town: Grafton. GPS: 48.420439, -97.420121

93 • B5 | Minto City Park

Total sites: 6, RV sites: 6, Elec sites: 6, Central water, Vault/pit toilet, No showers, Tent & RV camping: Fee unk, Elev: 807ft/246m, Tel: 701-248-3858, Nearest town: Minto. GPS: 48.286027, -97.371784

94 • B5 | Northwood City Park

Total sites: 5, RV sites: 5, Elec sites: 5, Tent & RV camping: $18, Very tight turn-around, Near RR, Elev: 1109ft/338m, Tel: 701-587-6301 x12, Nearest town: Northwood. GPS: 47.727031, -97.568182

95 • B5 | Willowood City CG

Total sites: 13, RV sites: 13, Elec sites: 13, Water at site, Flush toilet, Free showers, RV dump, Tent & RV camping: $25, 13 Full hookup, Elev: 945ft/288m, Tel: 701-788-8759, Nearest town: Mayville. GPS: 47.496713, -97.334654

96 • C1 | B and M Park

Dispersed sites, Central water, Vault/pit toilet, No showers, No RV dump, Tent & RV camping: Fee unk, Elev: 2622ft/799m, Tel: 701-579-4373, Nearest town: New England. GPS: 46.544734, -102.867628

97 • C1 | Golva City CG

Total sites: 5, RV sites: 5, Elec sites: 5, Central water, No toilets, No showers, No RV dump, Tent & RV camping: Fee unk, Open all year, Elev: 2805ft/855m, Tel: 701-872-3661, Nearest town: Golva. GPS: 46.732481, -103.984454

98 • C1 | Grassy Butte Community Park

Total sites: 25, RV sites: 25, Elec sites: 25, Vault/pit toilet, No showers, No RV dump, Tents: $5/RVs: $10, Elev: 2674ft/815m, Tel: 701-863-6906, Nearest town: Grassy Butte. GPS: 47.394372, -103.247199

99 • C1 | Killdeer City Park

Total sites: 12, RV sites: 12, Elec sites: 12, Central water, Flush toilet, Free showers, RV dump, Tent & RV camping: Donation, Reservations not accepted, Elev: 2241ft/683m, Tel: 701-764-5295, Nearest town: Killdeer. GPS: 47.364511, -102.753525

100 • C1 | Medora City CG

Total sites: 150, RV sites: 103, Elec sites: 108, Water at site, Flush toilet, Free showers, RV dump, Tents: $24/RVs: $30-46, Group tent site: $35, 85 Full hookup, Generator hours: 0700-2300, Open May-Sep, Reservations accepted, Elev: 2267ft/691m, Tel: 701-623-4444, Nearest town: Medora. GPS: 46.922343, -103.532917

101 • C1 | New England South Park

Dispersed sites, No water, Vault/pit toilet, Tent & RV camping: Fee unk, Elev: 2561ft/781m, Nearest town: New England. GPS: 46.531002, -102.867416

102 • C1 | Patterson Lake RA

Total sites: 60, RV sites: 20, Elec sites: 20, Central water, Flush toilet, Free showers, RV dump, Tents: $18/RVs: $28, Open May-Sep, Reservations accepted, Elev: 2441ft/744m, Tel: 701-456-2074, Nearest town: Dickinson. GPS: 46.866674, -102.851975

103 • C2 | Antelope Creek RV Park

Total sites: 45, RV sites: 45, Elec sites: 45, Water at site, Flush toilet, Free showers, RV dump, No tents/RVs: $25, 45 Full hookup, Reservations accepted, Elev: 1739ft/530m, Tel: 701-748-6948, Nearest town: Hazen. GPS: 47.303846, -101.620537

104 • C2 | Ball Park RV Park

Total sites: 10, RV sites: 10, Elec sites: 10, No water, Vault/pit toilet, Tent & RV camping: $10, Elev: 1959ft/597m, Tel: 701-794-3502, Nearest town: Center. GPS: 47.110074, -101.290369

105 • C2 | Beaver Bay RA - City

Total sites: 8, RV sites: 8, No water, No toilets, Tent & RV camping: Fee unk, Open May-Sep, Reservations not accepted, Elev: 1844ft/562m, Tel: 701-948-2256, Nearest town: Zap. GPS: 47.459087, -101.915456

106 • C2 | Centennial City Park

Total sites: 5, RV sites: 5, Elec sites: 5, Water at site, No toilets, No showers, RV dump, No tents/RVs: $20, 5 Full hookup, Elev: 1924ft/586m, Tel: 701-597-3127, Nearest town: Flasher. GPS: 46.452622, -101.233153

107 • C2 | Center RV Park

Total sites: 20, RV sites: 20, Elec sites: 20, Water at site, RV dump, No tents/RVs: Fee unk, 20 Full hookup, $400 monthly only, Reservations accepted, Elev: 1978ft/603m, Tel: 701-794-3502, Nearest town: Center. GPS: 47.113573, -101.295242

108 • C2 | Eagles RV Park

Total sites: 10, RV sites: 10, Elec sites: 10, Central water, RV dump, Tent & RV camping: $25, Open May-Oct, Elev: 1768ft/539m, Tel: 701-873-5852, Nearest town: Beulah. GPS: 47.255261, 101.786088

109 • C2 | Glen Ullin Memorial Park - City

Total sites: 26, RV sites: 26, Elec sites: 26, Water at site, No toilets, No showers, RV dump, Tents: $6/RVs: $15-25, Also cabins, 16 Full hookup, Elev: 2074ft/632m, Tel: 701-348-3950, Nearest town: Glen Ullin. GPS: 46.813180, -101.850890

110 • C2 | Heart Butte Res - Crappie Creek - BOR

Dispersed sites, No water, Vault/pit toilet, Tent & RV camping: $14, Open Mar-Nov, Reservations accepted, Elev: 2090ft/637m, Tel: 701-584-2201, Nearest town: New Ullin. GPS: 46.616636, -101.858435

111 • C2 | Heart Butte Res - Downstream RA - BOR

Total sites: 32, RV sites: 32, Elec sites: 22, No water, Vault/pit toilet, Tents: $14/RVs: $24, Open Mar-Nov, Max Length: 22ft, Reservations accepted, Elev: 2027ft/618m, Tel: 701-584-2201, Nearest town: New Ullin. GPS: 46.597038, -101.805084

112 • C2 | Heart Butte Res - Hawebesi - BOR

Total sites: 2, RV sites: 2, No water, Vault/pit toilet, Tent & RV camping: $14, Open Mar-Nov, Reservations accepted, Elev: 2079ft/634m, Tel: 701-584-2201, Nearest town: New Ullin. GPS: 46.602656, -101.855307

113 • C2 | Heart Butte Res - Koehlers Point - BOR

Dispersed sites, No water, Vault/pit toilet, Tent & RV camping: $14, Open Mar-Nov, Reservations not accepted, Elev: 2074ft/632m, Tel: 701-584-2201, Nearest town: New Ullin. GPS: 46.612284, -101.907565

114 • C2 | Heart Butte Res - Rattlesnake Point - BOR

Dispersed sites, No water, Vault/pit toilet, Tent & RV camping: $14, Open Mar-Nov, Reservations accepted, Elev: 2083ft/635m, Tel: 701-584-2201, Nearest town: New Ullin. GPS: 46.613785, -101.878143

115 • C2 | Heart Butte Res - Rimrock - BOR

Total sites: 48, RV sites: 48, Elec sites: 26, No water, Vault/pit toilet, Tents: $14/RVs: $24, Open Mar-Nov, Reservations accepted, Elev: 2085ft/636m, Tel: 701-584-2201, Nearest town: New Ullin. GPS: 46.590373, -101.816105

116 • C2 | Heart Butte Res - Schatz's Point - BOR

Total sites: 21, RV sites: 21, No water, Vault/pit toilet, Tent & RV camping: $14, Open Mar-Nov, Reservations accepted, Elev: 2077ft/633m, Tel: 701-584-2201, Nearest town: New Ullin. GPS: 46.604366, -101.870751

117 • C2 | Heart Butte Res - Schelle's Point - BOR

Dispersed sites, No water, Vault/pit toilet, Tent & RV camping: $14, Open Mar-Nov, Reservations not accepted, Elev: 2077ft/633m, Tel: 701-584-2201, Nearest town: New Ullin. GPS: 46.619046, -101.927771

118 • C2 | John Moses Memorial Park

Total sites: 4, RV sites: 4, Central water, No toilets, No tents/RVs: Free, Open May-Sep, Reservations not accepted, Elev: 1732ft/528m, Tel: 701-748-6948, Nearest town: Hazen. GPS: 47.298827, -101.619068

119 • C2 | Lewis and Clark City RV Park

Total sites: 28, RV sites: 28, Elec sites: 28, Water at site, Flush toilet, Free showers, RV dump, Tents: $10/RVs: $20, 28 Full hookup, Open Apr-Oct, Max Length: 45ft, Reservations accepted, Elev: 1749ft/533m, Tel: 701-748-2267, Nearest town: Hazen. GPS: 47.294022, -101.642954

120 • C2 | North City Park

Total sites: 6, RV sites: 6, Elec sites: 6, Water at site, No toilets, No showers, No RV dump, Tents: $10/RVs: $20, Reservations accepted, Elev: 2136ft/651m, Tel: 701-220-8453, Nearest town: New Salem. GPS: 46.850655, -101.418132

121 • C2 | Prairie Rose City Park

Total sites: 17, RV sites: 17, Elec sites: 17, Water at site, Vault/pit toilet, No showers, No RV dump, Tent & RV camping: Fee unk, Unconfirmed, Elev: 2375ft/724m, Tel: 701-225-7880, Nearest town: Gladstone. GPS: 46.862324, -102.569324

122 • C2 | Richardton City Park CG

Dispersed sites, No water, Tent & RV camping: Fee unk, Elev: 2460ft/750m, Tel: 701-974-3399, Nearest town: Richardton. GPS: 46.886637, -102.309026

123 • C2 | Riverside Park

Total sites: 20, RV sites: 8, Elec sites: 8, Water at site, Flush toilet, Free showers, Tents: $10/RVs: $25, Reservations accepted, Elev: 1782ft/543m, Tel: 701-873-5852, Nearest town: Beulah. GPS: 47.253788, -101.783844

124 • C2 | Sakakawea Park CG

Total sites: 8, RV sites: 8, Elec sites: 4, Central water, Flush toilet, Free showers, RV dump, Tents: $8/RVs: $15, Reservations not accepted, Elev: 1693ft/516m, Tel: 701-745-3202, Nearest town: Stanton. GPS: 47.322397, -101.376916

125 • C2 | Sun Valley RV Court

Total sites: 117, RV sites: 117, Elec sites: 117, Water at site, Flush toilet, Free showers, RV dump, No tents/RVs: $30-35, $35 Nov-Mar, 5 transient sites, Open all year, Reservations accepted, Elev: 1801ft/549m, Tel: 701-873-4637, Nearest town: Beulah. GPS: 47.266998, -101.772967

126 • C3 | Bowdon RV Park

Total sites: 6, RV sites: 6, Elec sites: 6, Water at site, Flush toilet, Free showers, RV dump, Tent & RV camping: $18, Elev: 1801ft/549m, Tel: 701-962-3749, Nearest town: Bowdon. GPS: 47.472742, -99.705015

127 • C3 | Braddock City Park CG

Total sites: 4, RV sites: 4, Elec sites: 4, Central water, RV dump, Tent & RV camping: Fee unk, Elev: 1867ft/569m, Tel: 701-332-6776, Nearest town: Braddock. GPS: 46.564423, -100.090953

128 • C3 | Dacotah Centennial Park

Total sites: 30, RV sites: 30, Elec sites: 30, Water at site, No tents/RVs: $25-35, 20 Full hookup, Operated by Bismarck-Mandan Stock Car Association, Open Apr-Nov, Reservations accepted, Elev: 1642ft/500m, Tel: 701-391-6211, Nearest town: Mandan. GPS: 46.818921, -100.858321

129 • C3 | General Sibley City Park

Total sites: 109, RV sites: 109, Elec sites: 109, Central water, Flush toilet, Free showers, RV dump, Tents: $12/RVs: $25, 5 double sites, Open May-Sep, Reservations accepted, Elev: 1640ft/500m, Tel: 701-222-1844, Nearest town: Bismarck. GPS: 46.744358, -100.788336

130 • C3 | Goodrich City Park CG

Total sites: 6, RV sites: 3, Elec sites: 3, Central water, Flush toilet, Free showers, RV dump, Tent & RV camping: Fee unk, Elev: 1962ft/598m, Tel: 701-884-2575, Nearest town: Goodrich. GPS: 47.474343, -100.122104

131 • C3 | Hazelton City Park CG

Total sites: 13, RV sites: 7, Elec sites: 13, Water at site, Flush toilet, Free showers, RV dump, Tents: $15/RVs: $20, 7 Full hookup, Reservations not accepted, Elev: 1968ft/600m, Tel: 701-782-6802, Nearest town: Hazelton. GPS: 46.483938, -100.283766

132 • C3 | McClusky City Park

Total sites: 6, RV sites: 6, Elec sites: 6, Water at site, RV dump, Tent & RV camping: $10, Elev: 1923ft/586m, Tel: 701-363-2543, Nearest town: McClusky. GPS: 47.480726, -100.445763

133 • C3 | Napoleon City Park and CG

Total sites: 12, RV sites: 10, Elec sites: 10, Water at site, No toilets, No showers, RV dump, Tent & RV camping: $25, 10 Full hookup, Open Apr-Oct, Reservations accepted, Elev: 1947ft/593m, Tel: 701-754-2320, Nearest town: Napoleon. GPS: 46.501619, -99.776157

134 • C3 | Pettibone City Park CG

Total sites: 3, RV sites: 3, Elec sites: 3, Water at site, Flush toilet, Free showers, No RV dump, Tents: $10/RVs: $15, Open all year, Elev: 1850ft/564m, Tel: 701-273-4029, Nearest town: Pettibone. GPS: 47.119797, -99.518961

135 • C3 | Riverside City Park

Dispersed sites, No water, Vault/pit toilet, Tent & RV camping: Fee unk, Reservations not accepted, Elev: 1713ft/522m, Tel: 701-462-8558, Nearest town: Washburn. GPS: 47.288092, -101.034962

136 • C3 | Robinson City Park

Total sites: 2, RV sites: 2, Elec sites: 2, RV dump, No tents/RVs: Fee unk, Elev: 1780ft/543m, Tel: 701-392-5221, Nearest town: Robinson. GPS: 47.141417, -99.775575

137 • C3 | Tuttle City Park CG

Dispersed sites, Central water, Flush toilet, Tent & RV camping: Fee unk, Reservations not accepted, Elev: 1860ft/567m, Tel: 701-867-2551, Nearest town: Tuttle. GPS: 47.145442, -99.990188

138 • C3 | Wilton City Park CG

Total sites: 8, RV sites: 8, Elec sites: 8, Water at site, Tents: $7/RVs: $11, No water in winter, Open all year, Elev: 2182ft/665m, Nearest town: Wilton. GPS: 47.154952, -100.786423

139 • C3 | Wing City Park CG

Total sites: 4, RV sites: 4, Elec sites: 4, Central water, Tent & RV camping: Free, Location approximate, Elev: 1899ft/579m, Nearest town: Wing. GPS: 47.141495, -100.284578

140 • C4 | C A Brown City Park

Total sites: 9, RV sites: 5, Elec sites: 9, Water at site, Flush toilet, Free showers, RV dump, Tents: $10-12/RVs: $12-15, 5 Full hookup, Reservations not accepted, Elev: 1365ft/416m, Tel: 701-769-2298, Nearest town: Hannaford. GPS: 47.312418, -98.180498

141 • C4 | Carrington City Park

Total sites: 8, RV sites: 8, Elec sites: 8, Water at site, Flush toilet, RV dump, Tent & RV camping: $20, Reservations not accepted, Elev: 1578ft/481m, Tel: 701-652-3184, Nearest town: Carrington. GPS: 47.443206, -99.114871

142 • C4 | Cooperstown City CG

Total sites: 10, RV sites: 6, Elec sites: 6, Water at site, Flush toilet, Free showers, RV dump, Tent & RV camping: $25, 12 Full hookup, Elev: 1417ft/432m, Tel: 701-797-3722, Nearest town: Cooperstown. GPS: 47.448467, -98.117126

143 • C4 | Dickey City Park CG

Total sites: 20, RV sites: 12, Elec sites: 12, Central water, No toilets, No showers, RV dump, Tent & RV camping: Fee unk, 12 Full hookup, Elev: 1316ft/401m, Tel: 701-320-5991, Nearest town: Dickey. GPS: 46.536627, -98.466177

144 • C4 | Gackle RV Park

Total sites: 6, RV sites: 6, Elec sites: 6, Water at site, Flush toilet, Free showers, RV dump, Tent & RV camping: Free, 6 Full hookup, Elev: 1936ft/590m, Tel: 701-485-3243, Nearest town: Gackle. GPS: 46.626316, -99.146876

145 • C4 | Glenfield City Park

Total sites: 5, RV sites: 5, Elec sites: 5, Water at site, Flush toilet, No showers, No RV dump, Tent & RV camping: Fee unk, Elev: 1493ft/455m, Tel: 701-785-2252, Nearest town: Glenfield. GPS: 47.456543, -98.564453

146 • C4 | Litchville City Park

Dispersed sites, No water, No toilets, Tent & RV camping: Free Elev: 1471ft/448m, Nearest town: Litchville. GPS: 46.655038, -98.191383

147 • C4 | Medina City Park

Total sites: 30, RV sites: 30, Elec sites: 30, Water at site, Flush toilet, Free showers, RV dump, Tents: $10/RVs: $15, Reservation accepted, Elev: 1814ft/553m, Tel: 701-659-0515, Nearest town Medina. GPS: 46.891311, -99.299515

148 • C4 | Sykeston City Park

Total sites: 10, RV sites: 10, Elec sites: 6, Water at site, No toilets No showers, RV dump, Tent & RV camping: $25, 6 Full hookup Elev: 1627ft/496m, Tel: 701-984-2380, Nearest town: Sykeston GPS: 47.466722, -99.401634

149 • C4 | Tourist Park CG

Total sites: 27, RV sites: 27, Elec sites: 27, Water at site, Flush toilet Free showers, RV dump, Tents: $10/RVs: $27, 27 Full hookup Open May-Oct, Reservations accepted, Elev: 1224ft/373m, Te

701-845-3294, Nearest town: Valley City. GPS: 46.923653, -97.993814

150 • C4 | Victory Park CG

Total sites: 4, RV sites: 4, Elec sites: 4, Tent & RV camping: Fee unk, Elev: 1480ft/451m, Nearest town: Wimbledon. GPS: 47.173131, -98.456309

151 • C4 | Woodworth City Park

Total sites: 4, RV sites: 2, Elec sites: 2, Central water, Flush toilet, Free showers, RV dump, Tent & RV camping: Fee unk, Elev: 2048ft/624m, Nearest town: Woodworth. GPS: 47.143467, -99.304778

152 • C5 | Alice City Park

Dispersed sites, Tent & RV camping: Fee unk, Unconfirmed, Elev: 1119ft/341m, Tel: 701-689-6421, Nearest town: Alice. GPS: 46.760144, -97.553596

153 • C5 | Arthur City Park

Dispersed sites, Tent & RV camping: Fee unk, Elev: 965ft/294m, Tel: 701-967-8327, Nearest town: Arthur. GPS: 47.101843, -97.212785

154 • C5 | Buffalo RV Park

Total sites: 8, RV sites: 8, Elec sites: 8, Water at site, RV dump, Tent & RV camping: $20, 8 Full hookup, Open May-Oct, Elev: 1207ft/368m, Tel: 701-351-1154, Nearest town: Buffalo. GPS: 46.922645, -97.547798

155 • C5 | City of Enderlin RV Park

Total sites: 3, RV sites: 3, Elec sites: 3, Water at site, Tent & RV camping: $10, 3 Full hookup, Elev: 1134ft/346m, Tel: 701-437-3476, Nearest town: Enderlin. GPS: 46.623981, -97.609049

156 • C5 | Fingal City CG

Total sites: 5, RV sites: 3, Elec sites: 3, Water at site, RV dump, Tent & RV camping: Fee unk, 3 Full hookup, Open May-Sep, Elev: 1283ft/391m, Tel: 701-924-8855, Nearest town: Fingal. GPS: 46.762842, -97.793961

157 • C5 | Galesburg City CG

Total sites: 5, RV sites: 2, Elec sites: 2, Central water, Tent & RV camping: Free, Elev: 1083ft/330m, Tel: 701-488-2220, Nearest town: Galesburg. GPS: 47.269041, -97.412571

158 • C5 | Hope City Park

Total sites: 10, RV sites: 10, Elec sites: 10, Water at site, Flush toilet, Free showers, Tent & RV camping: Fee unk, Elev: 1220ft/372m, Nearest town: Hope. GPS: 47.321099, -97.714061

159 • C5 | Hunter City Park CG

Total sites: 5, RV sites: 2, Elec sites: 2, Central water, Flush toilet, Tents: $5/RVs: $10, Elev: 1001ft/305m, Tel: 701-874-2112, Nearest town: Hunter. GPS: 47.191436, -97.227457

160 • C5 | Lindenwood City Park CG

Total sites: 58, RV sites: 47, Elec sites: 47, Water at site, Flush toilet, Free showers, RV dump, Tent & RV camping: $30, Open May-Oct, Reservations accepted, Elev: 915ft/279m, Tel: 701-232-3987, Nearest town: Fargo. GPS: 46.849137, -96.780448

161 • C5 | Mapleton City Park

Dispersed sites, No water, Vault/pit toilet, Tent & RV camping: Fee unk, Elev: 909ft/277m, Tel: 701-282-6992, Nearest town: Mapleton. GPS: 46.890463, -97.053101

162 • C5 | Norskie City Park

Dispersed sites, No water, No toilets, Tent & RV camping: Fee unk, Elev: 1047ft/319m, Nearest town: Clifford. GPS: 47.348177, -97.412681

163 • C5 | Page City Park CG

Total sites: 8, RV sites: 8, Elec sites: 8, Water at site, No toilets, No showers, RV dump, Tents: Free/RVs: $25, 8 Full hookup, Reservations accepted, Elev: 1173ft/358m, Tel: 701-668-2226, Nearest town: Page. GPS: 47.153833, -97.571446

164 • C5 | Sandager City Park

Total sites: 16, RV sites: 16, Elec sites: 16, Water at site, Flush toilet, Free showers, RV dump, Tents: $10/RVs: $20, 16 Full hookup, Reservations accepted, Elev: 1089ft/332m, Tel: 701-683-3010, Nearest town: Lisbon. GPS: 46.446348, -97.688533

165 • C5 | Tower City Campsite

Total sites: 15, RV sites: 15, Elec sites: 15, Water at site, Flush toilet, Free showers, RV dump, Tent & RV camping: Fee unk, Elev: 1200ft/366m, Tel: 701-749-2694, Nearest town: Tower City. GPS: 46.920353, -97.673909

166 • D1 | Bowman Lions Park CG

Total sites: 6, RV sites: 6, Flush toilet, No showers, RV dump, Tent & RV camping: Donation, Reservations not accepted, Elev: 2940ft/896m, Tel: 701-523-3251, Nearest town: Bowman. GPS: 46.176840, -103.390110

167 • D1 | Butte View Park

Total sites: 51, RV sites: 51, Elec sites: 51, Central water, Flush toilet, Free showers, RV dump, Tents: $15/RVs: $25-30, Near RR, Elev: 2969ft/905m, Tel: 701-523-3896, Nearest town: Bowman. GPS: 46.178629, -103.373058

168 • D1 | Gascoyne Lake City CG

Dispersed sites, No water, Vault/pit toilet, Tent & RV camping: Free, Elev: 2749ft/838m, Tel: 701-275-6264, Nearest town: Gascoyne. GPS: 46.126946, -103.091297

169 • D1 | Reeder City Park

Total sites: 10, RV sites: 10, Elec sites: 10, Water at site, Flush toilet, Free showers, RV dump, Tent & RV camping: Fee unk, 10 Full hookup, Elev: 2825ft/861m, Tel: 701-853-2664, Nearest town: Reeder. GPS: 46.106357, -102.940477

170 • D2 | Carson RV Site

Total sites: 2, RV sites: 2, Elec sites: 2, Water at site, No toilets, No showers, RV dump, No tents/RVs: Fee unk, 2 Full hookup, Elev: 2300ft/701m, Tel: 701-622-3395, Nearest town: Carson. GPS: 46.417285, -101.566491

171 • D2 | Haynes City Park CG

Dispersed sites, No water, No toilets, Tent & RV camping: Fee unk, Elev: 2536ft/773m, Tel: 701-567-2218, Nearest town: Haynes. GPS: 45.974186, -102.471107

172 • D2 | Lions and Elgin Parkboard City CG

Total sites: 14, RV sites: 7, Elec sites: 7, No toilets, No showers, RV dump, Tent & RV camping: Free, Open all year, Elev: 2336ft/712m, Tel: 701-584-3045, Nearest town: Elgin. GPS: 46.402140, -101.837068

173 • D2 | Mirror Lake City Park

Total sites: 26, RV sites: 16, Elec sites: 16, Water at site, Flush toilet, Free showers, Tent & RV camping: $15, Elev: 2667ft/813m, Tel: 701-567-2916, Nearest town: Hettinger. GPS: 45.997434, -102.637642

174 • D2 | New Leipzig City Park

Total sites: 14, RV sites: 14, Elec sites: 14, Water at site, No toilets, No showers, RV dump, Tent & RV camping: $10, 14 Full hookup, Elev: 2349ft/716m, Tel: 701-584-2278, Nearest town: New Leipzig. GPS: 46.372413, -101.940006

175 • D2 | Westside Trailer Park

Total sites: 9, RV sites: 9, Elec sites: 9, Central water, No toilets, No showers, RV dump, No tents/RVs: $30, 9 Full hookup, Elev: 2391ft/729m, Tel: 701-824-3360, Nearest town: Mott. GPS: 46.370638, -102.334628

176 • D3 | Hague City Park

Total sites: 4, RV sites: 4, Elec sites: 4, Water at site, Flush toilet, Free showers, RV dump, Tent & RV camping: Fee unk, 4 Full hookup, Elev: 1896ft/578m, Tel: 701-336-7529, Nearest town: Hague. GPS: 46.028917, -99.999185

177 • D3 | Seeman Park

Total sites: 10, RV sites: 10, Elec sites: 10, Central water, Flush toilet, Free showers, No RV dump, Tent & RV camping: $20, Reservations not accepted, Elev: 1716ft/523m, Tel: 701-254-4985, Nearest town: Linton. GPS: 46.249637, -100.213376

178 • D3 | Welk City Park

Total sites: 8, RV sites: 8, Elec sites: 8, Water at site, Flush toilet, RV dump, Tent & RV camping: $15, 8 Full hookup, Elev: 1818ft/554m, Tel: 701-336-7712, Nearest town: Strasburg. GPS: 46.135376, -100.167866

179 • D3 | Wishek City Park

Total sites: 8, RV sites: 8, Elec sites: 8, Central water, Flush toilet, Free showers, No RV dump, Tent & RV camping: Fee unk, Reservations not accepted, Elev: 2033ft/620m, Tel: 701-452-2350, Nearest town: Wishek. GPS: 46.254037, -99.555627

180 • D3 | Zeeland City Park

Dispersed sites, No water, No toilets, Tent & RV camping: Fee unk, Elev: 2014ft/614m, Tel: 701-423-5512, Nearest town: Zeeland. GPS: 45.968088, -99.828971

181 • D4 | Ashley RV Park

Total sites: 9, RV sites: 9, Elec sites: 9, Water at site, RV dump, Tent & RV camping: Fee unk, 9 Full hookup, Elev: 2005ft/611m, Tel: 701-288-3186, Nearest town: Ashley. GPS: 46.033214, -99.377873

182 • D4 | Forbes City Park

Dispersed sites, No water, Vault/pit toilet, Tent & RV camping: Fee unk, Location uncertain, Elev: 1563ft/476m, Tel: 701-357-7321, Nearest town: Forbes. GPS: 45.943545, -98.782777

183 • D4 | Fullerton City Park

Total sites: 4, RV sites: 4, Elec sites: 4, Central water, Flush toilet, Free showers, RV dump, Tent & RV camping: Free, Elev: 1421ft/433m, Tel: 701-375-7261, Nearest town: Fullerton. GPS: 46.162271, -98.422516

184 • D4 | Green Lake RA

Total sites: 30, RV sites: 15, Elec sites: 15, Central water, Flush toilet, Free showers, Tents: $10/RVs: $15, Reservations accepted, Elev: 2005ft/611m, Tel: 701-329-0375, Nearest town: Wishek. GPS: 46.205540, -99.479730

185 • D4 | Hoskins Lake Recreation Park

Total sites: 28, RV sites: 18, Elec sites: 18, Water available, Flush toilet, Pay showers, RV dump, Tent & RV camping: $20, Elev: 1982ft/604m, Tel: 701-288-3347, Nearest town: Ashley. GPS: 46.048396, -99.442359

186 • D4 | Kulm City CG

Total sites: 10, RV sites: 10, Elec sites: 10, Flush toilet, Tent & RV camping: Fee unk, Double sites, Elev: 1972ft/601m, Tel: 701-269-3256, Nearest town: Kulm. GPS: 46.298498, -98.943833

187 • D4 | Monango City Park CG

Total sites: 4, RV sites: 4, Elec sites: 4, Vault/pit toilet, Tent & RV camping: Fee unk, Elev: 1496ft/456m, Tel: 701-349-2650, Neares town: Monango. GPS: 46.171981, -98.590318

188 • D4 | Oster City Park

Total sites: 3, RV sites: 3, Elec sites: 3, Water at site, RV dump Tent & RV camping: Fee unk, Reservations not accepted, Elev 1457ft/444m, Tel: 701-349-3252, Nearest town: Ellendale. GPS 46.008579, -98.521693

189 • D4 | Weaver Park

Total sites: 29, RV sites: 29, Elec sites: 29, Water at site, Flush toile Free showers, RV dump, No tents/RVs: $20, 29 Full hookup, Ope Apr-Oct, Elev: 1550ft/472m, Tel: 701-493-2208, Nearest town Edgeley. GPS: 46.363055, -98.711696

190 • D5 | American Legion Memorial Park

Dispersed sites, Central water, Vault/pit toilet, Tents only: Fe unk, Reservations not accepted, Elev: 1082ft/330m, Tel: 701-899 3087, Nearest town: Hankinson. GPS: 46.043616, -96.924765

191 • D5 | Barney City Park

Total sites: 2, RV sites: 2, Elec sites: 2, Central water, No toilets, N showers, No RV dump, Tent & RV camping: Free, Open all yea

Reservations not accepted, Elev: 1017ft/310m, Nearest town: Barney. GPS: 46.268355, -96.999039

192 • D5 | Chahinkapa Park

Total sites: 6, RV sites: 6, Elec sites: 6, Central water, Flush toilet, Free showers, RV dump, Tents: $20/RVs: $35, Beside zoo, Reservations accepted, Elev: 958ft/292m, Tel: 701-642-8709, Nearest town: Wahpeton. GPS: 46.273505, -96.598432

193 • D5 | Forman Lions CG

Total sites: 4, RV sites: 4, Elec sites: 4, Water at site, No toilets, No showers, RV dump, Tents: $5/RVs: $10, 4 Full hookup, Elev: 1237ft/377m, Tel: 701-724-3338, Nearest town: Forman. GPS: 46.105682, -97.633121

194 • D5 | Hankinson City Park

Total sites: 8, RV sites: 8, Elec sites: 8, Central water, Flush toilet, Tent & RV camping: $15, Reservations not accepted, Elev: 1066ft/325m, Tel: 701-242-7885, Nearest town: Hankinson. GPS: 46.064191, -96.906146

195 • D5 | Havana City Park

Total sites: 2, RV sites: 2, Elec sites: 1, Water at site, No toilets, Tent & RV camping: Fee unk, Elev: 1283ft/391m, Tel: 701-724-6373, Nearest town: Havana. GPS: 45.953276, -97.615583

196 • D5 | Kidder RA

Total sites: 8, RV sites: 8, Elec sites: 8, Water at site, Flush toilet, Free showers, RV dump, Tents: $20/RVs: $35, Reservations accepted, Elev: 955ft/291m, Tel: 701-642-2811, Nearest town: Wahpeton. GPS: 46.288391, -96.597366

197 • D5 | Lidgerwood City Park

Total sites: 6, RV sites: 6, Elec sites: 6, Water at site, No toilets, No showers, RV dump, Tent & RV camping: $15, $5 dump fee, Reservations accepted, Elev: 1096ft/334m, Tel: 701-640-8320, Nearest town: Lidgerwood. GPS: 46.075527, -97.142441

198 • D5 | Milnor City Park CG

Total sites: 8, RV sites: 8, Elec sites: 8, Central water, Flush toilet, Free showers, RV dump, Tent & RV camping: Fee unk, Elev: 1099ft/335m, Tel: 701-427-5272, Nearest town: Milnor. GPS: 46.256928, -97.451273

199 • D5 | Mooreton City Park CG

Dispersed sites, Central water, Vault/pit toilet, No showers, No RV dump, Tent & RV camping: Fee unk, Elev: 958ft/292m, Tel: 701-274-8827, Nearest town: Mooreton. GPS: 46.268561, -96.841645

200 • D5 | Rutland RV Camp

Total sites: 6, RV sites: 6, Elec sites: 6, No tents/RVs: $15, Reservations not accepted, Elev: 1226ft/374m, Tel: 701-724-3019, Nearest town: Rutland. GPS: 46.051218, -97.507474

Ohio

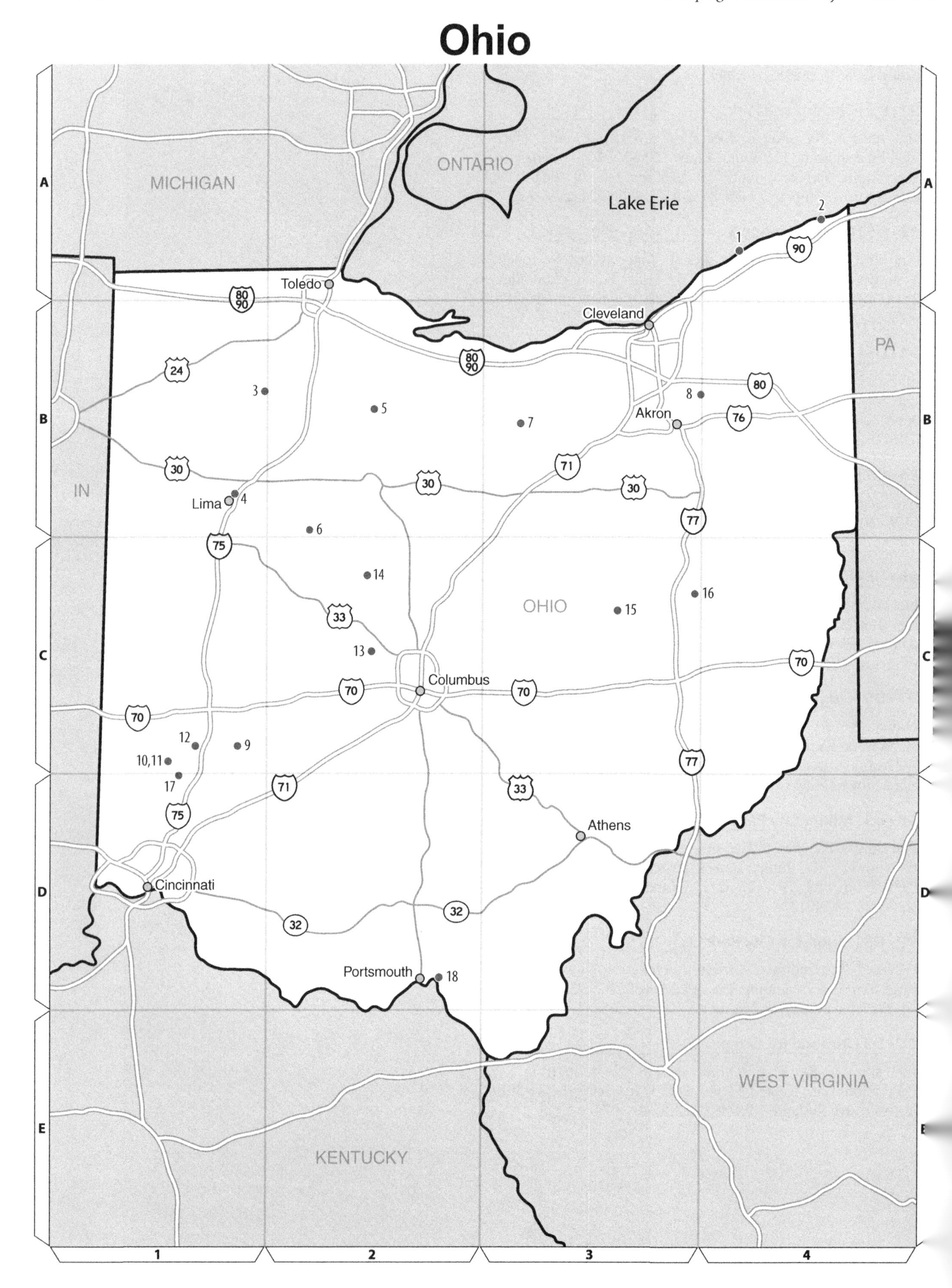

MICHIGAN
ONTARIO
Lake Erie
PA
IN
OHIO
WEST VIRGINIA
KENTUCKY
Toledo
Cleveland
Akron
Lima
Columbus
Athens
Cincinnati
Portsmouth
1
2
3
4
5
6
7
8
9
10,11
12
13
14
15
16
17
18
A
B
C
D
E

Map	ID	Map	ID
A4	1-2	C2	13-14
B1	3-4	C3	15-16
B2	5-6	D1	17
B3	7-8	D2	18
C1	9-12		

Alphabetical List of Camping Areas

1 • A4 | Perry Township Park

Total sites: 30, RV sites: 25, Elec sites: 25, Water at site, Flush toilet, Free showers, Tent & RV camping: $15-30, Elev: 614ft/187m, Tel: 440-259-5957, Nearest town: Perry. GPS: 41.795180, -81.163120

2 • A4 | Village Green CG

Total sites: 72, RV sites: 60, Elec sites: 60, Water at site, Flush toilet, Free showers, RV dump, Tents: $12-20/RVs: $25, Open Apr-Oct, Reservations accepted, Elev: 663ft/202m, Tel: 440-224-0310, Nearest town: North Kingsville. GPS: 41.920201, -80.688554

3 • B1 | Deshler Crossroads Park

Dispersed sites, No water, Vault/pit toilet, Tent & RV camping: Free, Railfan park with many trains, Reservations not accepted, Elev: 713ft/217m, Nearest town: Deshler. GPS: 41.206012, -83.902402

4 • B1 | Ottawa Metro Park

Total sites: 30, RV sites: 30, Elec sites: 30, Water at site, Flush toilet, Free showers, RV dump, Tent & RV camping: $25, $5 senior discount, Open Apr-Oct, Reservations not accepted, Elev: 876ft/267m, Tel: 419-221-1232, Nearest town: Lima. GPS: 40.753629, -84.056482

5 • B2 | Meadowbrook Park

Total sites: 220, RV sites: 220, Elec sites: 220, Flush toilet, Free showers, RV dump, Tent & RV camping: $38, 60 transient sites, Open Apr-Oct, Reservations accepted, Elev: 778ft/237m, Tel: 419-937-2242, Nearest town: Bascom. GPS: 41.130382, -83.274451

6 • B2 | Saulisberry Park (France Lake)

Total sites: 20, RV sites: 20, Tent & RV camping: Fee unk, Elev: 1004ft/306m, Nearest town: Kenton. GPS: 40.622549, -83.630947

7 • B3 | New London Reservoir Park

Total sites: 102, RV sites: 102, Elec sites: 92, Water at site, Flush toilet, Free showers, RV dump, Tents: $20/RVs: $30-35, 57 Full hookup, Open Apr-Oct, Reservations accepted, Elev: 1001ft/305m, Tel: 419-929-8609, Nearest town: New London. GPS: 41.072595, -82.422842

8 • B3 | Silver Springs CG

Total sites: 27, RV sites: 27, Elec sites: 27, Central water, Vault/pit toilet, No showers, RV dump, Tent & RV camping: $13-15, Open Apr-Oct, Reservations required, Elev: 1106ft/337m, Tel: 330-689-5100, Nearest town: Stow. GPS: 41.193868, -81.405657

9 • C1 | Beaver Creek Community Park

Total sites: 6, RV sites: 0, Central water, Flush toilet, No showers, No RV dump, Tents only: $10, Reservations required, Elev: 798ft/243m, Nearest town: Beaver Creek. GPS: 39.711146, -84.028222

10 • C1 | Germantown Metropark - Oak Ridge TC

Total sites: 3, RV sites: 0, No water, Vault/pit toilet, Tents only: $3-5, Hike-in, Open all year, Reservations accepted, Elev: 880ft/268m, Tel: 937-275-7275, Nearest town: Germantown. GPS: 39.637876, -84.426498

11 • C1 | Germantown Metropark - Old Mill

Dispersed sites, No water, Vault/pit toilet, Tents only: $18-35, Walk-to sites, Open all year, Reservations accepted, Elev: 809ft/247m, Tel: 937-275-7275, Nearest town: Germantown. GPS: 39.640046, -84.399342

12 • C1 | Possum Creek Metropark

Total sites: 5, RV sites: 0, Central water, Flush toilet, Tents only: $15-28, Open all year, Reservations accepted, Elev: 810ft/247m, Tel: 937-275-7275, Nearest town: Dayton. GPS: 39.706125, -84.268176

13 • C2 | Pastime Park

Total sites: 40, RV sites: 40, Elec sites: 40, Water at site, Flush toilet, Free showers, RV dump, Tent & RV camping: $25, $3 senior discount, Open Apr-Oct, Reservations accepted, Elev: 928ft/283m, Tel: 614-873-3527, Nearest town: Plain City. GPS: 40.115524, -83.271598

14 • C2 | Richwood Park

Total sites: 4, RV sites: 4, No tents/RVs: $10, Parking lot, Reservations not accepted, Elev: 949ft/289m, Nearest town: Richwood. GPS: 40.434261, -83.301435

15 • C3 | Coshocton Lake Park

Total sites: 69, RV sites: 69, Elec sites: 69, Central water, Flush toilet, Free showers, RV dump, Tents: $20/RVs: $26, Elev: 738ft/225m, Tel: 740-622-7528, Nearest town: Coshocton. GPS: 40.287927, -81.878117

16 • C3 | Gnadenhutten Primitive Camping

Dispersed sites, No water, Tent & RV camping: $5, Stay limit: 2 days, Reservations not accepted, Elev: 822ft/251m, Nearest town: Gnadenhutten. GPS: 40.356409, -81.438244

17 • D1 | Twin Creek Metropark - Pine Ridge TC

Total sites: 3, No water, Vault/pit toilet, Tents only: $3-5, Hike-in, Open all year, Reservations accepted, Elev: 791ft/241m, Tel: 937-275-7275, Nearest town: Germantown. GPS: 39.583469, -84.350921

18 • D2 | Riverfront Camping Area

Total sites: 51, RV sites: 51, Elec sites: 51, Water available, Flush toilet, Free showers, Tent & RV camping: Fee unk, Elev: 558ft/170m, Tel: 740-354-8807, Nearest town: Portsmouth. GPS: 38.748139, -82.874843

Oklahoma

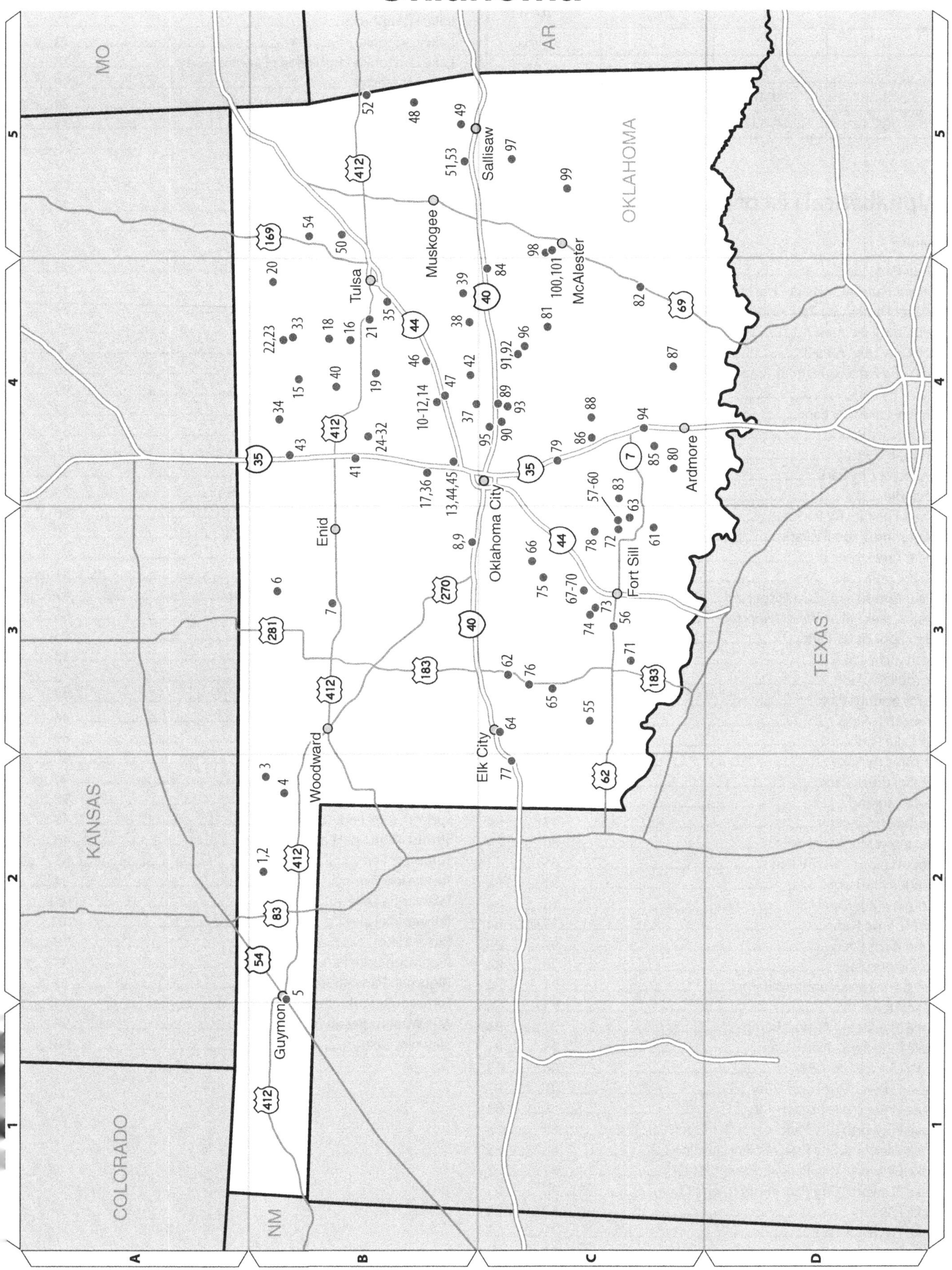
MO
AR
KANSAS
COLORADO
NM
TEXAS
OKLAHOMA
Tulsa
Muskogee
Sallisaw
McAlester
Oklahoma City
Enid
Woodward
Guymon
Elk City
Fort Sill
Ardmore

Map	ID	Map	ID
B2	1-5	C3	55-78
B3	6-9	C4	79-96
B4	10-47	C5	97-101
B5	48-54		

Alphabetical List of Camping Areas

Name	ID	Map
Adair Park	48	B5
Beaver Dunes City Park - Hackberry Bend CG	1	B2
Beaver Dunes City Park - Pioneer CG	2	B2
Bell Cow Lake Area A	10	B4
Bell Cow Lake Area B	11	B4
Bell Cow Lake Equestrian Area C	12	B4
Blair City Park	55	C3
Brushy Lake City Park	49	B5
Cache City Park	56	C3
Central SP - City	13	B4
Chandler City Park	79	C4
Chandler Lake	14	B4
Cherokee City RV Park	6	B3
Claremore Expo RV Park	50	B5
Clear Creek Lake	57	C3
Clear Creek Lake - Area D	58	C3
Clear Creek Lake - East Dispersed	59	C3
Clear Creek Lake - West Dispersed	60	C3
Cleo Springs RV Park	7	B3
Comanche Lake	61	C3
Cordell RV Park	62	C3
Doby Springs Park	3	B2
Duncan Lake	63	C3
Elk Lake Park	64	C3
Fairfax City Lake	15	B4
Feyodi Creek Park	16	B4
Gore Landing	51	B5
Guthrie Lake - City	17	B4
Healdton Municipal Lake	80	C4
Hobart Lions Club RV Park	65	C3
Holdenville Lake	81	C4
Hominy Municipal Lake	18	B4
Jim Thorpe Park	19	B4
John Wells Park	97	C5
Johnstone Park	20	B4
Keystone New Mannford Ramp	21	B4
Lake Atoka	82	C4
Lake Bluestem - Airport Ramp	22	B4
Lake Bluestem - North Dam	23	B4
Lake Chickasha - CPWD	66	C3
Lake El Reno East Loop - City	8	B3
Lake El Reno West Loop - City	9	B3
Lake Ellsworth City Park - Chandler Creek CG	67	C3
Lake Ellsworth City Park - Collier Landing CG	68	C3
Lake Ellsworth City Park - Edgewater CG	69	C3
Lake Ellsworth City Park - Fisherman's Cove	70	C3
Lake Frances	52	B5
Lake Frederick Park	71	C3
Lake Fuqua City Park	83	C4
Lake Henryetta	84	C4
Lake Humphreys	72	C3
Lake Lawtonka - East Side	73	C3
Lake Lawtonka - Robinson's Landing - City	74	C3
Lake McAlester	98	C5
Lake McMurtry - Bobcat Point	24	B4
Lake McMurtry - Bullfrog Flat	25	B4
Lake McMurtry - Catfish Cove	26	B4
Lake McMurtry - Locust Grove	27	B4
Lake McMurtry - Roadrunner Ridge	28	B4
Lake McMurtry East	29	B4
Lake McMurtry West	30	B4
Lake McMurtry Whitetail Trail North	31	B4
Lake McMurtry Whitetail Trail South	32	B4
Lake Pawhuska	33	B4
Lake Ponca	34	B4
Lake Sahoma	35	B4
Laverne Municipal Park	4	B2
Liberty Lake	36	B4
Lloyd Church Lake	99	C5
Meeker Lake	37	B4
Mountain Lake	85	C4
No Man's Land RP	5	B2
Okemah Lake	38	B4
Okmulgee and Dripping Springs RA	39	B4
Pauls Valley City Lake	86	C4
Pawnee Lake	40	B4
Pennington Creek Park	87	C4
Perry Lake	41	B4
Prague City Lake	42	B4
R.C. Longmire Lake	88	C4
Randlett Park	75	C3
Ray See Park	43	B4
Rocky Lake	76	C3
Sayre City Park	77	C3
Scissortail Park	44	B4
Shawnee Expo Center	89	C4
Shawnee Twin Lakes	90	C4
Sportsmans Lake - Cove 3	91	C4
Sportsmans Lake - Equestrian	92	C4
Spring Creek Park	45	B4
Stroud Municipal Lake	46	B4
Summers Ferry	53	B5
Sunnyside Ramp	54	B5
Talawanda Lake 1	100	C5
Talawanda Lake 2	101	C5
Taylor Lake	78	C3
Tecumseh Lake Park	93	C4
Tilghman Park/Route 66 RV Park	47	B4
Turner Falls Park	94	C4
Wes Watkins Reservoir	95	C4
Wewoka Lake	96	C4

1 • B2 | Beaver Dunes City Park - Hackberry Bend CG

Total sites: 17, RV sites: 7, Elec sites: 7, Water at site, Flush toilet, Free showers, RV dump, Tents: $12/RVs: $20-25, Also cabins, Elev: 2487ft/758m, Tel: 580-625-3373, Nearest town: Beaver. GPS: 36.840212, -100.513712

2 • B2 | Beaver Dunes City Park - Pioneer CG

Total sites: 13, RV sites: 13, Elec sites: 13, Water at site, Flush toilet, Free showers, RV dump, Tent & RV camping: $20, Elev: 2426ft/739m, Tel: 580-625-3373, Nearest town: Beaver. GPS: 36.835582, -100.515376

3 • B2 | Doby Springs Park

Total sites: 18, RV sites: 18, Elec sites: 18, Central water, No toilets, No showers, No RV dump, Tent & RV camping: $15, $10 for seniors, Dump station for gray water only, Elev: 1974ft/602m, Tel: 580-735-2654, Nearest town: Buffalo. GPS: 36.827609, -99.775616

4 • B2 | Laverne Municipal Park

Total sites: 4, RV sites: 4, Elec sites: 4, Water at site, No toilets, No showers, RV dump, Tent & RV camping: Fee unk, 4 Full hookup, Elev: 2152ft/656m, Tel: 580-921-5121, Nearest town: Laverne. GPS: 36.708623, -99.903157

5 • B2 | No Man's Land RP

Total sites: 5, RV sites: 5, Central water, Flush toilet, No showers, No RV dump, No tents/RVs: Free, Cold showers, Reservations not accepted, Elev: 3121ft/951m, Tel: 580-338-0478, Nearest town: Guymon. GPS: 36.675733, -101.467697

6 • B3 | Cherokee City RV Park

Total sites: 16, RV sites: 16, Elec sites: 16, Water at site, RV dump, No tents/RVs: $20, 16 Full hookup, Elev: 1207ft/368m, Tel: 580-596-3326, Nearest town: Cherokee. GPS: 36.757251, -98.348047

7 • B3 | Cleo Springs RV Park

Total sites: 5, RV sites: 5, Elec sites: 5, Water at site, RV dump, No tents/RVs: Fee unk, 5 Full hookup, Elev: 1286ft/392m, Tel: 580-438-2243, Nearest town: Cleo Springs. GPS: 36.407166, -98.441965

8 • B3 | Lake El Reno East Loop - City

Total sites: 20, RV sites: 20, Elec sites: 20, Water at site, Flush toilet, Free showers, RV dump, Tent & RV camping: $15, Stay limit: 7 days, Reservations not accepted, Elev: 1391ft/424m, Tel: 405-422-2139, Nearest town: El Reno. GPS: 35.518567, -97.986335

9 • B3 | Lake El Reno West Loop - City

Total sites: 32, RV sites: 32, Elec sites: 32, Water at site, Flush toilet, Free showers, RV dump, Tent & RV camping: $20, 32 Full hookup, Stay limit: 7 days, Reservations not accepted, Elev: 1382ft/421m, Tel: 405-422-2139, Nearest town: El Reno. GPS: 35.518646, -97.988986

10 • B4 | Bell Cow Lake Area A

Total sites: 12, RV sites: 12, Central water, Flush toilet, Free showers, Tent & RV camping: $10, Stay limit: 14 days, Max Length: 40ft, Elev: 928ft/283m, Tel: 405-258-1460, Nearest town: Chandler. GPS: 35.737639, -96.918394

11 • B4 | Bell Cow Lake Area B

Total sites: 16, RV sites: 16, Elec sites: 16, No water, Vault/pit toilet, No showers, Tent & RV camping: $20, Stay limit: 14 days, Max Length: 40ft, Elev: 928ft/283m, Tel: 405-258-1460, Nearest town: Chandler. GPS: 35.738082, -96.932768

12 • B4 | Bell Cow Lake Equestrian Area C

Total sites: 39, RV sites: 39, Elec sites: 39, Water at site, Flush toilet, Free showers, Tent & RV camping: $20, Stay limit: 14 days, Max Length: 40ft, Elev: 925ft/282m, Tel: 405-258-1460, Nearest town: Chandler. GPS: 35.730696, -96.938793

13 • B4 | Central SP - City

Total sites: 50, RV sites: 50, Elec sites: 50, Water at site, Flush toilet, Free showers, RV dump, Tents: $20/RVs: $20-24, 12 Full hookup, Elev: 1056ft/322m, Tel: 405-359-4630, Nearest town: Edmond. GPS: 35.647947, -97.378804

14 • B4 | Chandler Lake

Dispersed sites, No water, Tents: $10/RVs: $20, Stay limit: 14 days, Elev: 902ft/275m, Tel: 405-258-3210, Nearest town: Chandler. GPS: 35.739173, -96.910283

15 • B4 | Fairfax City Lake

Dispersed sites, Central water, Vault/pit toilet, Tent & RV camping: Fee unk, Unconfirmed, Elev: 860ft/262m, Tel: 918-642-5211, Nearest town: Fairfax. GPS: 36.605787, -96.725843

16 • B4 | Feyodi Creek Park

Total sites: 56, RV sites: 56, Elec sites: 19, Water at site, Flush toilet, Free showers, RV dump, Tents: $6/RVs: $11-15, 19 Full hookup, Open Mar-Nov, Elev: 768ft/234m, Tel: 918-358-2844, Nearest town: Cleveland. GPS: 36.279471, -96.433943

17 • B4 | Guthrie Lake - City

Total sites: 8, RV sites: 8, Elec sites: 8, Central water, Tent & RV camping: Fee unk, Open Apr-Sep, Reservations not accepted, Elev: 1001ft/305m, Tel: 405-282-3535, Nearest town: Guthrie. GPS: 35.816351, -97.442727

18 • B4 | Hominy Municipal Lake

Total sites: 100, RV sites: 100, Elec sites: 100, Central water, No toilets, No showers, RV dump, Tents: Free/RVs: $15, 50% for over 65, Check-in at Police Station, Mostly seasonal, Stay limit: 14 days, Elev: 866ft/264m, Tel: 918-885-4545, Nearest town: Hominy. GPS: 36.405667, -96.425636

19 • B4 | Jim Thorpe Park

Total sites: 4, RV sites: 4, Elec sites: 4, Water at site, No toilets, No showers, No RV dump, Tent & RV camping: Fee unk, Elev: 942ft/287m, Tel: 918-387-2405, Nearest town: Yale. GPS: 36.118411, -96.686954

20 • B4 | Johnstone Park

Total sites: 6, RV sites: 6, Elec sites: 6, No water, No toilets, No tents/RVs: $3, Elev: 672ft/205m, Tel: 918-338-4226, Nearest town: Bartlesville. GPS: 36.755689, -95.973285

21 • B4 | Keystone New Mannford Ramp

Total sites: 47, RV sites: 44, Elec sites: 44, Water at site, Flush toilet, Free showers, RV dump, Tents: $14/RVs: $22-30, Full hookup sites, Open Apr-Oct, Elev: 742ft/226m, Tel: 918-865-2621, Nearest town: Mannford. GPS: 36.158578, -96.285711

22 • B4 | Lake Bluestem - Airport Ramp

Total sites: 111, RV sites: 111, Elec sites: 111, Central water, Tents: $5/RVs: $15, Mostly seasonal, Open all year, Elev: 906ft/276m, Tel: 918-287-4545, Nearest town: Pawhuska. GPS: 36.698905, -96.417683

23 • B4 | Lake Bluestem - North Dam

Total sites: 50, RV sites: 40, Elec sites: 40, Central water, Tents: $5/RVs: $15, Mostly seasonal, Open all year, Elev: 909ft/277m, Tel: 918-287-4545, Nearest town: Pawhuska. GPS: 36.698686, -96.396601

24 • B4 | Lake McMurtry - Bobcat Point

Dispersed sites, No water, No toilets, Tents only: $15, Open all year, Reservations accepted, Elev: 974ft/297m, Tel: 405-747-8085, Nearest town: Stillwater. GPS: 36.178402, -97.192826

25 • B4 | Lake McMurtry - Bullfrog Flat

Dispersed sites, No water, No toilets, Tents only: $15, Open all year, Reservations accepted, Elev: 978ft/298m, Tel: 405-747-8085, Nearest town: Stillwater. GPS: 36.178861, -97.193201

26 • B4 | Lake McMurtry - Catfish Cove

Dispersed sites, No water, No toilets, Tents only: $15, Open all year, Reservations accepted, Elev: 980ft/299m, Tel: 405-747-8085, Nearest town: Stillwater. GPS: 36.163656, -97.190961

27 • B4 | Lake McMurtry - Locust Grove

Dispersed sites, No water, No toilets, Tents only: $15, Open all year, Reservations accepted, Elev: 969ft/295m, Tel: 405-747-8085, Nearest town: Stillwater. GPS: 36.179395, -97.193527

28 • B4 | Lake McMurtry - Roadrunner Ridge

Dispersed sites, No water, No toilets, Tents only: $15, Open all year, Reservations accepted, Elev: 969ft/295m, Tel: 405-747-8085, Nearest town: Stillwater. GPS: 36.179774, -97.193906

29 • B4 | Lake McMurtry East

Total sites: 23, RV sites: 10, Elec sites: 10, Water at site, Flush toilet, RV dump, Tents: $10/RVs: $25, Open all year, Reservations accepted, Elev: 997ft/304m, Tel: 405-747-8085, Nearest town: Stillwater. GPS: 36.182779, -97.176983

30 • B4 | Lake McMurtry West

Total sites: 23, RV sites: 14, Elec sites: 14, Water at site, Flush toilet, Free showers, RV dump, Tents: $10/RVs: $25, Open all year, Reservations accepted, Elev: 1017ft/310m, Tel: 405-747-8085, Nearest town: Stillwater. GPS: 36.170331, -97.188016

31 • B4 | Lake McMurtry Whitetail Trail North

Dispersed sites, No water, No toilets, Tents only: $15, Open all year, Reservations accepted, Elev: 970ft/296m, Tel: 405-747-8085, Nearest town: Stillwater. GPS: 36.167752, -97.190777

32 • B4 | Lake McMurtry Whitetail Trail South

Dispersed sites, No water, No toilets, Tents only: $15, Open all year, Reservations accepted, Elev: 968ft/295m, Tel: 405-747-8085, Nearest town: Stillwater. GPS: 36.166306, -97.189426

33 • B4 | Lake Pawhuska

Dispersed sites, No water, No toilets, Tent & RV camping: Fee unk, Elev: 965ft/294m, Tel: 918-287-3040, Nearest town: Pawhuska. GPS: 36.645218, -96.391681

34 • B4 | Lake Ponca

Total sites: 12, RV sites: 12, Elec sites: 12, Central water, Flush toilet, Free showers, RV dump, Tents: $8/RVs: $12, 5-day limit, Open Feb-Oct, Reservations not accepted, Elev: 1081ft/329m, Tel: 580-767-0430, Nearest town: Ponca City. GPS: 36.737611, -97.027198

35 • B4 | Lake Sahoma

Total sites: 10, RV sites: 10, Elec sites: 10, Central water, Flush toilet, Tents: $6/RVs: $12, Elev: 751ft/229m, Tel: 918-227-1534, Nearest town: Sapulpa. GPS: 36.036379, -96.151926

36 • B4 | Liberty Lake

Total sites: 8, RV sites: 8, Elec sites: 8, Central water, Vault/pit toilet, No showers, No RV dump, Tent & RV camping: Fee unk, Stay limit: 7 days, Generator hours: 0600-2200, Open all year, Elev: 1037ft/316m, Tel: 405-282-8400, Nearest town: Guthrie. GPS: 35.802271, -97.462757

37 • B4 | Meeker Lake

Dispersed sites, Tent & RV camping: Fee unk, Unconfirmed, Elev: 922ft/281m, Tel: 405-279-3321, Nearest town: Meeker. GPS: 35.493144, -96.936616

38 • B4 | Okemah Lake

Total sites: 25, RV sites: 18, Elec sites: 18, Water at site, Flush toilet Free showers, RV dump, Tents: $11/RVs: $21, Senior discount Open all year, Reservations accepted, Elev: 817ft/249m, Tel: 918-623-1050, Nearest town: Okemah. GPS: 35.521214, -96.320261

39 • B4 | Okmulgee and Dripping Springs RA

Total sites: 93, RV sites: 76, Elec sites: 76, Water at site, Flush toilet Free showers, RV dump, Tents: $12/RVs: $16-20, Open all year Elev: 768ft/234m, Tel: 918-756-5971, Nearest town: Okmulgee GPS: 35.564597, -96.104082

40 • B4 | Pawnee Lake

Total sites: 20, RV sites: 5, Elec sites: 5, Water at site, Flush toilet Tents: $7/RVs: $11-15, Senior/disabled discount: $1, Elev: 886ft 270m, Tel: 918-762-3166, Nearest town: Pawnee. GPS: 36.370967 -96.797401

41 • B4 | Perry Lake

Total sites: 10, RV sites: 10, Elec sites: 10, Water at site, No toilets No showers, RV dump, Tents: $5/RVs: $25, 10 Full hookup Elev: 1108ft/338m, Tel: 580-572-9465, Nearest town: Perry. GPS 36.256715, -97.337961

42 • B4 | Prague City Lake

Total sites: 12, RV sites: 8, Elec sites: 8, Water at site, Flush toilet, Free showers, RV dump, Tents: $6/RVs: $15, Reservations accepted, Elev: 886ft/270m, Tel: 405-567-2805, Nearest town: Prague. GPS: 35.522316, -96.723623

43 • B4 | Ray See Park

Dispersed sites, Central water, No toilets, No showers, RV dump, Tent & RV camping: Free, Unconfirmed, Get permit at police station, Elev: 967ft/295m, Nearest town: Tonkawa. GPS: 36.673975, -97.310335

44 • B4 | Scissortail Park

Total sites: 38, RV sites: 20, Elec sites: 20, Central water, Flush toilet, Free showers, RV dump, Tent & RV camping: $15-19, Elev: 1063ft/324m, Tel: 405-359-4570, Nearest town: Edmond. GPS: 35.631296, -97.397318

45 • B4 | Spring Creek Park

Total sites: 20, RV sites: 20, Elec sites: 20, Central water, Flush toilet, Free showers, Tents: $15-20/RVs: $15-25, Open all year, Elev: 1047ft/319m, Tel: 405-359-4570, Nearest town: Edmond. GPS: 35.638229, -97.383681

46 • B4 | Stroud Municipal Lake

Total sites: 76, RV sites: 76, Elec sites: 26, Water at site, Flush toilet, Free showers, RV dump, Tents: $8/RVs: $18, Over 55/disabled: $15, Stay limit: 14 days, Generator hours: 0600-2200, Reservations not accepted, Elev: 860ft/262m, Tel: 918-968-3890, Nearest town: Stroud. GPS: 35.799301, -96.605745

47 • B4 | Tilghman Park/Route 66 RV Park

Total sites: 40, RV sites: 40, Elec sites: 40, Water at site, Flush toilet, RV dump, Tent & RV camping: $15, Elev: 843ft/257m, Nearest town: Chandler. GPS: 35.701689, -96.887064

48 • B5 | Adair Park

Total sites: 27, RV sites: 27, Elec sites: 7, Water at site, Flush toilet, Free showers, Tent & RV camping: Fee unk, Elev: 1105ft/337m, Nearest town: Stillwell. GPS: 35.833354, -94.627782

49 • B5 | Brushy Lake City Park

Total sites: 23, RV sites: 23, Elec sites: 23, Water at site, Flush toilet, Free showers, Tent & RV camping: $20, Nov-Feb: $15, Stay limit: 14-21 days, Reservations not accepted, Elev: 715ft/218m, Tel: 918-775-6507, Nearest town: Sallisaw. GPS: 35.542236, -94.817627

50 • B5 | Claremore Expo RV Park

Total sites: 44, RV sites: 44, Elec sites: 44, Water at site, Flush toilet, Free showers, RV dump, No tents/RVs: $12-37, Near RR, Reservations not accepted, Elev: 646ft/197m, Tel: 918-342-5357, Nearest town: Claremore. GPS: 36.315449, -95.630515

51 • B5 | Gore Landing

Total sites: 24, RV sites: 24, Elec sites: 24, Water at site, Vault/pit toilet, No showers, RV dump, Tent & RV camping: $15, 1/2 price with Golden Age Pass, Open all year, Elev: 499ft/152m, Tel: 918-489-2636, Nearest town: Gore. GPS: 35.524141, -95.095819

52 • B5 | Lake Frances

Dispersed sites, No toilets, Tent & RV camping: Free, Elev: 922ft/281m, Nearest town: Siloam Springs. GPS: 36.129569, -94.564398

53 • B5 | Summers Ferry

Total sites: 10, RV sites: 10, Central water, Vault/pit toilet, Tent & RV camping: $8, 1/2 price with Golden Age Pass, Open all year, Reservations not accepted, Elev: 508ft/155m, Tel: 918-489-2636, Nearest town: Gore. GPS: 35.523464, -95.122316

54 • B5 | Sunnyside Ramp

Total sites: 12, RV sites: 12, No water, Vault/pit toilet, Tent & RV camping: Fee unk, Elev: 653ft/199m, Tel: 918-443-2250, Nearest town: Talala. GPS: 36.524258, -95.633718

55 • C3 | Blair City Park

Total sites: 5, RV sites: 5, Elec sites: 5, Water at site, No tents/RVs: $15, 5 Full hookup, Reservations not accepted, Elev: 1476ft/450m, Tel: 580-563-2406, Nearest town: Blair. GPS: 34.781344, -99.329115

56 • C3 | Cache City Park

Dispersed sites, No tents/RVs: $20-30, Unconfirmed, Elev: 1250ft/381m, Tel: 580-429-3354, Nearest town: Cache. GPS: 34.623536, -98.633904

57 • C3 | Clear Creek Lake

Dispersed sites, Central water, Flush toilet, Tent & RV camping: Fee unk, Elev: 1164ft/355m, Tel: 580-255-9538, Nearest town: Duncan. GPS: 34.584869, -97.846083

58 • C3 | Clear Creek Lake - Area D

Total sites: 30, RV sites: 30, Elec sites: 30, Central water, Flush toilet, Free showers, Tent & RV camping: Fee unk, Elev: 1184ft/361m, Tel: 580-255-9538, Nearest town: Duncan. GPS: 34.595154, -97.837617

59 • C3 | Clear Creek Lake - East Dispersed

Dispersed sites, No water, Tent & RV camping: Fee unk, Elev: 1172ft/357m, Tel: 580-255-9538, Nearest town: Duncan. GPS: 34.603408, -97.843221

60 • C3 | Clear Creek Lake - West Dispersed

Dispersed sites, No water, Tent & RV camping: Fee unk, Elev: 1159ft/353m, Tel: 580-255-9538, Nearest town: Duncan. GPS: 34.595869, -97.847585

61 • C3 | Comanche Lake

Total sites: 13, RV sites: 13, Elec sites: 13, Central water, Tent & RV camping: Fee unk, Elev: 1063ft/324m, Tel: 580-439-6308, Nearest town: Comanche. GPS: 34.368838, -97.894274

62 • C3 | Cordell RV Park

Total sites: 5, RV sites: 5, Elec sites: 5, Central water, Flush toilet, Free showers, RV dump, No tents/RVs: $10, Stay limit: 3 days, Open all year, Elev: 1558ft/475m, Tel: 580-832-3825, Nearest town: Cordell. GPS: 35.297487, -98.987002

63 • C3 | Duncan Lake

Total sites: 44, RV sites: 44, Elec sites: 44, Central water, Flush toilet, Free showers, RV dump, Tents: $12/RVs: $16-20, Elev: 1142ft/348m, Tel: 580-255-9397, Nearest town: Duncan. GPS: 34.523864, -97.813039

64 • C3 | Elk Lake Park

Total sites: 5, RV sites: 5, Elec sites: 5, Water at site, Tent & RV camping: $15, No water in winter, Open all year, Elev: 1926ft/587m, Tel: 580-225-3990, Nearest town: Elk City. GPS: 35.366325, -99.415865

65 • C3 | Hobart Lions Club RV Park

Total sites: 9, RV sites: 9, Elec sites: 9, Water at site, RV dump, No tents/RVs: $10, 1 Full hookup, Stay limit: 7 days, Open all year, Max Length: 40ft, Elev: 1558ft/475m, Tel: 580-726-2553, Nearest town: Hobart. GPS: 35.022163, -99.093347

66 • C3 | Lake Chickasha - CPWD

Total sites: 50, RV sites: 50, Elec sites: 50, Water at site, Flush toilet, Free showers, RV dump, Tents: $10/RVs: $10-15, Stay limit: 10 days, Reservations not accepted, Elev: 1204ft/367m, Tel: 405-412-6545, Nearest town: Verden. GPS: 35.147358, -98.128864

67 • C3 | Lake Ellsworth City Park - Chandler Creek CG

Dispersed sites, No water, No toilets, Tents: $8/RVs: $17-20, Stay limit: 14 days, Generator hours: 0700-2300, Elev: 1250ft/381m, Tel: 580-529-2663, Nearest town: Elgin. GPS: 34.806588, -98.385231

68 • C3 | Lake Ellsworth City Park - Collier Landing CG

Total sites: 9, RV sites: 9, No toilets, Tents: $8/RVs: $17-20, Stay limit: 14 days, Generator hours: 0700-2300, Elev: 1243ft/379m, Tel: 580-529-2663, Nearest town: Elgin. GPS: 34.832992, -98.341797

69 • C3 | Lake Ellsworth City Park - Edgewater CG

Total sites: 4, RV sites: 4, No toilets, Tents: $8/RVs: $17-20, Stay limit: 14 days, Generator hours: 0700-2300, Elev: 1250ft/381m, Tel: 580-529-2663, Nearest town: Elgin. GPS: 34.826066, -98.370673

70 • C3 | Lake Ellsworth City Park - Fisherman's Cove

Total sites: 42, RV sites: 42, Central water, RV dump, Tents: $8/RVs: $17-20, Stay limit: 14 days, Generator hours: 0700-2300, Open all year, Elev: 1253ft/382m, Tel: 580-529-2663, Nearest town: Elgin. GPS: 34.809898, -98.345026

71 • C3 | Lake Frederick Park

Total sites: 50, RV sites: 50, Elec sites: 30, Water at site, Flush toilet, Free showers, RV dump, Tents: $5/RVs: $15, Seniors $9, Open all year, Max Length: 40ft, Elev: 1224ft/373m, Tel: 580-397-7551, Nearest town: Manitou. GPS: 34.516256, -98.890031

72 • C3 | Lake Humphreys

Total sites: 44, RV sites: 44, Elec sites: 44, RV dump, Tent & RV camping: Fee unk, Elev: 1220ft/372m, Tel: 580-658-6268, Nearest town: Duncan. GPS: 34.597298, -97.891736

73 • C3 | Lake Lawtonka - East Side

Total sites: 45, RV sites: 45, Elec sites: 45, Central water, Flush toilet, Free showers, RV dump, Tents: $7/RVs: $17-20, Open all year, Reservations not accepted, Elev: 1381ft/421m, Tel: 580-529-2663, Nearest town: Lawton. GPS: 34.750579, -98.487321

74 • C3 | Lake Lawtonka - Robinson's Landing - City

Total sites: 28, RV sites: 28, Elec sites: 28, Water at site, Flush toilet, Free showers, RV dump, Tent & RV camping: $17-20, Open all year, Reservations not accepted, Elev: 1384ft/422m, Tel: 580-529-2663, Nearest town: Lawton. GPS: 34.777032, -98.533165

75 • C3 | Randlett Park

Total sites: 26, RV sites: 26, Elec sites: 26, Water available, Flush toilet, Free showers, RV dump, Tent & RV camping: $10, Elev: 1207ft/368m, Tel: 405-247-6484, Nearest town: Anadarko. GPS: 35.073261, -98.261041

76 • C3 | Rocky Lake

Dispersed sites, No water, Vault/pit toilet, Tent & RV camping: Fee unk, Unconfirmed, Elev: 1663ft/507m, Nearest town: Rocky. GPS: 35.165938, -99.070294

77 • C3 | Sayre City Park

Total sites: 80, RV sites: 80, Elec sites: 80, Central water, Flush toilet, Free showers, RV dump, Tent & RV camping: $12, Open all year, Elev: 1818ft/554m, Tel: 580-928-2260, Nearest town: Sayre. GPS: 35.273229, -99.645306

78 • C3 | Taylor Lake

Total sites: 30, RV sites: 20, Elec sites: 10, Water at site, Flush toilet, Free showers, RV dump, Tent & RV camping: Fee unk, 2 Full hookup, Elev: 1289ft/393m, Tel: 580-658-5401, Nearest town: Marlow. GPS: 34.753398, -97.927575

79 • C4 | Chandler City Park

Total sites: 22, RV sites: 22, Elec sites: 22, Water at site, RV dump, Tent & RV camping: $22, Elev: 1102ft/336m, Tel: 405-527-5114, Nearest town: Purcell. GPS: 34.986845, -97.376527

80 • C4 | Healdton Municipal Lake

Total sites: 19, RV sites: 19, Elec sites: 19, Water at site, Flush toilet, Free showers, RV dump, Tent & RV camping: Fee unk, 19 Full hookup, Open all year, Elev: 906ft/276m, Tel: 580-229-1100, Nearest town: Healdton. GPS: 34.238761, -97.453356

81 • C4 | Holdenville Lake

Total sites: 33, RV sites: 33, Elec sites: 33, Water at site, Flush toilet, RV dump, Tents: $5-10/RVs: $20, Numerous dispersed sites around lake, Elev: 809ft/247m, Tel: 405-712-0976, Nearest town: Holdenville. GPS: 35.035399, -96.367927

82 • C4 | Lake Atoka

Dispersed sites, No water, Vault/pit toilet, Tent & RV camping: Fee unk, Generators allowed/hours unknown, Elev: 594ft/181m, Tel: 580-889-3250, Nearest town: Atoka. GPS: 34.433208, -96.09289

83 • C4 | Lake Fuqua City Park

Total sites: 54, RV sites: 54, Elec sites: 54, Water at site, Flush toile

Free showers, RV dump, Tent & RV camping: Fee unk, Elev: 1147ft/350m, Tel: 580-255-9538, Nearest town: Duncan. GPS: 34.594873, -97.676215

84 • C4 | Lake Henryetta

Dispersed sites, No water, Vault/pit toilet, Tent & RV camping: Fee unk, Pay at City Hall, Elev: 682ft/208m, Tel: 918-652-3348, Nearest town: Henryetta. GPS: 35.412735, -95.922863

85 • C4 | Mountain Lake

Total sites: 7, RV sites: 4, Elec sites: 4, Vault/pit toilet, Tent & RV camping: Fee unk, Reservations not accepted, Elev: 1043ft/318m, Tel: 580-561-6145, Nearest town: Ardmore. GPS: 34.366465, -97.286205

86 • C4 | Pauls Valley City Lake

Total sites: 28, RV sites: 22, Elec sites: 22, Water at site, Flush toilet, Free showers, RV dump, Tents: $12/RVs: $12-15, Full hookup sites, Stay limit: 14 days, Generator hours: 0600-2200, Reservations not accepted, Elev: 935ft/285m, Tel: 405-238-5134, Nearest town: Pauls Valley. GPS: 34.770498, -97.207381

87 • C4 | Pennington Creek Park

Total sites: 24, RV sites: 19, Elec sites: 19, Water at site, Flush toilet, Free showers, RV dump, Tents: $5/RVs: $20, 15 Full hookup - may be no elec due to flooding, Open all year, Max Length: 40+ft, Reservations not accepted, Elev: 656ft/200m, Tel: 580-371-2369, Nearest town: Tishomingo. GPS: 34.233254, -96.682634

88 • C4 | R.C. Longmire Lake

Total sites: 20, RV sites: 12, Elec sites: 12, Central water, Flush toilet, Free showers, RV dump, Tents: $5/RVs: $10, Elev: 1030ft/314m, Tel: 405-238-2007, Nearest town: Pauls Valley. GPS: 34.758978, -97.055308

89 • C4 | Shawnee Expo Center

Total sites: 740, RV sites: 740, Elec sites: 740, Water at site, Flush toilet, Free showers, RV dump, No tents/RVs: Fee unk, 366 Full hookup, Open all year, Elev: 1056ft/322m, Tel: 405-275-7020, Nearest town: Shawnee. GPS: 35.352979, -96.950251

90 • C4 | Shawnee Twin Lakes

Total sites: 15, RV sites: 15, Central water, Flush toilet, Tent & RV camping: $5, Open Mar-Nov, Reservations not accepted, Elev: 1093ft/333m, Tel: 405-878-1529, Nearest town: Shawnee. GPS: 35.333463, -97.069808

91 • C4 | Sportsmans Lake - Cove 3

Total sites: 45, RV sites: 30, Elec sites: 30, Water at site, Flush toilet, Free showers, RV dump, Tents: $8/RVs: $15-20, Full hookup sites, Open all year, Reservations not accepted, Elev: 899ft/274m, Tel: 405-257-3600, Nearest town: Seminole. GPS: 35.209471, -96.551723

92 • C4 | Sportsmans Lake - Equestrian

Total sites: 12, RV sites: 12, Elec sites: 12, Water at site, Flush toilet, Free showers, RV dump, Tents: $15/RVs: $15-20, Open all year, Reservations not accepted, Elev: 938ft/286m, Tel: 405-257-3600, Nearest town: Seminole. GPS: 35.220413, -96.568767

93 • C4 | Tecumseh Lake Park

Total sites: 10, RV sites: 10, Central water, Vault/pit toilet, No showers, Tent & RV camping: Fee unk, Elev: 1043ft/318m, Tel: 405-275-0022, Nearest town: Tecumseh. GPS: 35.290175, -96.957325

94 • C4 | Turner Falls Park

Total sites: 545, RV sites: 45, Elec sites: 45, Water at site, Flush toilet, Free showers, RV dump, Tents: $13/RVs: $25, Also cabins, Must purchase tickets for EVERY PERSON for EVERY DAY they occupy the park before 4:00PM, No pets, Generator hours: 0800-2200, Open all year, Reservations not accepted, Elev: 1073ft/327m, Tel: 580-369-2988, Nearest town: Davis. GPS: 34.426157, -97.150508

95 • C4 | Wes Watkins Reservoir

Total sites: 62, RV sites: 29, Elec sites: 29, Central water, Flush toilet, Free showers, RV dump, Tents: $10/RVs: $25, Elev: 1129ft/344m, Tel: 405-964-4507, Nearest town: McLoud. GPS: 35.411041, -97.113824

96 • C4 | Wewoka Lake

Total sites: 26, RV sites: 26, Elec sites: 26, Water at site, Flush toilet, Free showers, RV dump, Tents: $8/RVs: $20, Seniors: $18, Reservations accepted, Elev: 866ft/264m, Tel: 405-257-5140, Nearest town: Wewoka. GPS: 35.182787, -96.521738

97 • C5 | John Wells Park

Total sites: 15, RV sites: 15, Elec sites: 15, Tent & RV camping: $5, Elev: 659ft/201m, Tel: 918-967-2164, Nearest town: Stigler. GPS: 35.230074, -95.097618

98 • C5 | Lake McAlester

Dispersed sites, No water, Vault/pit toilet, Tents only: Fee unk, Elev: 623ft/190m, Tel: 918-423-9300, Nearest town: McAlester. GPS: 35.019533, -95.806713

99 • C5 | Lloyd Church Lake

Dispersed sites, Vault/pit toilet, Tents only: Fee unk, Reservations not accepted, Elev: 830ft/253m, Tel: 918-465-2262, Nearest town: Wilburton. GPS: 34.879079, -95.334158

100 • C5 | Talawanda Lake 1

Dispersed sites, No water, No toilets, Tent & RV camping: Fee unk, Elev: 663ft/202m, Tel: 918-423-9300, Nearest town: McAlester. GPS: 34.973968, -95.792128

101 • C5 | Talawanda Lake 2

Dispersed sites, No water, Vault/pit toilet, Tent & RV camping: Fee unk, Elev: 673ft/205m, Tel: 918-423-9300, Nearest town: McAlester. GPS: 34.978694, -95.794327

Oregon

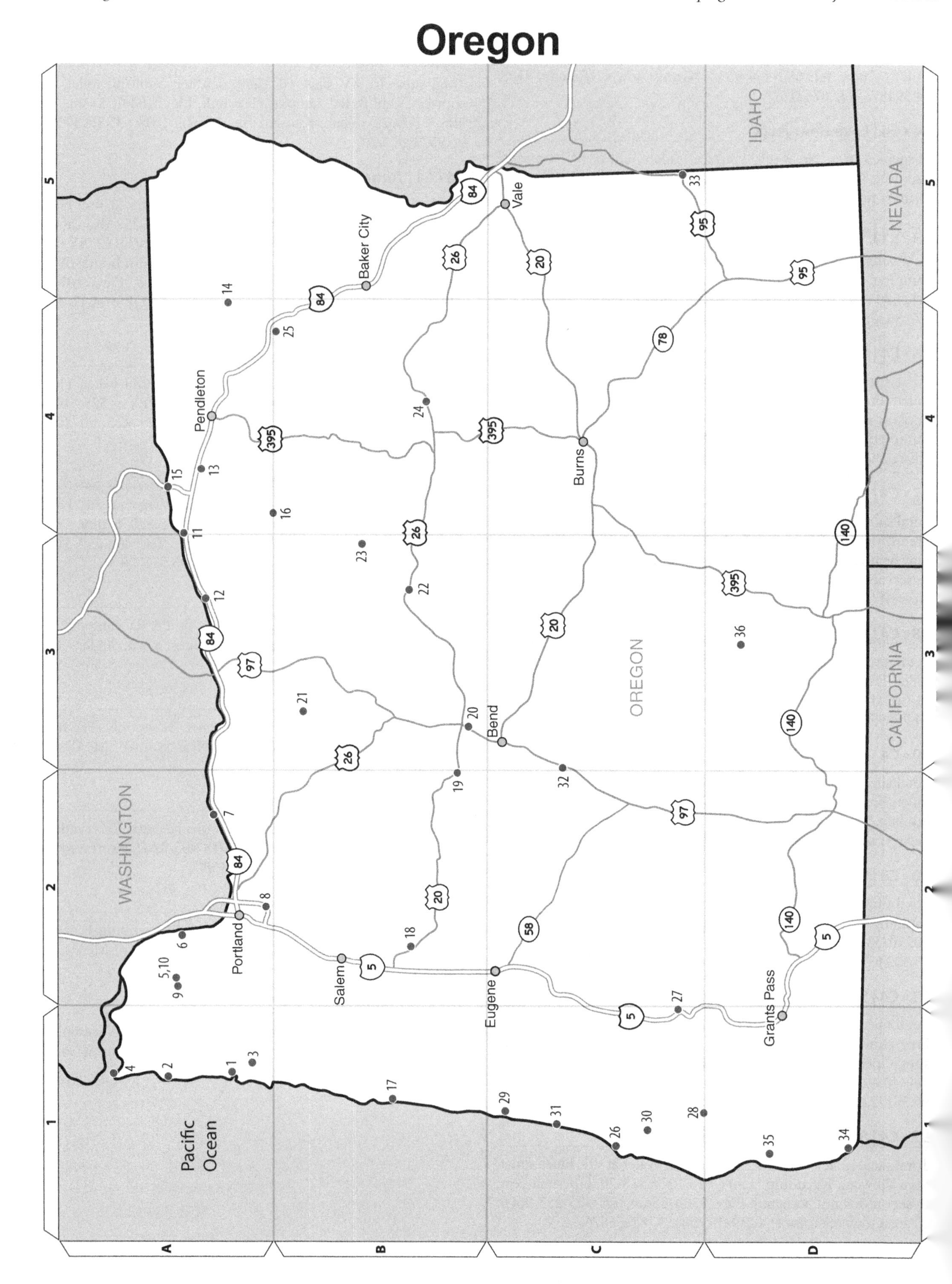
WASHINGTON
IDAHO
NEVADA
CALIFORNIA
OREGON
Pacific Ocean
Baker City
Vale
Pendleton
Burns
Bend
Portland
Salem
Eugene
Grants Pass
84
26
20
95
78
395
97
140
58
5
A
B
C
D
1
2
3
4
5
1
2
3
4
5,10
6
7
8
9
11
12
13
14
15
16
17
18
19
20
21
22
23
24
25
26
27
28
29
30
31
32
33
34
35
36

Map	ID	Map	ID
A1	1-4	B4	24-25
A2	5-10	C1	26-31
A3	11-12	C3	32
A4	13-16	C5	33
B1	17	D1	34-35
B2	18-19	D3	36
B3	20-23		

Alphabetical List of Camping Areas

1 • A1 | Al Griffin Memorial Park

Total sites: 12, RV sites: 4, Elec sites: 4, Central water, No toilets, No showers, No RV dump, Tents: $17/RVs: $30, 4 Full hookup, Open May-Oct, Max Length: 20ft, Reservations not accepted, Elev: 16ft/5m, Tel: 503-377-2288, Nearest town: Bay City. GPS: 45.526304, -123.891522

2 • A1 | Cannon Beach RV Resort

Total sites: 100, RV sites: 100, Elec sites: 100, Water at site, Flush toilet, Free showers, RV dump, No tents/RVs: $62, 100 Full hookup, $51 shoulder season/$43 winter, Concessionaire, Open all year, Max Length: 50ft, Elev: 37ft/11m, Tel: 503-436-2231, Nearest town: Cannon Beach. GPS: 45.889671, -123.955096

3 • A1 | Port of Tillamook Bay Blimp Base RV Park

Total sites: 52, RV sites: 52, Central water, Flush toilet, No RV dump, Tent & RV camping: $15, Dry-camp in parking lot, Stay limit: 14 days, Open Mar-Oct, Reservations not accepted, Elev: 16ft/5m, Tel: 503-842-7152, Nearest town: Tillamook. GPS: 45.418461, -123.820048

4 • A1 | Seafarer's City Park

Total sites: 20, RV sites: 20, Water at site, Tent & RV camping: $30, Elev: 20ft/6m, Tel: 503-861-3822, Nearest town: Hammond. GPS: 46.204912, -123.952351

5 • A2 | Anderson City Park

Total sites: 56, RV sites: 56, Elec sites: 19, Water at site, Flush toilet, Free showers, RV dump, Tents: $15/RVs: $20-30, 19 Full hookup, Open all year, Elev: 630ft/192m, Tel: 503-429-2531, Nearest town: Vernonia. GPS: 45.856241, -123.192743

6 • A2 | Bayport RV Park

Total sites: 23, RV sites: 23, Elec sites: 23, Water at site, Flush toilet, Pay showers, No RV dump, Tent & RV camping: $30, Stay limit: 14 days, Reservations accepted, Elev: 36ft/11m, Tel: 503-397-2888, Nearest town: St Helens. GPS: 45.828568, -122.839469

7 • A2 | Cascade Locks Marine Park - Port Authority

Total sites: 16, RV sites: 16, Elec sites: 12, Water at site, Flush toilet, Free showers, RV dump, Tents: $15/RVs: $20-40, 2 Full hookup, 12' clearance into park, Biker/hiker camping: $5, No water/power Nov-Apr, No fires, No generators, Open all year, Reservations accepted, Elev: 105ft/32m, Tel: 541-374-8619, Nearest town: Cascade Locks. GPS: 45.667509, -121.895826

8 • A2 | Clackamette RV Park

Total sites: 38, RV sites: 38, Elec sites: 38, Water at site, No toilets, No showers, RV dump, Tent & RV camping: $25-30, $5 dump fee, Open all year, Max Length: 40ft, Reservations not accepted, Elev: 33ft/10m, Tel: 503-496-1201, Nearest town: Oregon City. GPS: 45.371020, -122.603530

9 • A2 | Nehalem River Park

Total sites: 23, RV sites: 23, Central water, Vault/pit toilet, No showers, No RV dump, Tent & RV camping: $20, Reservable group site $00-$150, Open May-Nov, Max Length: 40ft, Reservations not accepted, Elev: 656ft/200m, Tel: 503-429-5291, Nearest town: Vernonia. GPS: 45.846805, -123.234806

10 • A2 | Vernonia Lake

Dispersed sites, Central water, Vault/pit toilet, No showers, No RV dump, Tents only: $10-15, Walk-to/group sites, Group site: $40-$75, Reservations not accepted, Elev: 643ft/196m, Tel: 503-429-2531, Nearest town: Vernonia. GPS: 45.856548, -123.176098

11 • A3 | Boardman Marina Park

Total sites: 67, RV sites: 63, Elec sites: 63, Water at site, Flush toilet, Free showers, RV dump, Tent & RV camping: $39, 63 Full hookup, Open all year, Reservations accepted, Elev: 285ft/87m, Tel: 541-481-7217, Nearest town: Arlington. GPS: 45.844499, -119.708018

12 • A3 | Port Of Arlington RV Park

Total sites: 13, RV sites: 11, Elec sites: 11, Water at site, Flush toilet, RV dump, Tents: $9/RVs: $30, 11 Full hookup, Limited services in winter, Near RR, Open all year, Max Length: 50ft, Reservations accepted, Elev: 272ft/83m, Tel: 541-454-2868, Nearest town: Arlington. GPS: 45.723237, -120.205145

13 • A4 | Fort Henrietta RV Park

Total sites: 9, RV sites: 9, Elec sites: 9, Water at site, Flush toilet, Free showers, RV dump, Tents: $20/RVs: $26, 7 Full hookup, Max Length: 80ft, Elev: 636ft/194m, Tel: 541-571-3597, Nearest town: Echo. GPS: 45.741956, -119.198099

14 • A4 | Hu-Na-Ha RV Park

Total sites: 55, RV sites: 45, Elec sites: 45, Water at site, Flush toilet, Free showers, RV dump, Tents: $20/RVs: $30-35, 45 Full hookup, 20% military discount, Open all year, Reservations accepted, Elev: 2648ft/807m, Tel: 541-786-1662, Nearest town: Elgin. GPS: 45.562610, -117.910480

15 • A4 | Umatilla Marina and RV Park

Total sites: 35, RV sites: 26, Elec sites: 26, Water at site, Flush toilet, Free showers, RV dump, Tents: $20/RVs: $34, 26 Full hookup, Dump fee $3, Open all year, Reservations accepted, Elev: 279ft/85m, Tel: 541-922-3939, Nearest town: Umatilla. GPS: 45.923921, -119.329056

16 • A4 | Willow Creek Park

Total sites: 24, RV sites: 24, Elec sites: 24, Water at site, Flush toilet, Pay showers, Tents: $6/RVs: $16-18, 9 Full hookup, Open Mar-Nov, Reservations accepted, Elev: 2151ft/656m, Tel: 541-676-5576, Nearest town: Heppner. GPS: 45.344523, -119.547892

17 • B1 | Port of Newport Marina RV Park

Total sites: 144, RV sites: 144, Elec sites: 144, Water at site, Flush toilet, Free showers, RV dump, No tents/RVs: $38-50, 144 Full hookup, Dry camping $27, High traffic surcharge $20-$50 for certain events/holidays, Nov-Apr $37-43, Generator hours: 0800-2200, Max Length: 60ft, Reservations accepted, Elev: 7ft/2m, Tel: 541-867-3321, Nearest town: Newport. GPS: 44.620697, -124.048832

18 • B2 | Gill's Landing RV Park

Total sites: 21, RV sites: 21, Elec sites: 21, Water at site, Flush toilet, Free showers, RV dump, Tent & RV camping: $35, 21 Full hookup, Seniors/veterans: $5 discount, $5 dump fee, Stay limit: 14 days, Open all year, Reservations accepted, Elev: 361ft/110m, Tel: 541-258-4917, Nearest town: Lebanon. GPS: 44.537072, -122.889286

19 • B2 | Sisters Creekside City Park

Total sites: 67, RV sites: 67, Elec sites: 25, Central water, Flush toilet, Pay showers, RV dump, Tents: $20/RVs: $20-45, 27 Full hookup, Hiker/biker sites: $5, Senior Discount: $5, RV Dump fee: $10, Firewood: $5, Open Apr-Nov, Reservations accepted, Elev: 3189ft/972m, Tel: 541-323-5218, Nearest town: Sisters. GPS: 44.287821, -121.541457

20 • B3 | Expo Center RV Park

Total sites: 115, RV sites: 105, Elec sites: 115, Water at site, Flush toilet, Free showers, RV dump, Tents: $22/RVs: $35, 105 Full hookup, Open all year, Reservations accepted, Elev: 3081ft/939m, Tel: 541-548-2711, Nearest town: Redmond. GPS: 44.233445, -121.186205

21 • B3 | Maupin City Park

Total sites: 47, RV sites: 25, Elec sites: 25, Water at site, Flush toilet, Pay showers, RV dump, Tents: $28-34/RVs: $36-42, 25 Full hookup, 3 group sites, $6 senior discount, Lower rates Nov-Apr, No open fires, Reservations accepted, Elev: 876ft/267m, Tel: 541-395-2252, Nearest town: Maupin. GPS: 45.173231, -121.073415

22 • B3 | Mitchell City Park

Total sites: 4, RV sites: 4, Elec sites: 4, No toilets, No showers, No RV dump, Tents: $12/RVs: $25, Open all year, Reservations not accepted, Elev: 2835ft/864m, Tel: 541-462-3121, Nearest town: Mitchell. GPS: 44.566889, -120.151955

23 • B3 | Spray Riverfront Park

Total sites: 8, RV sites: 8, No toilets, Tent & RV camping: $12, Reservations not accepted, Elev: 1837ft/560m, Tel: 541-468-2069, Nearest town: Spray. GPS: 44.833553, -119.791023

24 • B4 | Depot Park

Total sites: 20, RV sites: 20, Elec sites: 20, Water at site, Flush toilet, Pay showers, RV dump, Tents: $10-16/RVs: $20, 20 Full hookup, Open May-Oct, Reservations not accepted, Elev: 3527ft/1075m, Tel: 541-820-3605, Nearest town: Prairie City. GPS: 44.458096, -118.706023

25 • B4 | Morgan Lake Park

Dispersed sites, No water, Vault/pit toilet, Tent & RV camping Free, Stay limit: 3 days, Open Apr-Oct, Reservations not accepted Elev: 4171ft/1271m, Tel: 541-962-1352, Nearest town: La Grande GPS: 45.301419, -118.139267

26 • C1 | Charleston Marina RV Park

Total sites: 100, RV sites: 100, Elec sites: 100, Water at site, Flush toilet, Free showers, RV dump, No tents/RVs: $37-41, 100 Full hookup, $5 dump fee, No open fires, Open all year, Reservation accepted, Elev: 13ft/4m, Tel: 541-888-9512, Nearest town Charleston. GPS: 43.344107, -124.325697

27 • C1 | Millsite Municipal Park

Total sites: 13, RV sites: 13, Elec sites: 13, Flush toilet, Free showers RV dump, Tent & RV camping: $25, No fires, Dump fee $5, Besid RR, Elev: 607ft/185m, Tel: 541-643-0379, Nearest town: Myrtl Creek. GPS: 43.023944, -123.293364

28 • C1 | Orchard City Park

Total sites: Unk, Tent & RV camping: $10, Elev: 317ft/97m Tel: 541-439-3331, Nearest town: Powers. GPS: 42.859408, 124.051333

29 • C1 | Port Of Siuslaw CG and Marina

Total sites: 105, RV sites: 105, Elec sites: 92, Water at site, Flush toilet, Free showers, RV dump, No tents/RVs: $28-35, 66 Full hookup, Hiker-Biker tent sites, Open all year, Reservations accepted, Elev: 10ft/3m, Tel: 541-997-3040, Nearest town: Florence. GPS: 43.969136, -124.100836

30 • C1 | Sturdivant City Park

Total sites: 9, RV sites: 9, Central water, Flush toilet, No showers, No RV dump, Tent & RV camping: $10, Open all year, Max Length: 25ft, Reservations not accepted, Elev: 13ft/4m, Tel: 541-396-5131, Nearest town: Coquille. GPS: 43.175858, -124.200198

31 • C1 | Winchester Bay RV Resort

Total sites: 138, RV sites: 138, Elec sites: 138, Water at site, Flush toilet, Free showers, RV dump, No tents/RVs: $47-60, 138 Full hookup, Dry camping: $22, Winter rates: $38-$44 10/15-5/14, Open all year, Reservations accepted, Elev: 7ft/2m, Tel: 541-271-0287, Nearest town: Winchester Bay. GPS: 43.678342, -124.185639

32 • C3 | Rosland City Park

Total sites: 11, RV sites: 11, Elec sites: 1, Central water, Vault/pit toilet, Tents: $12/RVs: $15-18, Open May-Aug, Reservations not accepted, Elev: 4216ft/1285m, Tel: 541-536-2223, Nearest town: La Pine. GPS: 43.702131, -121.504886

33 • C5 | Jordan Valley City Park

Dispersed sites, Central water, No toilets, No showers, No RV dump, No tents/RVs: Fee unk, Unconfirmed, Reservations not accepted, Elev: 4401ft/1341m, Tel: 541-586-2460, Nearest town: Jordan Valley. GPS: 42.979604, -117.052863

34 • D1 | Beachfront RV Park

Total sites: 137, RV sites: 109, Elec sites: 90, Water at site, Flush toilet, Free showers, RV dump, Tents: $27/RVs: $32-51, 33 Full hookup, No tent/dry camping UFN, Lower winter rates, Stay limit: 14 days, Max Length: 40ft, Reservations accepted, Elev: 10ft/3m, Tel: 541-469-5867, Nearest town: Brookings. GPS: 42.043943, -124.266947

35 • D1 | Huntley City Park

Total sites: 70, RV sites: 70, Central water, Flush toilet, Free showers, No RV dump, Tent & RV camping: $15, Open all year, Max Length: 40ft, Elev: 89ft/27m, Tel: 541-247-9377, Nearest town: Gold Beach. GPS: 42.480141, -124.327321

36 • D3 | Paisley Airport

Dispersed sites, No water, No toilets, No tents/RVs: Fee unk, Reservations not accepted, Elev: 4393ft/1339m, Nearest town: Paisley. GPS: 42.711763, -120.560810

Pennsylvania

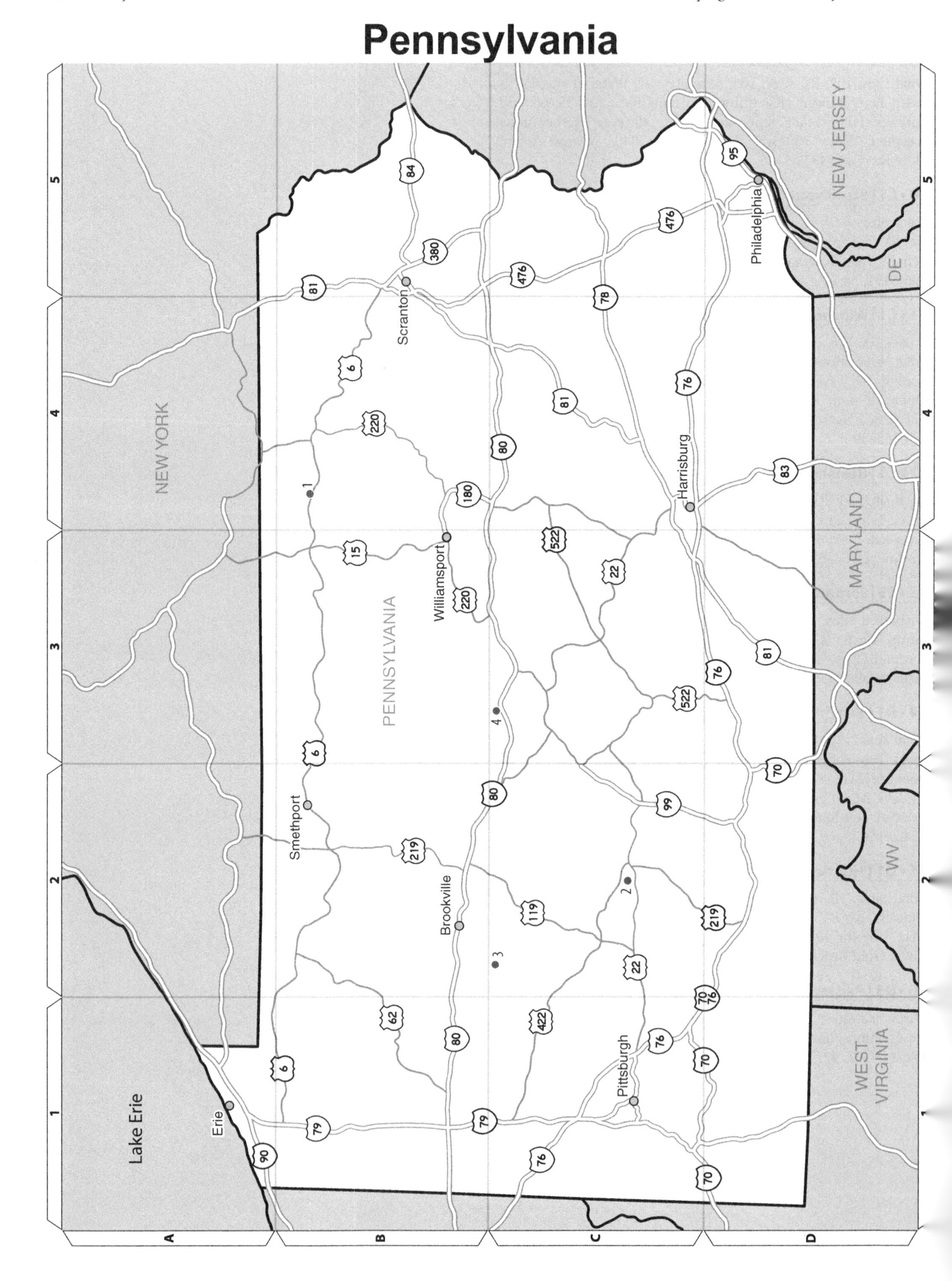

Map	ID	Map	ID
B4	1	C2	2-4

Alphabetical List of Camping Areas

1 • B4 | Alparon Community Park

Total sites: 22, RV sites: 22, Elec sites: 22, Water at site, Flush toilet, Free showers, RV dump, No tents/RVs: $27-32, 22 Full hookup, Reservations accepted, Elev: 1099ft/335m, Tel: 570-297-3648, Nearest town: Troy. GPS: 41.800844, -76.777779

2 • C2 | Nanty Glo Municipal Authority Pool and Park

Total sites: 10, RV sites: 5, Elec sites: 5, Water at site, Flush toilet, Pay showers, RV dump, Tents: $15/RVs: $25, Open May-Sep, Reservations accepted, Elev: 1870ft/570m, Tel: 814-650-4986, Nearest town: Nanty Glo. GPS: 40.478564, -78.826716

3 • C2 | Redbank Valley Municipal Park

Total sites: 79, RV sites: 79, Elec sites: 79, Water at site, Flush toilet, Free showers, RV dump, Tents: $17/RVs: $22-30, Full hookup sites, A/C surcharge $5, Dump fee $10, Open Apr-Oct, Elev: 1148ft/350m, Nearest town: Redbank. GPS: 41.015137, -79.291966

4 • C4 | Snow Shoe City Park

Total sites: 90, RV sites: 90, Elec sites: 90, Water at site, Flush toilet, Free showers, RV dump, Tents: $45/RVs: $45-65, 4 over-night spots, 84 Full hookup, Mostly long-term, Open Apr-Oct, Elev: 1752ft/534m, Tel: 814-387-6299, Nearest town: Snow Shoe. GPS: 41.024980, -77.943597

Rhode Island

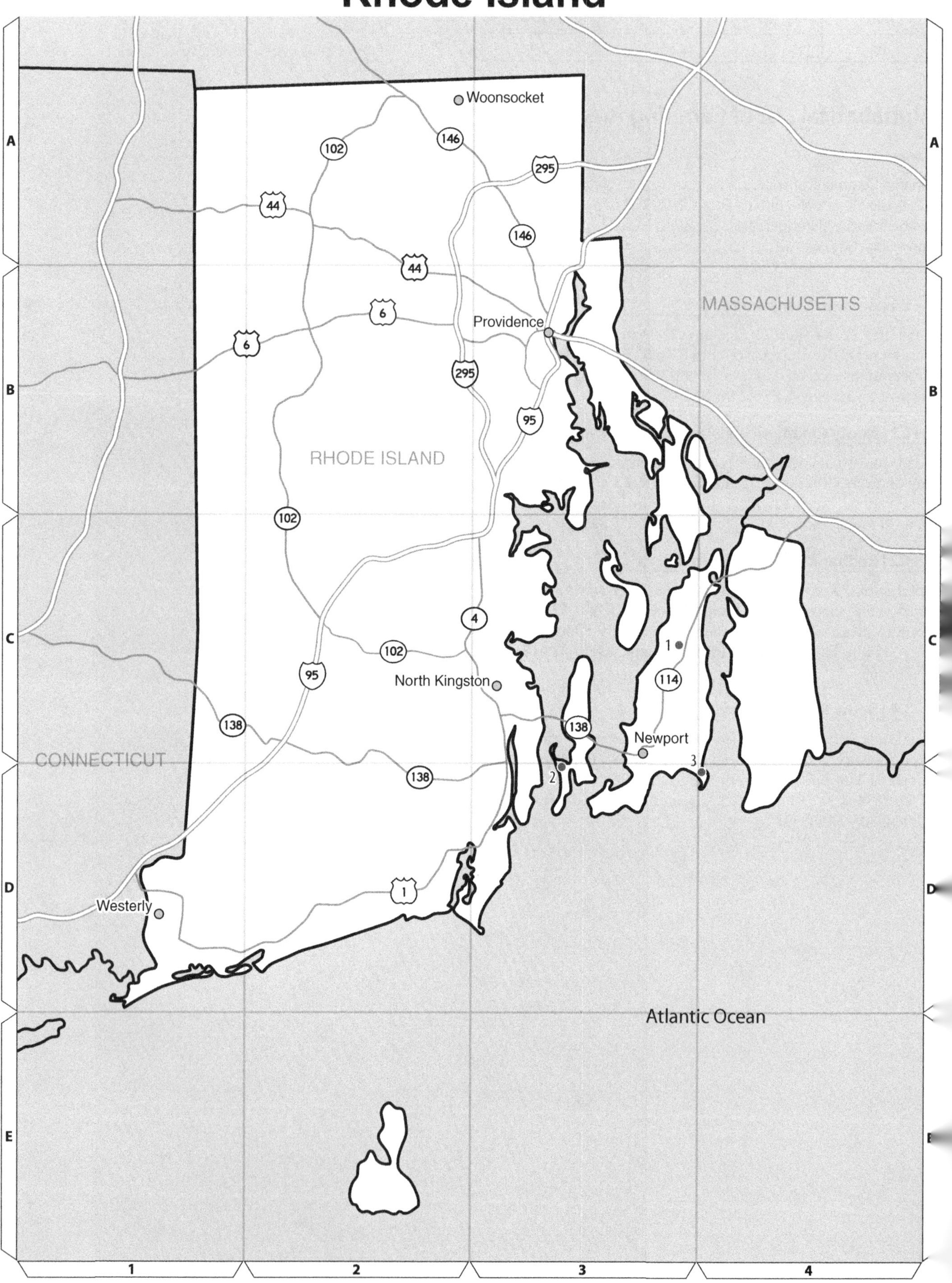

Map	ID	Map	ID
C3	1	D4	3
D3	2		

Alphabetical List of Camping Areas

1 • C3 | Melville Ponds City Park

Total sites: 133, RV sites: 70, Elec sites: 70, Water at site, Flush toilet, Free showers, RV dump, No tents/RVs: $55-120, 15 Full hookup, Open Apr-Oct, Reservations accepted, Elev: 125ft/38m, Tel: 401-682-2424, Nearest town: Portsmouth. GPS: 41.585412, -71.275317

2 • D3 | Fort Getty RA

Total sites: 109, RV sites: 83, Elec sites: 83, Water available, Flush toilet, Free showers, RV dump, Tents: $35/RVs: $60, 2 week stay minimum, Mostly seasonal, Open May-Sep, Reservations accepted, Elev: 62ft/19m, Tel: 401-423-7211, Nearest town: Newport. GPS: 41.491471, -71.398624

3 • D4 | Second Beach

Total sites: 39, RV sites: 39, Elec sites: 39, Water at site, Flush toilet, Free showers, RV dump, No tents/RVs: $110-130, 39 Full hookup, No pets, Open May-Sep, Max Length: 40ft, Reservations accepted, Elev: 72ft/22m, Tel: 401-846-6273, Nearest town: Middletown. GPS: 41.486841, -71.251694

South Dakota

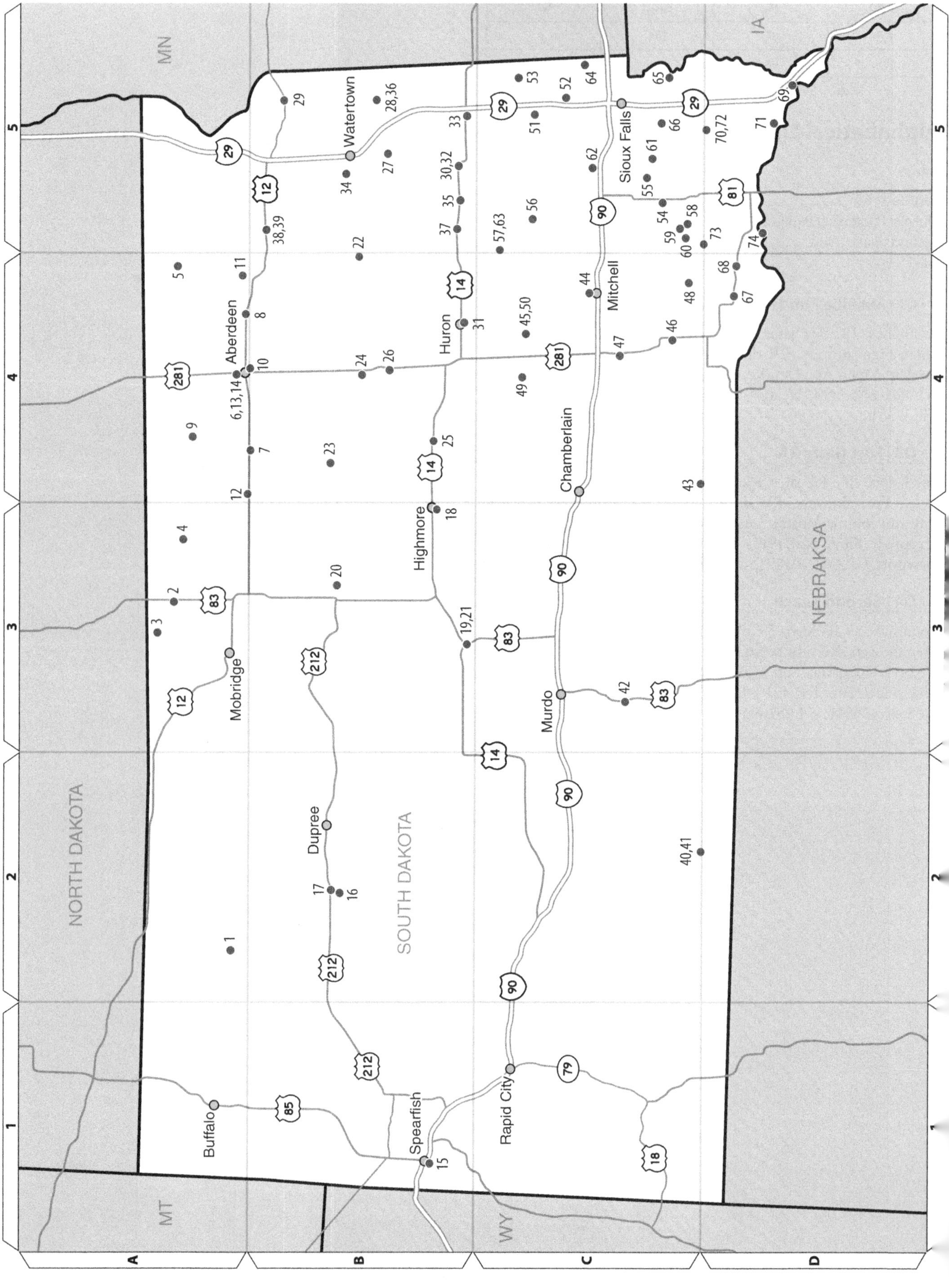

Map	ID	Map	ID
A2	1	B5	27-39
A3	2-4	C2	40-41
A4	5-14	C3	42
B1	15	C4	43-50
B2	16-17	C5	51-66
B3	18-21	D4	67-68
B4	22-26	D5	69-74

Alphabetical List of Camping Areas

Name	ID	Map
Avon City Park	67	D4
Bison City Park	1	A2
Britton RV Park	5	A4
Brooks Memorial Park	40	C2
Brown County Fairgrounds	6	A4
Burke City Park	43	C4
Castlewood City Park	27	B5
City Park East	18	B3
Clear Lake City Park	28	B5
Collier's Park	7	A4
Colman City Park	51	C5
Dell Rapids CG	52	C5
Dickinson City Park	22	B4
Durkee Lake City Park	16	B2
Elk Point City Park	69	D5
Faith City Park	17	B2
Faulkton City Park	23	B4
Fischers Lilly Park	19	B3
Flandreau Municipal Park	53	C5
Freeman City Park	54	C5
Gettysburg City Park	20	B3
Griffin City Park	21	B3
Groton City Park	8	A4
Gunderson Park	70	D5
Hav-A-Rest Park	24	B4
Herreid Memorial Park	2	A3
Hieb Memorial Park	55	C5
Hodson Memorial Park	41	C2
Howard City Park	56	C5
Lake Carthage	57	C5
Lake Farley City CG	29	B5
Lake Mitchell City CG	44	C4
Lake Pocasse	3	A3
Lake Prior City Park	45	C4
Lakeside City Park	4	A3
Leola City Park at Lundquist Dam	9	A4
Lion's Park	71	D5
Lions City Park	46	C4
Maxwell Park CG	30	B5
Melgaard Park City CG	10	A4
Memorial Park CG	31	B5
Menno City Park	58	C5
Menno Lake RA	59	C5
Miller City Park aka Crystal Park	25	B4
Nordland Park CG	32	B5
Olivet Park	60	C5
Parker RV Park	61	C5
Peder Larsen City Park	72	D5
Pierpont City Park	11	A4
Pioneer City CG	62	C5
Redstone City Park	63	C5
Roscoe City Park	12	A4
Scotland City Park (Ballfield)	73	D5
Sexauer City Park	33	B5
Spearfish City CG	15	B1
Split Rock Park	64	C5
Stickney City Park	47	C4
Stokes - Thomas Lake	34	B5
Tabor RA	74	D5
Thorness Park	35	B5
Tripp City Park	48	C4
Tulare City Park	26	B4
Tyndall City Park	68	D4
Ulven City Park	36	B5
Washington Park	37	B5
Webster Overnight RV Park	38	B5
Webster RV Park	39	B5
Wessington Springs City Park	49	C4
West Ball Park	65	C5
Westerman City Park	66	C5
White River City Park	42	C3
Woonsocket RV Park	50	C4
Wylie Park North CG	13	A4
Wylie Park South CG	14	A4

1 • A2 | Bison City Park

Total sites: 4, RV sites: 4, Elec sites: 4, Water at site, Flush toilet, Free showers, RV dump, No tents/RVs: $16, Reservations not accepted, Elev: 2780ft/847m, Nearest town: Bison. GPS: 45.520651, -102.465724

2 • A3 | Herreid Memorial Park

Dispersed sites, No water, No toilets, No tents/RVs: Free, Overnight parking allowed, Elev: 1690ft/515m, Nearest town: Herreid. GPS: 45.825735, -100.069360

3 • A3 | Lake Pocasse

Total sites: 7, RV sites: 2, Vault/pit toilet, Tent & RV camping: $5, Open all year, Elev: 1634ft/498m, Tel: 605-889-2490, Nearest town: Pollock. GPS: 45.904317, -100.290461

4 • A3 | Lakeside City Park

Total sites: 18, RV sites: 18, Elec sites: 18, Flush toilet, Free showers, RV dump, Tent & RV camping: $15, Open Apr-Nov, Reservations not accepted, Elev: 1847ft/563m, Tel: 605-284-2441, Nearest town: Eureka. GPS: 45.772083, -99.633588

5 • A4 | Britton RV Park

Total sites: 10, RV sites: 10, Elec sites: 10, Central water, No toilets, No showers, No RV dump, Tent & RV camping: $15, 2 nights free, Sign in at Police Station, Stay limit: 10 days, Reservations not accepted, Elev: 1345ft/410m, Tel: 605-448-5721, Nearest town: Britton. GPS: 45.784251, -97.749816

6 • A4 | Brown County Fairgrounds

Total sites: 278, RV sites: 278, Elec sites: 278, Water at site, Flush toilet, No showers, RV dump, Tents: $20/RVs: $20-23, 118 Full hookup, Reservations not accepted, Elev: 1309ft/399m, Tel: 605-626-7116, Nearest town: Aberdeen. GPS: 45.488515, -98.490709

7 • A4 | Collier's Park

Total sites: 4, RV sites: 4, RV dump, Tent & RV camping: Fee unk, Elev: 1544ft/471m, Nearest town: Ipswich. GPS: 45.448138, -99.031674

8 • A4 | Groton City Park

Total sites: 12, RV sites: 5, Elec sites: 5, Water at site, Flush toilet, No showers, RV dump, Tents: $10/RVs: $20, 5 Full hookup, Open May-Nov, Reservations not accepted, Elev: 1309ft/399m, Tel: 605-397-8422, Nearest town: Groton. GPS: 45.453215, -98.097953

9 • A4 | Leola City Park at Lundquist Dam

Total sites: 12, RV sites: 12, Elec sites: 12, Central water, Vault/pit toilet, No showers, No RV dump, Tent & RV camping: $10, First night free, Open all year, Reservations accepted, Elev: 1575ft/480m, Tel: 605-439-3299, Nearest town: Leola. GPS: 45.729585, -98.931199

10 • A4 | Melgaard Park City CG

Total sites: 25, RV sites: 16, Elec sites: 16, Central water, Flush toilet, Free showers, RV dump, Tents: $22/RVs: $32, Open Apr-Oct, Reservations not accepted, Elev: 1302ft/397m, Tel: 605-626-7015, Nearest town: Aberdeen. GPS: 45.445801, -98.478271

11 • A4 | Pierpont City Park

Total sites: 20, RV sites: 20, Central water, Vault/pit toilet, No showers, No RV dump, Tent & RV camping: Free, Unconfirmed, Open all year, Elev: 1516ft/462m, Nearest town: Pierpont. GPS: 45.462415, -97.833411

12 • A4 | Roscoe City Park

Dispersed sites, Central water, No toilets, No showers, RV dump, Tent & RV camping: Free, Unconfirmed, Open May-Sep, Elev: 1821ft/555m, Nearest town: Roscoe. GPS: 45.454402, -99.334375

13 • A4 | Wylie Park North CG

Total sites: 38, RV sites: 23, Elec sites: 23, Water at site, Flush toilet, Free showers, RV dump, Tents: $24/RVs: $36-37, 23 Full hookup, Open May-Sep, Reservations accepted, Elev: 1322ft/403m, Tel: 605-626-3512, Nearest town: Aberdeen. GPS: 45.493726, -98.525052

14 • A4 | Wylie Park South CG

Total sites: 92, RV sites: 82, Elec sites: 92, Water at site, Flush toilet, Free showers, RV dump, Tents: $24/RVs: $36-37, Also cabins, 44 Full hookup, Open May-Sep, Reservations accepted, Elev: 1326ft/404m, Tel: 605-626-3512, Nearest town: Aberdeen. GPS: 45.489597, -98.523995

15 • B1 | Spearfish City CG

Total sites: 211, RV sites: 161, Elec sites: 161, Water at site, Flush toilet, Free showers, RV dump, Tents: $25/RVs: $30-45, 61 Full hookup, Higher rally rates, Limited services Oct-May, Open all year, Reservations accepted, Elev: 3720ft/1134m, Tel: 605-642-1340, Nearest town: Spearfish. GPS: 44.479961, -103.857586

16 • B2 | Durkee Lake City Park

Total sites: 50, RV sites: 50, Central water, Vault/pit toilet, No showers, No RV dump, Tent & RV camping: $10, Shared hookups, Reservations not accepted, Elev: 2430ft/741m, Nearest town: Faith. GPS: 44.982462, -102.050646

17 • B2 | Faith City Park

Total sites: 10, RV sites: 10, Elec sites: 6, Central water, Flush toilet, No showers, RV dump, Tent & RV camping: $10, Open all year, Reservations not accepted, Elev: 2592ft/790m, Tel: 605-967-2261, Nearest town: Faith. GPS: 45.018940, -102.036510

18 • B3 | City Park East

Total sites: 10, RV sites: 5, Elec sites: 5, Central water, Flush toilet, No showers, RV dump, Tent & RV camping: $8, 20 amps, NearRR, Open Apr-Oct, Elev: 1880ft/573m, Tel: 605-852-2716, Nearest town: Highmore. GPS: 44.519691, -99.438183

19 • B3 | Fischers Lilly Park

Total sites: 12, RV sites: 12, Elec sites: 12, Water at site, Flush toilet, No showers, RV dump, Tent & RV camping: $15, Reservations not accepted, Elev: 1408ft/429m, Tel: 605-223-7690, Nearest town: Fort Pierre. GPS: 44.352333, -100.368424

20 • B3 | Gettysburg City Park

Total sites: 3, RV sites: 3, Elec sites: 3, Central water, Flush toilet, No showers, RV dump, Tent & RV camping: Donation, Stay limit: 3 days, Reservations not accepted, Elev: 2057ft/627m, Nearest town: Gettysburg. GPS: 45.007601, -99.958985

21 • B3 | Griffin City Park

Total sites: 16, RV sites: 16, Elec sites: 16, Central water, Flush toilet, No showers, RV dump, Tent & RV camping: $25, $10 Nov-Mar - bathrooms closed, Stay limit: 14 days, Open all year Reservations not accepted, Elev: 1437ft/438m, Tel: 605-773-7445 Nearest town: Pierre. GPS: 44.359092, -100.345250

22 • B4 | Dickinson City Park

Total sites: 4, RV sites: 4, Elec sites: 4, Water at site, Flush toilet Free showers, RV dump, Tent & RV camping: $15, 4 Full hookup Reservations not accepted, Elev: 1788ft/545m, Tel: 605-532-5665 Nearest town: Clark. GPS: 44.878642, -97.730146

23 • B4 | Faulkton City Park

Total sites: 6, RV sites: 6, Elec sites: 6, Central water, Flush toilet No showers, RV dump, Tent & RV camping: $20, 1st 4 night free or donation, Reservations not accepted, Elev: 1572ft/479m Tel: 605-598-6515, Nearest town: Faulkton. GPS: 45.036463, 99.126401

24 • B4 | Hav-A-Rest Park

Total sites: 21, RV sites: 19, Elec sites: 19, Water available, Flus toilet, Free showers, RV dump, Tent & RV camping: $20, Ope Apr-Nov, Reservations accepted, Elev: 1296ft/395m, Tel: 605 472-4550, Nearest town: Redfield. GPS: 44.878584, -98.530375

25 • B4 | Miller City Park aka Crystal Park

Total sites: 20, RV sites: 20, Elec sites: 20, Central water, Flush toilet, No showers, RV dump, No tents/RVs: Donation, Open May-Sep, Max Length: 40ft, Reservations not accepted, Elev: 1558ft/475m, Tel: 605-853-2705, Nearest town: Miller. GPS: 44.524816, -98.994464

26 • B4 | Tulare City Park

Total sites: 5, RV sites: 3, Elec sites: 3, Central water, Flush toilet, Tent & RV camping: Donation, Location approximate, Reservations not accepted, Elev: 1306ft/398m, Nearest town: Tulare. GPS: 44.737492, -98.505587

27 • B5 | Castlewood City Park

Total sites: 6, RV sites: 6, Elec sites: 6, Central water, No toilets, No showers, RV dump, Tent & RV camping: $15, Reservations accepted, Elev: 1673ft/510m, Tel: 605-793-2220, Nearest town: Castlewood. GPS: 44.717754, -97.034372

28 • B5 | Clear Lake City Park

Total sites: 18, RV sites: 18, Elec sites: 18, Water at site, Flush toilet, Free showers, RV dump, Tent & RV camping: $15, Reservations not accepted, Elev: 1782ft/543m, Tel: 605-874-2121, Nearest town: Clear Lake. GPS: 44.760729, -96.683853

29 • B5 | Lake Farley City CG

Total sites: 10, RV sites: 10, Elec sites: 10, Water at site, Flush toilet, Free showers, RV dump, Tent & RV camping: $22, 10 Full hookup, Fee for Wi-Fi, Open May-Sep, Reservations accepted, Elev: 1143ft/348m, Nearest town: Millbank. GPS: 45.225937, -96.641741

30 • B5 | Maxwell Park CG

Total sites: 10, RV sites: 4, Elec sites: 4, Water at site, No toilets, No showers, RV dump, Tents: Free/RVs: $10, Near RR, Open Jun-Sep, Elev: 1854ft/565m, Tel: 605-983-5251, Nearest town: Arlington. GPS: 44.364857, -97.134133

31 • B5 | Memorial Park CG

Total sites: 73, RV sites: 24, Elec sites: 24, Water at site, Flush toilet, Free showers, RV dump, Tents: $20/RVs: $30, 24 Full hookup sites, Reservations accepted, Elev: 1253ft/382m, Tel: 605-353-8533, Nearest town: Huron. GPS: 44.368716, -98.192722

32 • B5 | Nordland Park CG

Total sites: 10, RV sites: 5, Elec sites: 5, Central water, No toilets, No showers, No RV dump, Tents: Free/RVs: $10, Open Jun-Sep, Reservations not accepted, Elev: 1831ft/558m, Tel: 605-983-5251, Nearest town: Arlington. GPS: 44.360798, -97.129071

33 • B5 | Sexauer City Park

Total sites: 30, RV sites: 18, Elec sites: 18, Central water, Flush toilet, Free showers, RV dump, Tents: $10/RVs: $25, Reservations accepted, Elev: 1604ft/489m, Tel: 605-692-2708, Nearest town: Brookings. GPS: 44.317940, -96.804920

34 • B5 | Stokes - Thomas Lake

Total sites: 72, RV sites: 72, Elec sites: 72, Water available, Flush toilet, Free showers, RV dump, Tent & RV camping: $21, 6 Full hookup, Limited services Oct, Stay limit: 14 days, Open May-Oct, Reservations not accepted, Elev: 1722ft/525m, Tel: 605-882-6264, Nearest town: Watertown. GPS: 44.931799, -97.168877

35 • B5 | Thorness Park

Total sites: 7, RV sites: 7, Elec sites: 7, Central water, Flush toilet, No showers, RV dump, Tent & RV camping: $10, Tight for RVs >30ft, Reservations accepted, Elev: 1720ft/524m, Tel: 605-847-4140, Nearest town: Lake Preston. GPS: 44.359713, -97.370193

36 • B5 | Ulven City Park

Total sites: 24, RV sites: 24, Elec sites: 24, Water at site, No toilets, No showers, No RV dump, Tent & RV camping: $15, 6 Full hookup, Reservations not accepted, Elev: 1788ft/545m, Tel: 605-874-2121, Nearest town: Clear Lake. GPS: 44.756737, -96.657151

37 • B5 | Washington Park

Total sites: 10, RV sites: 3, Elec sites: 3, Water available, Flush toilet, Free showers, No RV dump, Tents: $10/RVs: $10-20, Max Length: 20ft, Reservations not accepted, Elev: 1755ft/535m, Tel: 605-854-3731, Nearest town: De Smet. GPS: 44.385699, -97.559602

38 • B5 | Webster Overnight RV Park

Total sites: 3, RV sites: 3, Elec sites: 3, No water, No toilets, No showers, RV dump, Tent & RV camping: $20, 1st night free, Water for dumping only, Reservations not accepted, Elev: 1817ft/554m, Tel: 605-345-3241, Nearest town: Webster. GPS: 45.340475, -97.517637

39 • B5 | Webster RV Park

Total sites: 10, RV sites: 10, Elec sites: 10, Water at site, No toilets, No showers, RV dump, No tents/RVs: $20, 7 Full hookup, 1st night free, Reservations not accepted, Elev: 1812ft/552m, Tel: 605-345-3241, Nearest town: Webster. GPS: 45.340087, -97.518504

40 • C2 | Brooks Memorial Park

Total sites: 4, RV sites: 4, Central water, Vault/pit toilet, No showers, No RV dump, Tent & RV camping: Donation, Reservations not accepted, Elev: 3317ft/1011m, Tel: 605-685-6330, Nearest town: Martin. GPS: 43.176314, -101.730881

41 • C2 | Hodson Memorial Park

Dispersed sites, Tent & RV camping: Donation, Elev: 3327ft/1014m, Tel: 605-685-6330, Nearest town: Martin. GPS: 43.168892, -101.731266

42 • C3 | White River City Park

Total sites: 12, RV sites: 12, Central water, Vault/pit toilet, No showers, No RV dump, Tent & RV camping: Free, Call city clerk for permission to run 100' hose and 100' electric cord to your camper for free, Open all year, Max Length: 25ft, Elev: 2132ft/650m, Nearest town: White River. GPS: 43.564955, -100.741975

43 • C4 | Burke City Park

Total sites: 5, RV sites: 5, Elec sites: 5, Water at site, Flush toilet, Free showers, No RV dump, Tent & RV camping: $10, Unconfirmed, Open all year, Max Length: 40ft, Elev: 2169ft/661m, Nearest town: Burke. GPS: 43.185018, -99.297401

44 • C4 | Lake Mitchell City CG

Total sites: 59, RV sites: 50, Elec sites: 55, Water at site, Flush toilet,

Free showers, RV dump, Tents: $22-24/RVs: $37, Open Apr-Oct, Reservations accepted, Elev: 1280ft/390m, Tel: 605-995-8457, Nearest town: Mitchell. GPS: 43.734812, -98.027169

45 • C4 | Lake Prior City Park

Total sites: 5, RV sites: 5, Elec sites: 5, Water at site, No toilets, No showers, RV dump, Tent & RV camping: $15, Elev: 1299ft/396m, Tel: 605-796-4112, Nearest town: Woonsocket. GPS: 44.057247, -98.277518

46 • C4 | Lions City Park

Total sites: 10, RV sites: 10, Elec sites: 10, Central water, Flush toilet, Free showers, RV dump, Tent & RV camping: Donation, Also cabins, Call for rate for stays over 5 days, Reservations not accepted, Elev: 1522ft/464m, Tel: 605-724-2245, Nearest town: Armour. GPS: 43.322246, -98.343087

47 • C4 | Stickney City Park

Total sites: 2, RV sites: 2, Elec sites: 2, Central water, Flush toilet, Free showers, Tent & RV camping: Donation, Reservations not accepted, Elev: 1647ft/502m, Tel: 605-732-4204, Nearest town: Stickney. GPS: 43.589261, -98.441872

48 • C4 | Tripp City Park

Total sites: 5, RV sites: 5, No toilets, No showers, No RV dump, Tent & RV camping: $5, Elev: 1516ft/462m, Nearest town: Tripp. GPS: 43.233032, -97.965846

49 • C4 | Wessington Springs City Park

Total sites: 13, RV sites: 13, Elec sites: 13, Flush toilet, Free showers, RV dump, Tents: $10/RVs: $15, Reservations not accepted, Elev: 1706ft/520m, Tel: 605-539-1691, Nearest town: Wessington Springs. GPS: 44.075706, -98.572538

50 • C4 | Woonsocket RV Park

Total sites: 6, RV sites: 6, Elec sites: 6, Water at site, Flush toilet, No tents/RVs: $15, Elev: 1302ft/397m, Tel: 605-796-4112, Nearest town: Woonsocket. GPS: 44.056471, -98.274645

51 • C5 | Colman City Park

Total sites: 27, RV sites: 27, Elec sites: 24, Water at site, Flush toilet, Free showers, No RV dump, Tents: $18/RVs: $18-27, 5 Full hookup, Reservations accepted, Elev: 1706ft/520m, Tel: 605-534-3121, Nearest town: Colman. GPS: 43.978528, -96.809776

52 • C5 | Dell Rapids CG

Total sites: 15, RV sites: 15, Elec sites: 15, Central water, No toilets, No showers, RV dump, Tent & RV camping: $25, Open May-Sep, Reservations accepted, Elev: 1483ft/452m, Tel: 605-428-3595, Nearest town: Dell Rapids. GPS: 43.818898, -96.706877

53 • C5 | Flandreau Municipal Park

Total sites: 16, RV sites: 16, Elec sites: 16, Water at site, Flush toilet, Free showers, RV dump, Tents: $5/RVs: $12, Reservations not accepted, Elev: 1539ft/469m, Tel: 605-573-2056, Nearest town: Flandreau. GPS: 44.055806, -96.567919

54 • C5 | Freeman City Park

Total sites: 7, RV sites: 7, Central water, Flush toilet, Free showers, No RV dump, Tents: $6/RVs: $10, No bathhouse water Oct-May, Open all year, Reservations not accepted, Elev: 1509ft/460m, Tel: 605-925-7127, Nearest town: Freeman. GPS: 43.356002, -97.431058

55 • C5 | Hieb Memorial Park

Total sites: 7, RV sites: 7, Elec sites: 3, Water at site, Free showers, RV dump, Tent & RV camping: Free, Showers at pool, Near RR, Reservations not accepted, Elev: 1430ft/436m, Tel: 605-648-2869, Nearest town: Marion. GPS: 43.426518, -97.265049

56 • C5 | Howard City Park

Total sites: 7, RV sites: 7, Elec sites: 6, Water at site, Flush toilet, Free showers, RV dump, Tent & RV camping: $18, 6 Full hookup, Reservations accepted, Elev: 1558ft/475m, Tel: 605-772-4391, Nearest town: Howard. GPS: 44.008649, -97.522319

57 • C5 | Lake Carthage

Total sites: 18, RV sites: 13, Elec sites: 13, Central water, Flush toilet, Tents: $11/RVs: $15, Reservations not accepted, Elev: 1430ft/436m, Tel: 605-256-5003, Nearest town: Carthage. GPS: 44.177351, -97.706364

58 • C5 | Menno City Park

Total sites: 4, RV sites: 4, Elec sites: 4, Central water, Flush toilet, Free showers, RV dump, No tents/RVs: $10, Reservations not accepted, Elev: 1322ft/403m, Tel: 605-387-2427, Nearest town: Menno. GPS: 43.235286, -97.584237

59 • C5 | Menno Lake RA

Total sites: 10, RV sites: 10, Elec sites: 10, Central water, Flush toilet, No showers, RV dump, Tent & RV camping: $10, Elev: 1263ft/385m, Tel: 605-387-2427, Nearest town: Menno. GPS: 43.262961, -97.607573

60 • C5 | Olivet Park

Dispersed sites, No toilets, Tent & RV camping: $5, 15 amp, Elev 1192ft/363m, Nearest town: Olivet. GPS: 43.240328, -97.668171

61 • C5 | Parker RV Park

Total sites: 7, RV sites: 7, Elec sites: 7, Water at site, Flush toilet RV dump, No tents/RVs: $10-15, 4 Full hookup, Reservations no accepted, Elev: 1351ft/412m, Tel: 605-297-4453, Nearest town Parker. GPS: 43.400149, -97.140753

62 • C5 | Pioneer City CG

Total sites: 31, RV sites: 31, Elec sites: 31, Water at site, Flush toilet Free showers, RV dump, Tent & RV camping: $20, Open May Oct, Reservations accepted, Elev: 1480ft/451m, Tel: 605-363 5065, Nearest town: Montrose. GPS: 43.703196, -97.181368

63 • C5 | Redstone City Park

Total sites: 5, RV sites: 5, Elec sites: 5, Central water, No toilets No showers, No RV dump, Tent & RV camping: $15, Elev 1427ft/435m, Tel: 605-772-4472, Nearest town: Carthage. GPS 44.171284, -97.723505

64 • C5 | Split Rock Park

Total sites: 26, RV sites: 19, Elec sites: 12, Central water, Flush toile Free showers, Tent & RV camping: Fee unk, Elev: 1476ft/450m

Tel: 605-594-2225, Nearest town: Garretson. GPS: 43.720071, -96.502442

65 • C5 | West Ball Park

Total sites: 7, RV sites: 7, Elec sites: 7, Vault/pit toilet, No showers, Tent & RV camping: $15, Elev: 1270ft/387m, Tel: 605-987-2881, Nearest town: Canton. GPS: 43.298999, -96.602488

66 • C5 | Westerman City Park

Total sites: 16, RV sites: 16, Elec sites: 16, Central water, Flush toilet, Free showers, RV dump, Tent & RV camping: $11, Dump fee, Open May-Sep, Reservations accepted, Elev: 1348ft/411m, Tel: 605-647-2286, Nearest town: Lennox. GPS: 43.348210, -96.895695

67 • D4 | Avon City Park

Total sites: 2, RV sites: 2, Elec sites: 2, No tents/RVs: Fee unk, Elev: 1619ft/493m, Nearest town: Avon. GPS: 43.005549, -98.059468

68 • D4 | Tyndall City Park

Total sites: 4, RV sites: 4, Elec sites: 4, Water at site, Flush toilet, Free showers, RV dump, Tent & RV camping: $10, Reservations not accepted, Elev: 1427ft/435m, Tel: 605-589-3781, Nearest town: Tyndall. GPS: 42.995126, -97.868566

69 • D5 | Elk Point City Park

Total sites: 23, RV sites: 23, Elec sites: 23, Central water, Flush toilet, No showers, No RV dump, Tent & RV camping: $15, Open May-Sep, Reservations not accepted, Elev: 1129ft/344m, Tel: 605 356-2141, Nearest town: Elk Point. GPS: 42.683580, -96.691222

70 • D5 | Gunderson Park

Dispersed sites, No toilets, Tents only: Free, Elev: 1207ft/368m, Tel: 605-563-2302, Nearest town: Centerville. GPS: 43.126852, -96.966514

71 • D5 | Lion's Park

Total sites: 10, RV sites: 10, Elec sites: 10, Central water, Flush toilet, Free showers, RV dump, Tent & RV camping: Free, Stay limit: 2 days, Open Apr-Oct, Reservations not accepted, Elev: 1230ft/375m, Tel: 605-677-7082, Nearest town: Vermilion. GPS: 42.786201, -96.937992

72 • D5 | Peder Larsen City Park

Total sites: 3, RV sites: 3, Elec sites: 3, No toilets, No showers, No RV dump, Tent & RV camping: Fee unk, Elev: 1243ft/379m, Tel: 605-563-2302, Nearest town: Centerville. GPS: 43.119794, -96.955241

73 • D5 | Scotland City Park (Ballfield)

Total sites: 12, RV sites: 12, Elec sites: 12, Water at site, No toilets, No showers, RV dump, Tent & RV camping: Fee unk, 7 Full hookup, Reservations not accepted, Elev: 1355ft/413m, Tel: 605-464-0238, Nearest town: Scotland. GPS: 43.151680, -97.713318

74 • D5 | Tabor RA

Dispersed sites, No water, Vault/pit toilet, Tent & RV camping: $15, SD state park sticker required, Elev: 1260ft/384m, Tel: 605-568-2985, Nearest town: Tabor. GPS: 42.860126, -97.654437

Tennessee

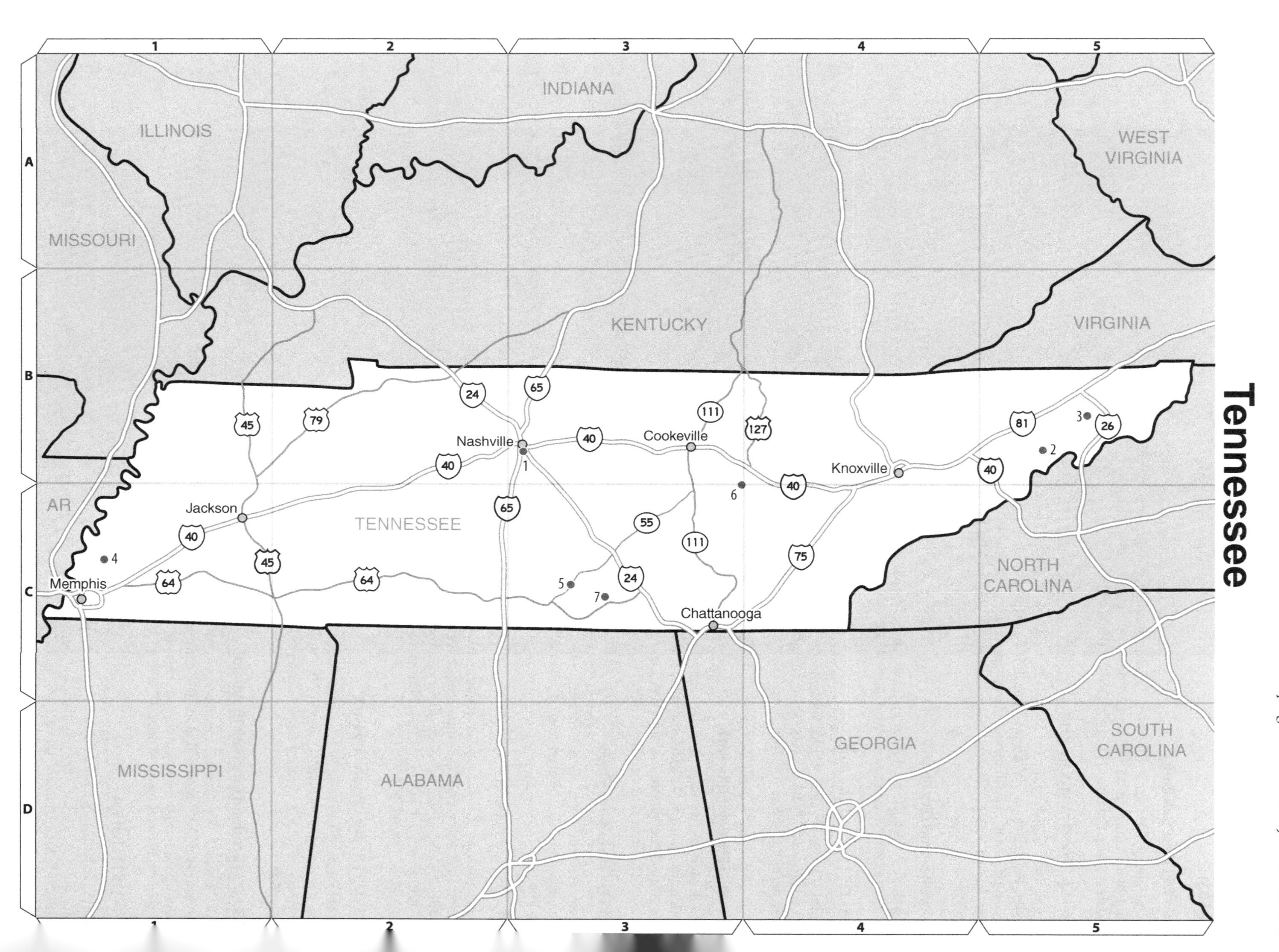
1
2
3
4
5
A
B
C
D
INDIANA
ILLINOIS
MISSOURI
WEST VIRGINIA
KENTUCKY
VIRGINIA
AR
TENNESSEE
NORTH CAROLINA
SOUTH CAROLINA
GEORGIA
ALABAMA
MISSISSIPPI
Memphis
Jackson
Nashville
Cookeville
Knoxville
Chattanooga
45
79
24
65
40
111
127
81
26
55
75
64

Map	ID	Map	ID
B3	1	C1	4
B5	2-3	C3	5-7

Alphabetical List of Camping Areas

1 • B3 | Nashville Fairgrounds RV Park

Total sites: 20, RV sites: 20, Elec sites: 20, Water at site, No tents/RVs: $35, Full hookup sites, Near RR, No open fires, Elev: 450ft/137m, Tel: 615-862-8994, Nearest town: Nashville. GPS: 36.134476, -86.762164

2 • B5 | Kinser City Park

Total sites: 132, RV sites: 132, Elec sites: 132, Water at site, Flush toilet, Free showers, RV dump, Tents: $15/RVs: $25, Open Apr-Oct, Elev: 1286ft/392m, Tel: 423-639-5912, Nearest town: Greeneville. GPS: 36.080549, -82.847142

3 • B5 | Persimmon Ridge City Park

Total sites: 46, RV sites: 46, Elec sites: 46, Water at site, Flush toilet, Free showers, RV dump, Tent & RV camping: $14, Open all year, Reservations accepted, Elev: 1749ft/533m, Tel: 423-753-2036, Nearest town: Jonesborough. GPS: 36.289524, -82.498747

4 • C1 | Navy Lake RA

Total sites: 24, RV sites: 24, Elec sites: 24, Water at site, Flush toilet, Free showers, RV dump, Tent & RV camping: $23-24, 12 Full hookup, Open all year, Reservations not accepted, Elev: 322ft/98m, Tel: 901-674-0378, Nearest town: Millington. GPS: 35.366781, -89.853991

5 • C3 | Lynchburg City Park

Total sites: 20, RV sites: 20, Elec sites: 20, No tents/RVs: $20, Max Length: 40ft, Elev: 779ft/237m, Nearest town: Lynchburg. GPS: 35.279922, -86.376952

6 • C3 | Meadow Lake City Park

Total sites: 13, RV sites: 8, Elec sites: 8, Water at site, Flush toilet, Free showers, RV dump, Tents: $15/RVs: $25-30, Also cabins, Reservations accepted, Elev: 1874ft/571m, Tel: 931-788-2034, Nearest town: Crossville. GPS: 35.902942, -85.095659

7 • C3 | Winchester City Park

Total sites: 30, RV sites: 23, Elec sites: 28, Water at site, Flush toilet, Free showers, RV dump, Tents: $15/RVs: $20, 9 Full hookup, Open Apr-Oct, Reservations accepted, Elev: 908ft/277m, Tel: 931-962-4204, Nearest town: Winchester. GPS: 35.204501, -86.133769

Texas

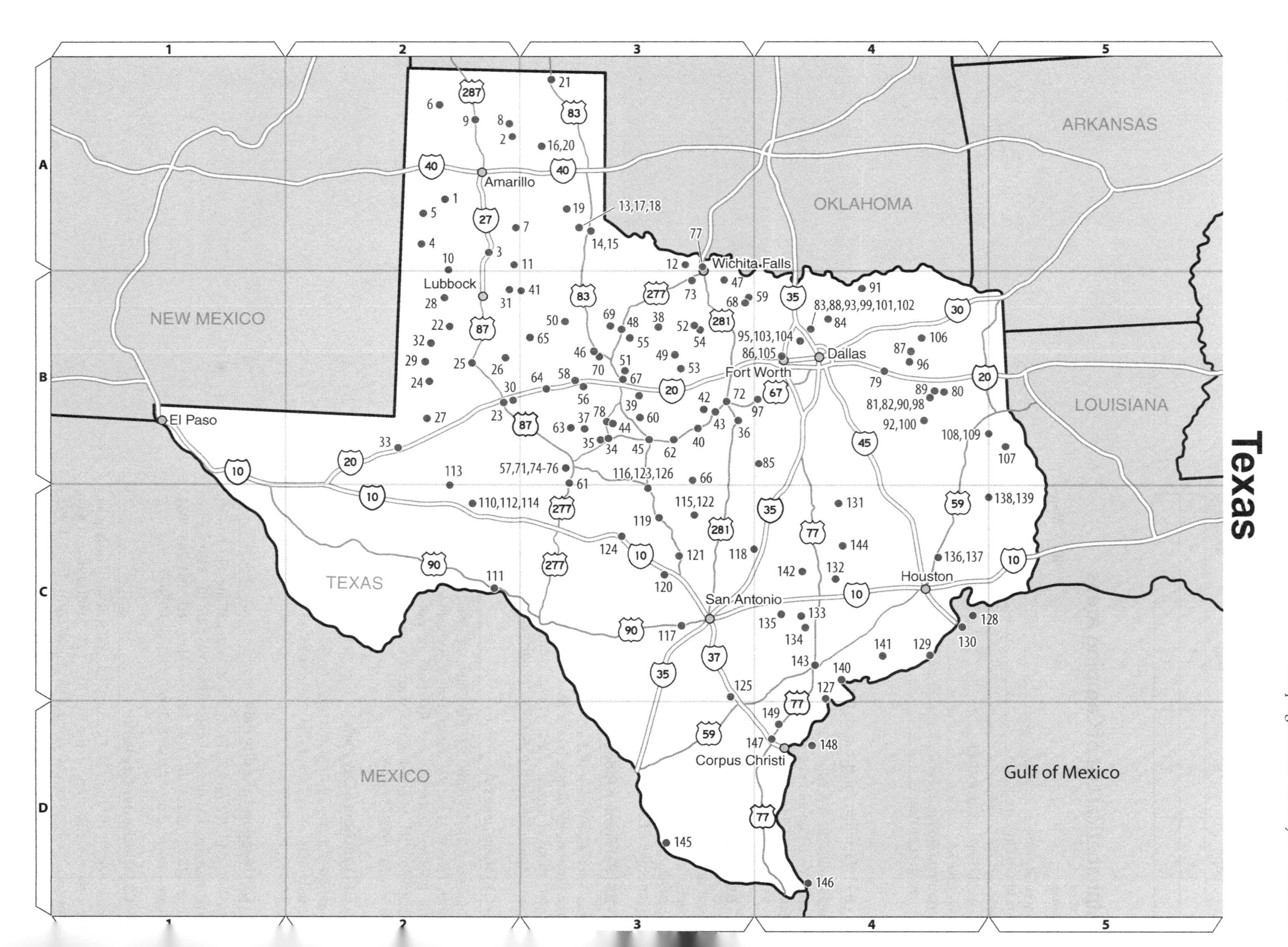
ARKANSAS
OKLAHOMA
LOUISIANA
NEW MEXICO
TEXAS
MEXICO
Gulf of Mexico
Amarillo
Lubbock
Wichita Falls
Dallas
Fort Worth
Houston
San Antonio
Corpus Christi
El Paso

Map	ID	Map	ID
A2	1-11	C2	110-114
A3	12-21	C3	115-126
B2	22-33	C4	127-144
B3	34-78	D3	145
B4	79-106	D4	146-149
B5	107-109		

Alphabetical List of Camping Areas

Name	ID	Map
Alley Oop City RV Park	110	C2
Austwell City Park	127	C4
Badu City Park	115	C3
Ballinger City Park	34	B3
Ballinger Lake Park	35	B3
Boca Chica Beach	146	D4
Bolivar Flats Beach Dispersed	128	C4
Bosque River RV Park	36	B3
Brady Lake City Park	116	C3
Bronte RV Park	37	B3
Bryan Beach	129	C4
Buffalo Creek Reservoir Boat Ramp	12	A3
Canton Civic Center and RV Park	79	B4
Castroville RP	117	C3
Childress Ramp	13	A3
Chldress City Fair Park	14	A3
City Park Camp	80	B4
City RV Park	38	B3
Clyde Lake	39	B3
Coleman City Park	22	B2
Comanche City Park	40	B3
Comanche Trail City Park	23	B2
Concession Park	81	B4
Crosbyton City Park	41	B3
De Leon Community Park	42	B3
Dellanera City RV Park	130	C4
Dublin City Park	43	B3
East Side Park #4	82	B4
Eastside City Park	131	C4
Eastvale Park	83	B4
Elm Creek Reservoir/W. Lee Colburn Park	44	B3
Emma Long Metropolitan Park	118	C3
Erwin Park	84	B4
Fair Park	15	A3
Falcon Heights Park	145	D3
Faunt Leroy City Park	85	B4
Fayetteville Town Square	132	C4
Florey City Park	24	B2
Forrest Park RV Park	25	B2
Fort Mason City Park	119	C3
Fort Worth Convention Center	86	B4
Gail RV Park	26	B2
Gary James Memorial Park	45	B3
Goldsmith City Park	27	B2
Governor Jim Hogg RV Park	87	B4
Green Dickson Park	133	C4
Hamlin City Park	46	B3
Hapgood City Park	47	B3
Haskell City Park	48	B3
Hereford City RV Park	1	A2
Hidden Cove City Park	88	B4
Highway 64 Ramp	89	B4
Hill Creek Park	90	B4
Hobart Street City Park	16	A3
Hub City RV Park	134	C4
Hubbard Creek Reservoir	49	B3
Huber City Park	2	A2
Independence City Park	135	C4
Jayton RV Park	50	B3
Johnson City Park	51	B3
Kerrville-Schreiner City Park	120	C3
Kindley City Park	52	B3
Labonte Park	147	D4
Lady Bird Johnson City Park	121	C3
Lake Baylor North Ramp	17	A3
Lake Baylor South Ramp	18	A3
Lake Bonham RA	91	B4
Lake Daniel	53	B3
Lake Eddleman City Park	54	B3
Lake Houston Wilderness Park - Platforms	136	C4
Lake Houston Wilderness Park -Backcountry	137	C4
Lake Jacksonville Park	92	B4
Lake Stamford Park	55	B3
Lake Sweetwater Park	56	B3
Lake Tejas City Park - Eastside	138	C4
Lake Tejas City Park - Westside	139	C4
Langtry Community Center	111	C2
Levelland City RV Park	28	B2
Lewisville Lake Park	93	B4
Lighthouse Beach RV Park	140	C4
Little Elm Park	94	B4
Llano River RV Park	122	C3
M.S. Doss City Park	29	B2
Meadowmere Park	95	B4
Memphis City Park	19	A3
Middle Concho Park	57	B3
Mineola Civic Center and RV Park	96	B4
Mission Dolores City Park	107	B5
Moss Creek Lake City Park	30	B2
Newman Park	58	B3
Oakdale City Park	97	B4
Old Omen West City Park	98	B4
Ollie Liner RV Park	3	A2
Pampa Recreation Park	20	A3
Pelham Park	59	B3
Pilot Knoll Park	99	B4
Pinkston Dam	108	B5
Port Aransas Beach Dispersed - City	148	D4
Press Morris Park	60	B3
Pugh River City Park	61	B3
Ralls Lions Park	31	B2
Ray and Donna West Free RV Park	4	A2
Reeve Lake RV Park	5	A2
Richards City Park	123	C3
Rita Blanca City Park	6	A2
Riverside City Park	141	C4
Riverside City Park	62	B3
Rob and Bessie Welder City Park	149	D4
Robert Lee Park	63	B3

1 • A2 | Hereford City RV Park

Total sites: 5, RV sites: 5, Elec sites: 5, Water at site, No toilets, No showers, RV dump, No tents/RVs: Free, 1-2 nights free, Open all year, Reservations not accepted, Elev: 3845ft/1172m, Tel: 806-363-7100, Nearest town: Hereford. GPS: 34.834821, -102.398244

2 • A2 | Huber City Park

Total sites: 10, RV sites: 10, Elec sites: 10, Water at site, Vault/pit toilet, No showers, RV dump, No tents/RVs: Donation, Near RR, Stay limit: 3 days, Elev: 3159ft/963m, Tel: 806-273-0975, Nearest town: Borger. GPS: 35.653431, -101.396171

3 • A2 | Ollie Liner RV Park

Total sites: 44, RV sites: 44, Elec sites: 44, Water at site, Flush toilet, No showers, RV dump, No tents/RVs: $25, 24 Full hookup, Stay limit: 7 days, Open all year, Reservations accepted, Elev: 3376ft/1029m, Tel: 806-293-2183, Nearest town: Plainview. GPS: 34.161123, -101.707782

4 • A2 | Ray and Donna West Free RV Park

Total sites: 8, RV sites: 8, Elec sites: 8, Water at site, RV dump, No tents/RVs: $25, 8 Full hookup, 1st 3 nights free, Stay limit: 8 days, Reservations not accepted, Elev: 3812ft/1162m, Tel: 806-272-4528, Nearest town: Muleshoe. GPS: 34.237536, -102.745848

5 • A2 | Reeve Lake RV Park

Total sites: 20, RV sites: 20, Elec sites: 20, Water at site, No toilets, No showers, RV dump, No tents/RVs: $15-20, Elev: 4015ft/1224m, Tel: 806-250-2761, Nearest town: Friona. GPS: 34.643586, -102.726537

6 • A2 | Rita Blanca City Park

Total sites: 8, RV sites: 8, Water at site, RV dump, Tent & RV camping: $15, 8 Full hookup, Max Length: 40ft, Reservations not accepted, Elev: 3940ft/1201m, Tel: 806-244-5511, Nearest town: Dalhart. GPS: 36.038723, -102.505311

7 • A2 | Silverton Municipal Park

Total sites: 2, RV sites: 2, Elec sites: 2, No water, No toilets, No showers, No RV dump, No tents/RVs: Free, Reservations not accepted, Elev: 3284ft/1001m, Tel: 506-823-2125, Nearest town: Silverton. GPS: 34.473854, -101.306869

8 • A2 | Stinnett City Park

Total sites: 4, RV sites: 4, Elec sites: 4, Water at site, No toilets, No showers, RV dump, No tents/RVs: Free, $10 after third night, Stay limit: 3 days, Elev: 3209ft/978m, Tel: 806-878-2422, Nearest town: Stinnett. GPS: 35.826807, -101.444169

9 • A2 | Texoma City Park

Total sites: 12, RV sites: 12, Elec sites: 12, Central water, Flush toilet, No showers, RV dump, Tent & RV camping: Free, Near RR, Stay limit: 1 day, Open Apr-Oct, Reservations not accepted, Elev: 3665ft/1117m, Tel: 806-934-0837, Nearest town: Dumas. GPS: 35.867101, -101.979386

10 • A2 | Waylon Jennings City RV Park

Total sites: 8, RV sites: 8, Elec sites: 8, Water at site, Flush toilet No showers, RV dump, No tents/RVs: $20, 1st 4 days free, Open all year, Reservations not accepted, Elev: 3560ft/1085m, Tel: 806-385-5161, Nearest town: Littlefield. GPS: 33.912394, -102.32657

11 • A2 | Wayne Russell City RV Park

Total sites: 8, RV sites: 8, Elec sites: 8, Water at site, No toilets No showers, RV dump, No tents/RVs: $10, 1st 2 nights free, Sta limit: 5 days, Open all year, Reservations not accepted, Elev 3189ft/972m, Tel: 806-983-2834, Nearest town: Floydada. GPS 33.993392, -101.341816

12 • A3 | Buffalo Creek Reservoir Boat Ramp

Dispersed sites, No water, No toilets, Tent & RV camping: Free Open all year, Elev: 1043ft/318m, Tel: 940-592-2642, Neare town: Iowa Park. GPS: 33.987417, -98.760187

13 • A3 | Childress Ramp

Dispersed sites, No water, No toilets, Tent & RV camping: Free Open all year, Elev: 1818ft/554m, Tel: 940-937-3684, Neare town: Childress. GPS: 34.466953, -100.357585

14 • A3 | Chldress City Fair Park

Total sites: 5, RV sites: 5, Elec sites: 5, Water at site, No RV dump, No tents/RVs: $15, Stay limit: 3 days, Open all year, Reservations not accepted, Elev: 1860ft/567m, Tel: 940-937-3684, Nearest town: Childress. GPS: 34.430176, -100.202127

15 • A3 | Fair Park

Total sites: 5, RV sites: 5, Elec sites: 5, Water at site, No toilets, No showers, No RV dump, Tent & RV camping: $15, Stay limit: 3 days, Reservations not accepted, Elev: 1857ft/566m, Tel: 940-937-3684, Nearest town: Childress. GPS: 34.432354, -100.202521

16 • A3 | Hobart Street City Park

Total sites: 10, RV sites: 10, Elec sites: 10, Water at site, No toilets, No showers, RV dump, Tent & RV camping: Fee unk, Elev: 3235ft/986m, Tel: 806-669-5740, Nearest town: Pampa. GPS: 35.527611, -100.971554

17 • A3 | Lake Baylor North Ramp

Total sites: 9, RV sites: 9, No water, No toilets, Tent & RV camping: Fee unk, Open all year, Elev: 1831ft/558m, Tel: 940-937-2102, Nearest town: Childress. GPS: 34.478886, -100.373806

18 • A3 | Lake Baylor South Ramp

Total sites: 13, RV sites: 13, Elec sites: 13, Water at site, Flush toilet, Free showers, Tent & RV camping: Fee unk, Open all year, Elev: 1804ft/550m, Tel: 940-937-2102, Nearest town: Childress. GPS: 34.471491, -100.370411

19 • A3 | Memphis City Park

Total sites: 8, RV sites: 8, Elec sites: 8, Water at site, No toilets, No RV dump, Tent & RV camping: Free, Obtain free permit at City Hall, Elev: 2005ft/611m, Tel: 806-259-3001, Nearest town: Memphis. GPS: 34.711568, -100.535574

20 • A3 | Pampa Recreation Park

Total sites: 25, RV sites: 25, Elec sites: 25, Water at site, Flush toilet, Free showers, RV dump, Tents: Free/RVs: $15-20, Stay limit: 60 days, Reservations not accepted, Elev: 3215ft/980m, Tel: 806-669-1044, Nearest town: Pampa. GPS: 35.537625, -100.933156

21 • A3 | Whigham Park

Total sites: 10, RV sites: 5, Elec sites: 5, Water at site, Flush toilet, No showers, RV dump, Tent & RV camping: Free, No restrooms in winter, Get code for utilities from police, Stay limit: 2 days, Reservations not accepted, Elev: 2946ft/898m, Tel: 806-435-4014, Nearest town: Perryton. GPS: 36.390113, -100.801923

22 • B2 | Coleman City Park

Total sites: 12, RV sites: 12, Elec sites: 12, Water at site, No toilets, No showers, RV dump, Tent & RV camping: Free, Stay limit: 5 days, Open all year, Reservations not accepted, Elev: 3280ft/1000m, Tel: 806-637-4547, Nearest town: Brownfield. GPS: 33.172692, -102.275833

23 • B2 | Comanche Trail City Park

Total sites: 5, RV sites: 5, No toilets, Tent & RV camping: Fee unk, Stay limit: 3 days, Elev: 2606ft/794m, Tel: 432-264-2323, Nearest town: Big Spring. GPS: 32.212935, -101.474643

24 • B2 | Florey City Park

Total sites: 130, RV sites: 20, Elec sites: 20, Water at site, Flush toilet, Free showers, RV dump, Tents: $10/RVs: $35, Stay limit: 7 days, Open all year, Reservations not accepted, Elev: 3173ft/967m, Tel: 432-524-1401, Nearest town: Andrews. GPS: 32.455188, -102.570653

25 • B2 | Forrest Park RV Park

Total sites: 8, RV sites: 8, Elec sites: 8, Central water, No toilets, No showers, RV dump, No tents/RVs: $20, 4 nights free, then $20, Stay limit: 10 days, Reservations not accepted, Elev: 2953ft/900m, Tel: 806-872-2124, Nearest town: Lamesa. GPS: 32.722697, -101.956761

26 • B2 | Gail RV Park

Total sites: 7, RV sites: 7, Tent & RV camping: Fee unk, Elev: 2533ft/772m, Nearest town: Gail. GPS: 32.771196, -101.441646

27 • B2 | Goldsmith City Park

Total sites: 12, RV sites: 12, Elec sites: 12, Water at site, No toilets, No showers, RV dump, Tent & RV camping: $15, Pay at City Hall, Open all year, Elev: 3169ft/966m, Nearest town: Goldsmith. GPS: 31.988939, -102.616519

28 • B2 | Levelland City RV Park

Total sites: 7, RV sites: 7, Elec sites: 7, Water at site, No toilets, No showers, RV dump, Tent & RV camping: Free, Beside runway, Stay limit: 3 days, Reservations not accepted, Elev: 3504ft/1068m, Tel: 806-894-0113, Nearest town: Levelland. GPS: 33.553607, -102.374612

29 • B2 | M.S. Doss City Park

Total sites: 6, RV sites: 6, Elec sites: 6, Central water, No toilets, No showers, RV dump, No tents/RVs: Free, Open all year, Max Length: 30ft, Elev: 3314ft/1010m, Tel: 432-758-3676, Nearest town: Seminole. GPS: 32.722153, -102.649441

30 • B2 | Moss Creek Lake City Park

Total sites: 26, RV sites: 26, Elec sites: 26, Water at site, No toilets, No showers, RV dump, Tents: $9/RVs: $12-15, Some Full hookup sites, Elev: 2362ft/720m, Tel: 432-393-5246, Nearest town: Big Spring. GPS: 32.241291, -101.316062

31 • B2 | Ralls Lions Park

Total sites: 3, RV sites: 3, Elec sites: 3, RV dump, Tent & RV camping: Fee unk, Elev: 3110ft/948m, Nearest town: Ralls. GPS: 33.671014, -101.387538

32 • B2 | Seagraves Chamber of Commerce RV Park

Total sites: 5, RV sites: 5, Elec sites: 5, No toilets, No showers, RV dump, No tents/RVs: Free, 3 nights free, then $5, Open all year, Elev: 3333ft/1016m, Nearest town: Seagraves. GPS: 32.942039, -102.559338

33 • B2 | Wickett City RV Park

Total sites: 30, RV sites: 30, Elec sites: 30, Water at site, No toilets, RV dump, No tents/RVs: $12, Open all year, Reservations not accepted, Elev: 2674ft/815m, Nearest town: Wickett. GPS: 31.570150, -103.001009

34 • B3 | Ballinger City Park

Total sites: 19, RV sites: 19, Elec sites: 19, Water at site, RV dump, Tent & RV camping: $15, Open all year, Reservations not accepted, Elev: 1611ft/491m, Tel: 325-365-3511, Nearest town: Ballinger. GPS: 31.749361, -99.945444

35 • B3 | Ballinger Lake Park

Total sites: 22, RV sites: 22, Elec sites: 11, Water at site, Flush toilet, No showers, RV dump, Tents: $9/RVs: $15, Open all year, Reservations not accepted, Elev: 1670ft/509m, Tel: 325-365-5411, Nearest town: Ballinger. GPS: 31.738826, -100.036344

36 • B3 | Bosque River RV Park

Total sites: 21, RV sites: 21, Elec sites: 21, Water at site, Tent & RV camping: $25, 21 Full hookup, $20 Nov-Feb, $30-$35 during festivals, Generator hours: 0700-2200, Open all year, Reservations accepted, Elev: 1014ft/309m, Tel: 254-796-4620, Nearest town: Hico. GPS: 31.975891, -98.031877

37 • B3 | Bronte RV Park

Total sites: 6, RV sites: 6, Elec sites: 6, Water at site, Flush toilet, Free showers, RV dump, Tent & RV camping: Fee unk, 6 Full hookup, Cold showers, 7-day limit, Elev: 1785ft/544m, Tel: 325-473-2401, Nearest town: Bronte. GPS: 31.882983, -100.283094

38 • B3 | City RV Park

Total sites: 11, RV sites: 11, Elec sites: 11, Water at site, No toilets, No showers, RV dump, No tents/RVs: $15, 11 Full hookup, Elev: 1309ft/399m, Tel: 940-849-4411, Nearest town: Throckmorton. GPS: 33.171456, -99.177117

39 • B3 | Clyde Lake

Total sites: 21, RV sites: 21, Elec sites: 10, Water at site, Vault/pit toilet, RV dump, Tents: $10/RVs: $18, 8 Full hookup, Open all year, Max Length: 8ft, Elev: 1894ft/577m, Tel: 325-893-5339, Nearest town: Clyde. GPS: 32.315772, -99.474086

40 • B3 | Comanche City Park

Total sites: 12, RV sites: 8, Elec sites: 8, No toilets, No showers, RV dump, Tent & RV camping: $20, Elev: 1398ft/426m, Tel: 325-356-2616, Nearest town: Comanche. GPS: 31.892694, -98.617271

41 • B3 | Crosbyton City Park

Total sites: 8, RV sites: 8, Elec sites: 8, Water at site, No toilets, No showers, RV dump, Tent & RV camping: $10, 8 Full hookup, First 2 nights free, Stay limit: 3 days, Elev: 3018ft/920m, Tel: 806-675-2301, Nearest town: Crosbyton. GPS: 33.657426, -101.232162

42 • B3 | De Leon Community Park

Total sites: 10, RV sites: 10, Elec sites: 10, RV dump, Tents: $20/RVs: $20-30, 10 Full hookup, Senior discount: $2, Reservations accepted, Elev: 1316ft/401m, Tel: 254-893-2065, Nearest town: De Leon. GPS: 32.117928, -98.523846

43 • B3 | Dublin City Park

Total sites: 8, RV sites: 8, Elec sites: 8, Water at site, Flush toilet, Tent & RV camping: $15, Reservations accepted, Elev: 1483ft/452m, Tel: 254-445-3331, Nearest town: Dublin. GPS: 32.090175, -98.352659

44 • B3 | Elm Creek Reservoir/W. Lee Colburn Park

Total sites: 14, RV sites: 14, Elec sites: 14, Water at site, Flush toilet, RV dump, Tent & RV camping: $15, 14 Full hookup, Open all year, Elev: 1821ft/555m, Tel: 915-723-2081, Nearest town: Winters. GPS: 31.940244, -99.862561

45 • B3 | Gary James Memorial Park

Total sites: 8, RV sites: 8, Elec sites: 8, Central water, RV dump, Tent & RV camping: $10, Elev: 1752ft/534m, Tel: 325-348-3232, Nearest town: Santa Anna. GPS: 31.739887, -99.318999

46 • B3 | Hamlin City Park

Total sites: 12, RV sites: 12, Elec sites: 8, Central water, Vault/pit toilet, No showers, No RV dump, No tents/RVs: $15, First night free, Elev: 1713ft/522m, Tel: 325-576-2711, Nearest town: Hamlin. GPS: 32.875443, -100.131168

47 • B3 | Hapgood City Park

Total sites: 12, RV sites: 12, Elec sites: 12, Water at site, No toilets, No showers, RV dump, No tents/RVs: $15, 12 Full hookup, Reservations not accepted, Elev: 886ft/270m, Tel: 940-538-4316, Nearest town: Henrietta. GPS: 33.801623, -98.180459

48 • B3 | Haskell City Park

Total sites: 36, RV sites: 36, Elec sites: 36, Water at site, Flush toilet, Free showers, RV dump, No tents/RVs: $16, First night free, 36 Full hookup, Pay at City Hall - 301 South 1st St, Open all year, Max Length: 32ft, Elev: 1572ft/479m, Tel: 940-864-2333, Nearest town: Haskell. GPS: 33.152788, -99.730917

49 • B3 | Hubbard Creek Reservoir

Dispersed sites, No water, Vault/pit toilet, Tent & RV camping: Free, Elev: 1190ft/363m, Nearest town: Breckenridge. GPS: 32.834943, -98.974989

50 • B3 | Jayton RV Park

Total sites: 8, RV sites: 8, Elec sites: 8, Water at site, No toilets, N showers, RV dump, No tents/RVs: Fee unk, Open all year, Elev 2009ft/612m, Tel: 806-237-3822, Nearest town: Jayton. GPS 33.252359, -100.573925

51 • B3 | Johnson City Park

Total sites: 5, RV sites: 5, No water, Flush toilet, Tent & R camping: Free, Stay limit: 2 days, Reservations not accepted, Elev 1657ft/505m, Tel: 325-676-6217, Nearest town: Abilene. GPS 32.613135, -99.680363

52 • B3 | Kindley City Park

Total sites: 6, RV sites: 6, Elec sites: 6, No toilets, No showers, N RV dump, No tents/RVs: $10, Reservations not accepted, Ele 1102ft/336m, Tel: 940-549-3324, Nearest town: Graham. GP 33.193854, -98.648285

53 • B3 | Lake Daniel

Dispersed sites, No water, Vault/pit toilet, Tent & RV campin Free, Open all year, Elev: 1322ft/403m, Tel: 254-559-8287, Neare town: Breckenridge. GPS: 32.646518, -98.872551

54 • B3 | Lake Eddleman City Park

Total sites: 22, RV sites: 12, Elec sites: 12, Water at site, No toilets, No showers, RV dump, Tent & RV camping: $12, Elev: 1112ft/339m, Tel: 940-549-3324, Nearest town: Graham. GPS: 33.138415, -98.597385

55 • B3 | Lake Stamford Park

Total sites: 75, RV sites: 75, Elec sites: 75, Water at site, Tents: $15/RVs: $35, Mostly seasonal, Elev: 1417ft/432m, Tel: 325-773-2095, Nearest town: Stamford. GPS: 33.045642, -99.609453

56 • B3 | Lake Sweetwater Park

Total sites: 32, RV sites: 19, Elec sites: 17, Water at site, Flush toilet, No showers, RV dump, Tents: $6/RVs: $10, Concessionaire, Reservations accepted, Elev: 2080ft/634m, Tel: 325-235-8816, Nearest town: Sweetwater. GPS: 32.440613, -100.303302

57 • B3 | Middle Concho Park

Dispersed sites, No water, Flush toilet, Tent & RV camping: $12, Residents $6, Open all year, Elev: 1883ft/574m, Tel: 325-657-4279, Nearest town: San Angelo. GPS: 31.379389, -100.520166

58 • B3 | Newman Park

Total sites: 6, RV sites: 6, Elec sites: 6, Central water, No toilets, No showers, RV dump, Tents: $6/RVs: $8, Elev: 2087ft/636m, Tel: 325-235-5003, Nearest town: Sweetwater. GPS: 32.485272, -100.410872

59 • B3 | Pelham Park

Total sites: 10, RV sites: 10, Elec sites: 10, Water at site, Flush toilet, Free showers, RV dump, Tent & RV camping: $15, Near RR, Stay limit: 7 days, Elev: 1116ft/340m, Tel: 940-872-1114, Nearest town: Bowie. GPS: 33.549172, -97.831135

60 • B3 | Press Morris Park

Total sites: 27, RV sites: 27, Elec sites: 27, Central water, Flush toilet, RV dump, Tents: $10/RVs: $15-20, 9 Full hookup, Open all year, Reservations not accepted, Elev: 1739ft/530m, Tel: 325-625-4116, Nearest town: Coleman. GPS: 32.036993, -99.462671

61 • B3 | Pugh River City Park

Dispersed sites, Vault/pit toilet, Tent & RV camping: Free, Stay limit: 3 days, Reservations not accepted, Elev: 2046ft/624m, Nearest town: Christoval. GPS: 31.184706, -100.496174

62 • B3 | Riverside City Park

Total sites: 26, RV sites: 26, Elec sites: 26, Central water, Flush toilet, Free showers, No RV dump, Tent & RV camping: $39, 24 Full hookup, TACO/ Good Sam/ AAA/AARP/active or retired military $35, Max Length: 100ft, Reservations accepted, Elev: 1333ft/406m, Tel: Info: 325-998-1969/Res: 325-642-1869, Nearest town: Brownwood. GPS: 31.736521, -98.975699

63 • B3 | Robert Lee Park

Total sites: 8, RV sites: 8, Elec sites: 8, Water at site, Flush toilet, No showers, RV dump, Tent & RV camping: Fee unk, Elev: 1841ft/561m, Nearest town: Robert Lee. GPS: 31.898247, -100.476558

64 • B3 | Ruddick City Park

Total sites: 5, RV sites: 5, No water, No toilets, No showers, No RV dump, No tents/RVs: Free, Must be self-contained, Elev: 2093ft/638m, Tel: 325-728-3464, Nearest town: Colorado City. GPS: 32.394607, -100.848358

65 • B3 | Samuel W. Wahl RA

Total sites: 40, RV sites: 40, Elec sites: 20, Water at site, Flush toilet, Pay showers, No RV dump, Tents: $10/RVs: $20, Plus $12/person, Generator use allowed overnight only on NORTH side of the parking lot, Generator hours: 0500-2200, Max Length: 25ft, Reservations not accepted, Elev: 2241ft/683m, Tel: 806-775-2673, Nearest town: Lubbock. GPS: 33.048819, -101.083069

66 • B3 | San Saba River RV Park

Total sites: 33, RV sites: 33, Elec sites: 33, Water at site, Flush toilet, Free showers, RV dump, No tents/RVs: $30-35, 33 Full hookup, New in 2008, Elev: 1194ft/364m, Tel: 325-372-3212, Nearest town: San Saba. GPS: 31.202509, -98.695107

67 • B3 | Seabee City Park

Total sites: 4, RV sites: 4, Central water, No toilets, No showers, No RV dump, No tents/RVs: Free, Stay limit: 2 days, Reservations not accepted, Elev: 1654ft/504m, Tel: 325-676-6217, Nearest town: Abilene. GPS: 32.538817, -99.715444

68 • B3 | Selma City Park

Total sites: 21, RV sites: 21, Elec sites: 21, Water at site, Flush toilet, Free showers, No RV dump, Tent & RV camping: $16, Cold showers, Open all year, Elev: 961ft/293m, Tel: 940-872-1114, Nearest town: Bowie. GPS: 33.484490, -97.887710

69 • B3 | Slim Sorrells Park

Total sites: 7, RV sites: 7, Elec sites: 7, Water at site, No tents/RVs: Free, Stay limit: 3 days, Elev: 1681ft/512m, Tel: 940-996-2214, Nearest town: Rule. GPS: 33.184782, -99.891133

70 • B3 | South Park

Dispersed sites, No water, No toilets, Tent & RV camping: Free, Rough access road - no large RVs, Open all year, Elev: 1768ft/539m, Tel: 325-576-2711, Nearest town: Hamlin. GPS: 32.819343, -100.076233

71 • B3 | Spring Creek Park

Dispersed sites, No water, Vault/pit toilet, Tent & RV camping: $12, City residents: $6, Stay limit: 14 days, Open all year, Elev: 1867ft/569m, Tel: 325-481-2617, Nearest town: San Angelo. GPS: 31.377067, -100.507187

72 • B3 | Stephenville City Park

Total sites: 7, RV sites: 7, Elec sites: 7, Water at site, Flush toilet, Free showers, RV dump, No tents/RVs: $20, Must be self-contained, Seniors $15, No open fires, Stay limit: 7 days, Reservations not accepted, Elev: 1283ft/391m, Tel: 254-918-1295, Nearest town: Stephenville. GPS: 32.213093, -98.197067

73 • B3 | Stonewall Jackson Camp

Total sites: 25, RV sites: 5, Central water, Vault/pit toilet, Tent & RV camping: Free, No water in winter, Open all year, Elev:

1024ft/312m, Tel: 940-586-1313, Nearest town: Holliday. GPS: 33.786211, -98.679041

74 • B3 | Twin Buttes Reservoir - 12-Mile Boat Ramp - City

Dispersed sites, No water, No toilets, Tent & RV camping: Fee unk, $12 annual Limited Public Use permit required, Elev: 1959ft/597m, Tel: 325-277-8766, Nearest town: San Angelo. GPS: 31.377765, -100.602697

75 • B3 | Twin Buttes Reservoir - Equalization Channel - City

Dispersed sites, No water, No toilets, Tent & RV camping: Fee unk, $12 annual Limited Public Use permit required, Elev: 1959ft/597m, Tel: 325-277-8766, Nearest town: San Angelo. GPS: 31.342309, -100.516851

76 • B3 | Twin Buttes Reservoir - Marina - City

Dispersed sites, No water, No toilets, Tent & RV camping: Fee unk, $12 annual Limited Public Use permit required, Elev: 1909ft/582m, Tel: 325-277-8766, Nearest town: San Angelo. GPS: 31.388966, -100.552234

77 • B3 | Wichita Bend RV Park

Total sites: 28, RV sites: 28, Elec sites: 28, Water at site, No toilets, No showers, RV dump, No tents/RVs: $17, RVs must be self-contained, Stay limit: 3 days, Elev: 942ft/287m, Tel: 940-761-7491, Nearest town: Wichita Falls. GPS: 33.916597, -98.511231

78 • B3 | Winters RV Park

Total sites: 6, RV sites: 6, Elec sites: 6, Water at site, No RV dump, No tents/RVs: $20, Elev: 1854ft/565m, Nearest town: Winters. GPS: 31.956996, -99.964491

79 • B4 | Canton Civic Center and RV Park

Total sites: 220, RV sites: 220, Elec sites: 220, Water at site, Flush toilet, Free showers, RV dump, No tents/RVs: $30-45, Full hookup sites, Open all year, Reservations accepted, Elev: 482ft/147m, Tel: 903-567-6556, Nearest town: Canton. GPS: 32.560713, -95.864464

80 • B4 | City Park Camp

Total sites: 33, RV sites: 33, Elec sites: 33, Water at site, Flush toilet, Free showers, RV dump, Tent & RV camping: $20, 33 Full hookup, Cold showers, Elev: 492ft/150m, Tel: 903-834-3171, Nearest town: Overton. GPS: 32.272009, -94.986336

81 • B4 | Concession Park

Dispersed sites, No water, Vault/pit toilet, Tent & RV camping: Free, Parking lot, Elev: 384ft/117m, Nearest town: Tyler. GPS: 32.211721, -95.180071

82 • B4 | East Side Park #4

Dispersed sites, No water, No toilets, Tent & RV camping: Free, Parking lot, Open all year, Max Length: 16ft, Reservations not accepted, Elev: 436ft/133m, Tel: 903-939-2724, Nearest town: Tyler. GPS: 32.229949, -95.162798

83 • B4 | Eastvale Park

Dispersed sites, No toilets, Tent & RV camping: Fee unk, Open all year, Elev: 558ft/170m, Tel: 972-625-1106, Nearest town: The Colony. GPS: 33.113753, -96.893386

84 • B4 | Erwin Park

Total sites: 10, RV sites: 0, Central water, No toilets, No showers, No RV dump, Tents only: $20, $70 to camp beside pavilion, $12.50 for local residents, No water in winter, Open all year, Reservations required, Elev: 640ft/195m, Tel: 972-547-7480, Nearest town: McKinney. GPS: 33.255286, -96.654867

85 • B4 | Faunt Leroy City Park

Total sites: 8, RV sites: 8, Elec sites: 8, Water at site, Flush toilet, Free showers, RV dump, No tents/RVs: $20, 8 Full hookup, Cold showers, Stay limit: 11 days, Open all year, Reservations accepted, Elev: 761ft/232m, Tel: 254-865-2226, Nearest town: Gatesville. GPS: 31.425162, -97.749151

86 • B4 | Fort Worth Convention Center

Total sites: 134, RV sites: 134, Elec sites: 134, Water at site, No tents/RVs: $30-60, 104 Full hookup, Some hookups shared - may be some distance from RV to pole, Open all year, Reservations not accepted, Elev: 611ft/186m, Tel: 817-392-7469, Nearest town: Fort Worth. GPS: 32.750207, -97.326872

87 • B4 | Governor Jim Hogg RV Park

Total sites: 19, RV sites: 19, Elec sites: 19, Water at site, Flush toilet, Free showers, RV dump, No tents/RVs: $20, 19 Full hookup, Elev: 407ft/124m, Tel: 903-763-0405, Nearest town: Quitman. GPS: 32.791798, -95.454071

88 • B4 | Hidden Cove City Park

Total sites: 100, RV sites: 100, Elec sites: 100, Water at site, Flush toilet, Free showers, RV dump, Tents: $25/RVs: $55-75, 56 Full hookup, Winter fees, Concessionaire, Open all year, Reservations accepted, Elev: 545ft/166m, Tel: 972-294-1443, Nearest town: The Colony. GPS: 33.130454, -96.939363

89 • B4 | Highway 64 Ramp

Dispersed sites, No water, No toilets, Tent & RV camping: Free Open all year, Reservations not accepted, Elev: 410ft/125m, Tel 903-939-2724, Nearest town: Tyler. GPS: 32.278496, -95.113168

90 • B4 | Hill Creek Park

Dispersed sites, No water, No toilets, Tent & RV camping: Free Open all year, Elev: 410ft/125m, Tel: 903-939-2724, Nearest town Tyler. GPS: 32.233955, -95.183367

91 • B4 | Lake Bonham RA

Total sites: 89, RV sites: 89, Elec sites: 89, Water at site, Vault pit toilet, No showers, RV dump, Tents: $6/RVs: $15-20, Senio discount, Stay limit: 14 days, No generators, Open all yea Reservations accepted, Elev: 584ft/178m, Tel: 903-227-751 Nearest town: Bonham. GPS: 33.642939, -96.136946

92 • B4 | Lake Jacksonville Park

Total sites: 17, RV sites: 10, Elec sites: 17, Water at site, Flush toile Free showers, RV dump, Tents: $25/RVs: $25-45, $45 include shelter, Reservations accepted, Elev: 459ft/140m, Tel: 903-58 4160, Nearest town: Jacksonville. GPS: 31.920471, -95.290292

93 • B4 | Lewisville Lake Park

Total sites: 97, RV sites: 80, Elec sites: 80, Water at site, Flush toilet, Free showers, RV dump, Tent & RV camping: $20-22, 50% senior discount on RV sites, Tent camping Fri-Sat only, Open all year, Reservations accepted, Elev: 548ft/167m, Tel: 972-219-3742, Nearest town: Lewisville. GPS: 33.075472, -97.001707

94 • B4 | Little Elm Park

Dispersed sites, Central water, Vault/pit toilet, No showers, No RV dump, Tents only: $5, Must bring approved fire pit, Stay limit: 4 days, Elev: 545ft/166m, Tel: 972-731-3296, Nearest town: Little Elm. GPS: 33.161672, -96.944799

95 • B4 | Meadowmere Park

Total sites: 46, Central water, Vault/pit toilet, Tents only: $35, Reservations accepted, Elev: 551ft/168m, Tel: 817-488-5272, Nearest town: Grapevine. GPS: 32.982279, -97.115145

96 • B4 | Mineola Civic Center and RV Park

Total sites: 44, RV sites: 44, Elec sites: 44, Water at site, No toilets, No showers, RV dump, No tents/RVs: $34-39, 44 Full hookup, Elev: 453ft/138m, Tel: 903-569-6115, Nearest town: Mineola. GPS: 32.675096, -95.480255

97 • B4 | Oakdale City Park

Total sites: 132, RV sites: 112, Elec sites: 112, Water at site, Flush toilet, Free showers, RV dump, Tents: $20/RVs: $25-38, 112 Full hookup, No fires, Reservations accepted, Elev: 621ft/189m, Tel: 254-897-2321, Nearest town: Glen Rose. GPS: 32.239494, -97.745186

98 • B4 | Old Omen West City Park

Total sites: 6, RV sites: 6, No water, Vault/pit toilet, Tent & RV camping: Free, Use street address - not GPS, Open all year, Reservations not accepted, Elev: 387ft/118m, Tel: 903-939-2724, Nearest town: Tyler. GPS: 32.240437, -95.136787

99 • B4 | Pilot Knoll Park

Total sites: 68, RV sites: 55, Elec sites: 55, Water at site, Flush toilet, Free showers, RV dump, Tent & RV camping: $30-35, 13 walk-to sites, $20-$25 for local residents, Open all year, Reservations accepted, Elev: 535ft/163m, Tel: 940-455-2228, Nearest town: Highland Village. GPS: 33.107677, -97.071761

100 • B4 | South Shore Park

Dispersed sites, No water, No toilets, Tent & RV camping: Free, Open all year, Elev: 426ft/130m, Tel: 903-586-3510, Nearest town: Jacksonville. GPS: 31.901649, -95.309308

101 • B4 | Stewart Creek Park

Total sites: 30, RV sites: 4, Elec sites: 4, Water at site, Flush toilet, Free showers, RV dump, Tents: $25/RVs: $30, Stay limit: 14 days, Open all year, Reservations accepted, Elev: 561ft/171m, Tel: 972-624-2248, Nearest town: The Colony. GPS: 33.082583, -96.920306

102 • B4 | Sycamore Bend

Dispersed sites, Tents only: $7, Stay limit: 3 days, Generator hours: 0700-2200, Open all year, Elev: 571ft/174m, Tel: 940-497-2528, Nearest town: Lewisville. GPS: 33.108835, -97.060581

103 • B4 | Twin Coves Park

Total sites: 22, RV sites: 22, Elec sites: 22, Water at site, Flush toilet, Free showers, RV dump, Tent & RV camping: $35-55, Also cabins, Some Full hookup, $10 daily entrance fee, Reservations accepted, Elev: 556ft/169m, Tel: 972-874-6399, Nearest town: Flower Mound. GPS: 33.005084, -97.105248

104 • B4 | Vineyards CG

Total sites: 93, RV sites: 93, Elec sites: 93, Flush toilet, Free showers, RV dump, No tents/RVs: $49-69, Also cabins, 93 Full hookup, Open all year, Max Length: 70ft, Reservations accepted, Elev: 577ft/176m, Tel: 888-329-8993, Nearest town: Grapevine. GPS: 32.954346, -97.059082

105 • B4 | Will Rogers Coliseum

Total sites: 78, RV sites: 78, Elec sites: 78, No tents/RVs: $60, 78 Full hookup, Open all year, Reservations not accepted, Elev: 593ft/181m, Tel: 866-630-2588, Nearest town: Fort Worth. GPS: 32.736709, -97.367322

106 • B4 | Winnsboro City Park

Total sites: 20, RV sites: 20, Elec sites: 20, Water at site, Flush toilet, Free showers, RV dump, Tent & RV camping: $15, Near RR, Open all year, Reservations accepted, Elev: 508ft/155m, Tel: 903-342-3564, Nearest town: Winnsboro. GPS: 32.952701, -95.276483

107 • B5 | Mission Dolores City Park

Total sites: 32, RV sites: 32, Elec sites: 32, Water at site, Flush toilet, Free showers, RV dump, Tent & RV camping: $22, 32 Full hookup, Open all year, Elev: 343ft/105m, Tel: 936-275-3815, Nearest town: San Augustine. GPS: 31.520956, -94.114691

108 • B5 | Pinkston Dam

Dispersed sites, No toilets, Tent & RV camping: Free, Open all year, Elev: 328ft/100m, Tel: 936-598-2941, Nearest town: Center. GPS: 31.710211, -94.363019

109 • B5 | Sandy Creek

Dispersed sites, No toilets, Tent & RV camping: Free, Open all year, Elev: 358ft/109m, Tel: 936-598-2941, Nearest town: Center. GPS: 31.704905, -94.336918

110 • C2 | Alley Oop City RV Park

Total sites: 10, RV sites: 10, Elec sites: 10, Water at site, No toilets, No showers, RV dump, No tents/RVs: $15, Mostly seasonal, Reservations not accepted, Elev: 2254ft/687m, Tel: 432-639-2301, Nearest town: Iraan. GPS: 30.917338, -101.908965

111 • C2 | Langtry Community Center

Dispersed sites, No water, No toilets, No tents/RVs: Donation, Judge Roy Bean Museum, Open all year, Elev: 1299ft/396m, Tel: 915-291-3340, Nearest town: Langtry. GPS: 29.808921, -101.560205

112 • C2 | Rocky Top City RV Park

Total sites: 14, RV sites: 14, Elec sites: 14, Water at site, No toilets, No showers, RV dump, No tents/RVs: Fee unk, Mostly seasonal, Elev: 2204ft/672m, Tel: 432-639-2301, Nearest town: Iraan. GPS: 30.911338, -101.892521

113 • C2 | Santa Fe City Park

Total sites: 4, RV sites: 4, Elec sites: 4, Water at site, RV dump, Tent & RV camping: Free, Permit required from City Hall, Elev: 2474ft/754m, Tel: 432-652-3333, Nearest town: McCamey. GPS: 31.137967, -102.216637

114 • C2 | The Landing RV Park

Total sites: 12, RV sites: 12, Elec sites: 12, Central water, No toilets, No showers, RV dump, Tent & RV camping: $12, Beside municipal runway, Open all year, Reservations not accepted, Elev: 2195ft/669m, Tel: 432-639-2301, Nearest town: Iraan. GPS: 30.908797, -101.895079

115 • C3 | Badu City Park

Total sites: 11, RV sites: 11, Elec sites: 11, Water at site, No toilets, No showers, RV dump, No tents/RVs: $35, 11 Full hookup, Stay limit: 7 days, Open all year, Reservations not accepted, Elev: 1040ft/317m, Tel: 325-247-4158 X 202, Nearest town: Llano. GPS: 30.754962, -98.676975

116 • C3 | Brady Lake City Park

Total sites: 38, RV sites: 20, Elec sites: 20, Water at site, Flush toilet, Free showers, RV dump, Tents: $5-10/RVs: $25-35, Reservations accepted, Elev: 1752ft/534m, Tel: 325-597-1823, Nearest town: Brady. GPS: 31.128633, -99.382991

117 • C3 | Castroville RP

Total sites: 44, RV sites: 40, Elec sites: 40, Water at site, Flush toilet, Free showers, RV dump, Tents: $10/RVs: $45, Stay limit: 180 days, Open all year, Reservations accepted, Elev: 748ft/228m, Tel: 830-931-4070, Nearest town: Castroville. GPS: 29.343764, -98.881647

118 • C3 | Emma Long Metropolitan Park

Total sites: 66, RV sites: 66, Elec sites: 20, Water at site, Flush toilet, Free showers, RV dump, Tents: $10-20/RVs: $20-25, Open all year, Reservations accepted, Elev: 522ft/159m, Tel: 512-346-1831, Nearest town: Austin. GPS: 30.326711, -97.840527

119 • C3 | Fort Mason City Park

Total sites: 24, RV sites: 24, Elec sites: 24, Water at site, Flush toilet, Free showers, RV dump, Tents: $10/RVs: $30, Reservations accepted, Elev: 1506ft/459m, Tel: 325-347-2064, Nearest town: Mason. GPS: 30.737497, -99.211958

120 • C3 | Kerrville-Schreiner City Park

Total sites: 124, RV sites: 124, Elec sites: 66, Water at site, Flush toilet, Free showers, RV dump, Tents: $20/RVs: $25-35, Also cabins, Open all year, Reservations accepted, Elev: 1680ft/512m, Tel: 830-257-7300, Nearest town: Kerrville. GPS: 30.002476, -99.127391

121 • C3 | Lady Bird Johnson City Park

Total sites: 98, RV sites: 98, Elec sites: 98, Water at site, Flush toilet, Free showers, RV dump, Tents: $10/RVs: $48-52, 98 Full hookup, Open all year, Reservations accepted, Elev: 1683ft/513m, Tel: 830-997-4202, Nearest town: Fredericksburg. GPS: 30.242376, -98.911484

122 • C3 | Llano River RV Park

Total sites: 25, RV sites: 25, Elec sites: 25, Water at site, Flush toilet, Free showers, RV dump, No tents/RVs: $30, 25 Full hookup, Tent camping: $7/person, Concessionaire, Open all year, Reservations accepted, Elev: 1050ft/320m, Tel: 325-247-7905, Nearest town: Llano. GPS: 30.749892, -98.705517

123 • C3 | Richards City Park

Total sites: 14, RV sites: 14, Elec sites: 14, Water at site, Flush toilet, Free showers, RV dump, Tents: $5/RVs: $20, 14 Full hookup, Stay limit: 10 days, Elev: 1676ft/511m, Tel: 325-597-2152, Nearest town: Brady. GPS: 31.131803, -99.351135

124 • C3 | Schreiner City Park

Dispersed sites, Central water, No toilets, Tent & RV camping: Free, No bathrooms in winter, Stay limit: 3 days, Elev: 1696ft/517m, Tel: 325-446-2622, Nearest town: Junction. GPS: 30.490650, -99.760680

125 • C3 | Tips Park

Total sites: 40, RV sites: 20, Elec sites: 20, Water at site, Flush toilet, Free showers, RV dump, Tents: $5/RVs: $15, Open all year, Elev: 141ft/43m, Tel: 361-786-4330, Nearest town: Three Rivers. GPS: 28.461899, -98.191496

126 • C3 | Willie Washington City Park

Total sites: 6, RV sites: 6, Elec sites: 6, Water at site, Tents: $5/RVs: $20, 6 Full hookup, Stay limit: 10 days, Elev: 1683ft/513m, Nearest town: Brady. GPS: 31.123858, -99.327281

127 • C4 | Austwell City Park

Total sites: 9, RV sites: 9, Elec sites: 9, Water at site, Flush toilet, Free showers, RV dump, Tents: $22/RVs: $22-26, 12 Full hookup, Open all year, Elev: 36ft/11m, Tel: 361-286-3523, Nearest town: Austwell. GPS: 28.389941, -96.846756

128 • C4 | Bolivar Flats Beach Dispersed

Dispersed sites, No water, Vault/pit toilet, Tent & RV camping $10, $10 annual pass, 27 miles of beach camping, Open all year Reservations not accepted, Elev: 3ft/1m, Nearest town: Crysta Beach. GPS: 29.382619, -94.723204

129 • C4 | Bryan Beach

Dispersed sites, No water, Vault/pit toilet, Tent & RV camping Free, Open all year, Reservations not accepted, Elev: 7ft/2m Tel: 979-233-3526, Nearest town: Brazosport. GPS: 28.912342, 95.335597

130 • C4 | Dellanera City RV Park

Total sites: 65, RV sites: 65, Elec sites: 65, Water at site, Flush toile Free showers, RV dump, No tents/RVs: $46-59, 65 Full hookup Add $10 holiday weekends, $41-$46 Oct to mid-May, No ope fires, Open all year, Reservations accepted, Elev: 20ft/6m, Tel: 409 797-5102, Nearest town: Galveston. GPS: 29.240893, -94.87297

131 • C4 | Eastside City Park

Total sites: 3, RV sites: 3, Elec sites: 3, Water at site, No toilets, N showers, RV dump, Tent & RV camping: Fee unk, Elev: 1240f 378m, Nearest town: Hearne. GPS: 30.885422, -96.584094

132 • C4 | Fayetteville Town Square

Dispersed sites, No water, No toilets, Tent & RV camping: Fre

Room for 1 or 2 rigs along Hwy 159 SE side of square, Permission required, Elev: 423ft/129m, Tel: 979-249-6702, Nearest town: Fayetteville. GPS: 29.904158, -96.675539

133 • C4 | Green Dickson Park

Total sites: 12, RV sites: 12, Elec sites: 12, Water at site, RV dump, Tent & RV camping: $30, 12 Full hookup, Reservations accepted, Elev: 384ft/117m, Tel: 361-594-3362, Nearest town: Shriner. GPS: 29.449901, -97.183416

134 • C4 | Hub City RV Park

Total sites: 50, RV sites: 50, Elec sites: 50, Water at site, Flush toilet, Free showers, RV dump, Tents: $8/RVs: $15-18, Senior discount, Open all year, Elev: 348ft/106m, Tel: 361-293-5682, Nearest town: Yoakum. GPS: 29.304781, -97.129597

135 • C4 | Independence City Park

Total sites: 21, RV sites: 21, Elec sites: 21, Central water, Flush toilet, RV dump, Tent & RV camping: $30, Elev: 274ft/84m, Tel: 830-672-1324, Nearest town: Gonzales. GPS: 29.485143, -97.451236

136 • C4 | Lake Houston Wilderness Park - Platforms

Total sites: 8, RV sites: 0, Central water, Flush toilet, Free showers, No RV dump, Tents only: $7, Platforms for tents, Open all year, Elev: 70ft/21m, Tel: 281-354-6881, Nearest town: New Caney. GPS: 30.139959, -95.168175

137 • C4 | Lake Houston Wilderness Park -Backcountry

Total sites: 24, RV sites: 0, Central water, Flush toilet, Free showers, No RV dump, Tents only: $7, Hike-in, - platforms, Open all year, Elev: 69ft/21m, Tel: 281-354-6881, Nearest town: New Caney. GPS: 30.136018, -95.174609

138 • C4 | Lake Tejas City Park - Eastside

Total sites: 2, RV sites: 2, Elec sites: 2, Water at site, No toilets, No showers, RV dump, Tent & RV camping: $25, Open May-Sep, Elev: 234ft/71m, Tel: 409-837-575 x103, Nearest town: Colmesneil. GPS: 30.902141, -94.403732

139 • C4 | Lake Tejas City Park - Westside

Total sites: 5, RV sites: 5, Elec sites: 5, Water at site, No toilets, No showers, RV dump, Tent & RV camping: $25, 5 Full hookup, Open May-Sep, Elev: 248ft/76m, Tel: 409-837-575 x103, Nearest town: Colmesneil. GPS: 30.903542, -94.405597

140 • C4 | Lighthouse Beach RV Park

Total sites: 63, RV sites: 55, Elec sites: 55, Water at site, Flush toilet, Free showers, RV dump, Tents: $10/RVs: $40, Also cabins, 55 Full hookup, Open all year, Reservations not accepted, Elev: 9ft/3m, Tel: 361-552-5311, Nearest town: Port Lavaca,. GPS: 28.638163, -96.613741

141 • C4 | Riverside City Park

Total sites: 74, RV sites: 74, Elec sites: 74, Water at site, Flush toilet, Free showers, RV dump, Tents: $5/RVs: $20-25, 40 Full hookup, Open all year, Reservations accepted, Elev: 72ft/22m, Tel: 979-245-0340, Nearest town: Bay City. GPS: 28.920727, -96.014364

142 • C4 | Vernon L Richards Riverbend Park

Total sites: 19, RV sites: 19, Elec sites: 19, Water at site, Flush toilet, Free showers, RV dump, Tent & RV camping: $20-25, Reservations accepted, Elev: 302ft/92m, Tel: 512-237-3282 x2323, Nearest town: Smithville. GPS: 30.022376, -97.142901

143 • C4 | Victoria RV Park

Total sites: 18, RV sites: 18, Elec sites: 18, Water at site, No toilets, No showers, RV dump, Tent & RV camping: $12, Stay limit: 30 days, Open all year, Reservations not accepted, Elev: 82ft/25m, Tel: 361-485-3200, Nearest town: Victoria. GPS: 28.814799, -97.009037

144 • C4 | Welch City Park

Total sites: 40, RV sites: 40, Elec sites: 13, Water at site, Flush toilet, Free showers, No RV dump, Tents: $8/RVs: $20, Open all year, Elev: 271ft/83m, Tel: 979-596-2286, Nearest town: Somerville. GPS: 30.337548, -96.550964

145 • D3 | Falcon Heights Park

Dispersed sites, Central water, Flush toilet, Free showers, Tents: Free/RVs: $0-10, Open all year, Reservations not accepted, Elev: 335ft/102m, Nearest town: Falcon Heights. GPS: 26.566322, -99.127848

146 • D4 | Boca Chica Beach

Dispersed sites, No water, No toilets, Tent & RV camping: Fee unk, 4x4 required for beach camping, Open all year, Reservations not accepted, Elev: 7ft/2m, Tel: 956-546-3721, Nearest town: Brownsville. GPS: 26.014488, -97.153031

147 • D4 | Labonte Park

Total sites: 20, RV sites: 20, No water, No toilets, No showers, No RV dump, Tent & RV camping: Free, Obtain permit at City Hall, $25-$50 holiday weekends, Stay limit: 3 days, Open all year, Reservations accepted, Elev: 10ft/3m, Tel: 361-826-7529, Nearest town: Corpus Christi. GPS: 27.893821, -97.631037

148 • D4 | Port Aransas Beach Dispersed - City

Dispersed sites, Flush toilet, Free showers, No tents/RVs: $45, $12 annual car permit required - additional $45 for RV beach parking, Stay limit: 3 days, Open all year, Reservations not accepted, Elev: 16ft/5m, Tel: 361-749-4158, Nearest town: Aransas Pass. GPS: 27.816441, -97.064726

149 • D4 | Rob and Bessie Welder City Park

Total sites: 60, RV sites: 60, Elec sites: 60, Water at site, Flush toilet, Free showers, No RV dump, No tents/RVs: $35, 60 Full hookup, Open all year, Reservations accepted, Elev: 79ft/24m, Tel: 361-437-6795, Nearest town: Sinton. GPS: 28.071127, -97.528121

Utah

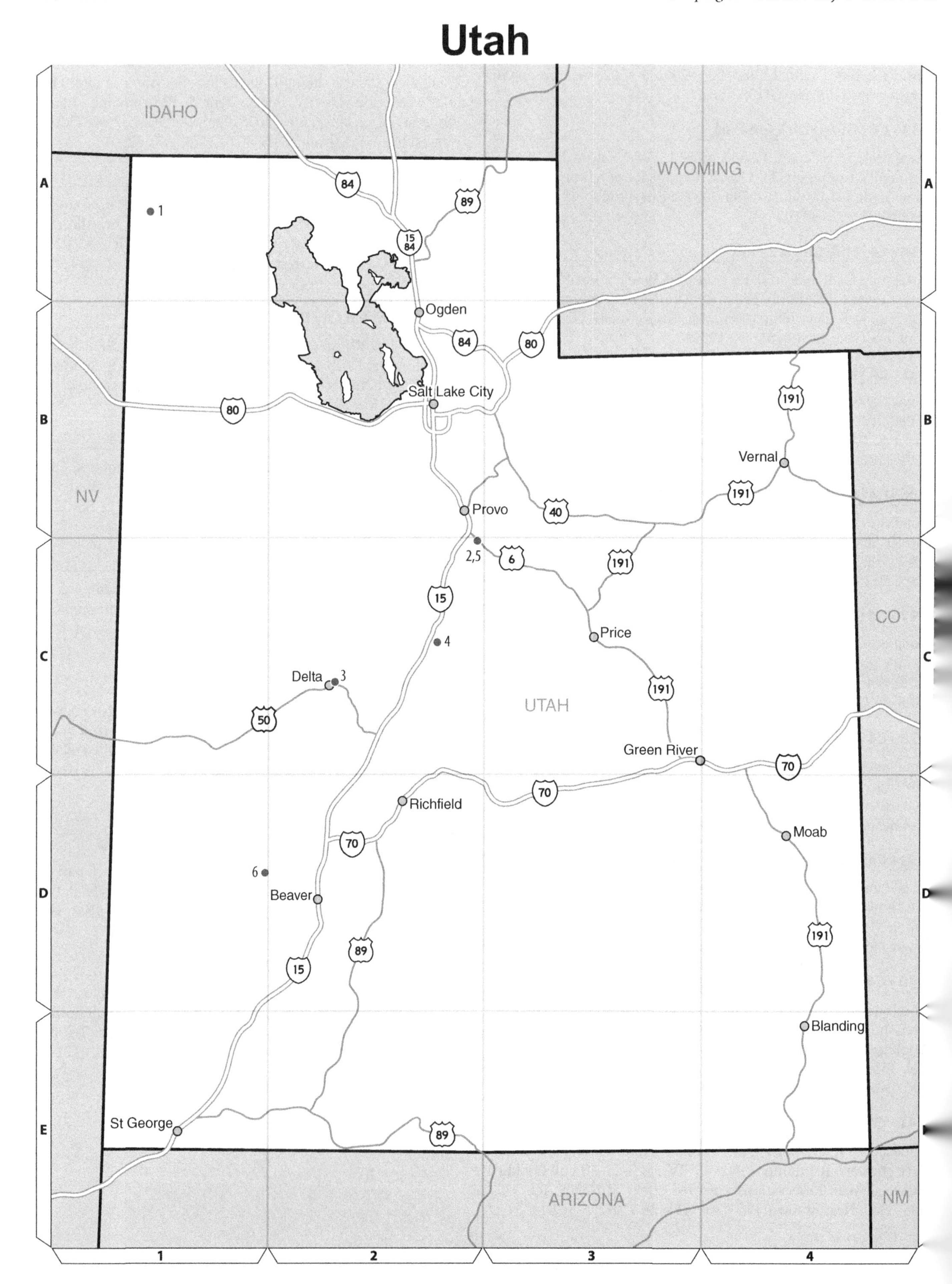
IDAHO
WYOMING
NV
CO
UTAH
ARIZONA
NM
Ogden
Salt Lake City
Provo
Vernal
Price
Delta
Green River
Richfield
Moab
Beaver
Blanding
St George
1
2,5
3
4
6
A
B
C
D
E
1
2
3
4
84
89
15
80
40
191
6
50
70

Map	ID	Map	ID
A1	1	D1	6
C2	2-5		

Alphabetical List of Camping Areas

Name	ID	Map
Canyon View RV Park	2	C2
Delta City RV Parking	3	C2
Grouse Creek Community Park and CG	1	A1
Levan Town Park	4	C2
Lions Club RV Park	6	D1
Spanish Oaks City CG	5	C2

1 • A1 | Grouse Creek Community Park and CG

Total sites: 9, RV sites: 9, Central water, Vault/pit toilet, No showers, No RV dump, Tent & RV camping: Fee unk, Camping also available at store, Elev: 5321ft/1622m, Tel: 801-678-6574, Nearest town: Grouse Creek. GPS: 41.708497, -113.884224

2 • C2 | Canyon View RV Park

Total sites: 24, RV sites: 24, Elec sites: 24, Water at site, RV dump, Tent & RV camping: $25, Stay limit: 14 days, Generator hours: 0700-2200, Open Apr-Oct, Reservations accepted, Elev: 4718ft/1438m, Tel: 801-798-5000, Nearest town: Spanish Fork. GPS: 40.081737, -111.601420

3 • C2 | Delta City RV Parking

Total sites: 1, RV sites: 1, Elec sites: 1, No water, No toilets, No tents/RVs: Fee unk, Unconfirmed, 2-day limit, Stay limit: 2 days, Elev: 4644ft/1415m, Nearest town: Delta. GPS: 39.353889, -112.578959

4 • C2 | Levan Town Park

Total sites: 6, RV sites: 6, Central water, Vault/pit toilet, No showers, No RV dump, No tents/RVs: Donation, Generator hours: 0700-2200, Reservations required, Elev: 5322ft/1622m, Tel: 435-623-1959, Nearest town: Levan. GPS: 39.563446, -111.862072

5 • C2 | Spanish Oaks City CG

Total sites: 24, RV sites: 12, Central water, Vault/pit toilet, Tents: $10/RVs: $25, Stay limit: 14 days, Open Apr-Oct, Reservations accepted, Elev: 5181ft/1579m, Tel: 801-804-4600, Nearest town: Spanish Fork. GPS: 40.070373, -111.599191

6 • D1 | Lions Club RV Park

Total sites: 6, RV sites: 6, Central water, No toilets, No showers, RV dump, Tent & RV camping: Donation, Elev: 5010ft/1527m, Nearest town: Milford. GPS: 38.401170, -113.014436

Vermont

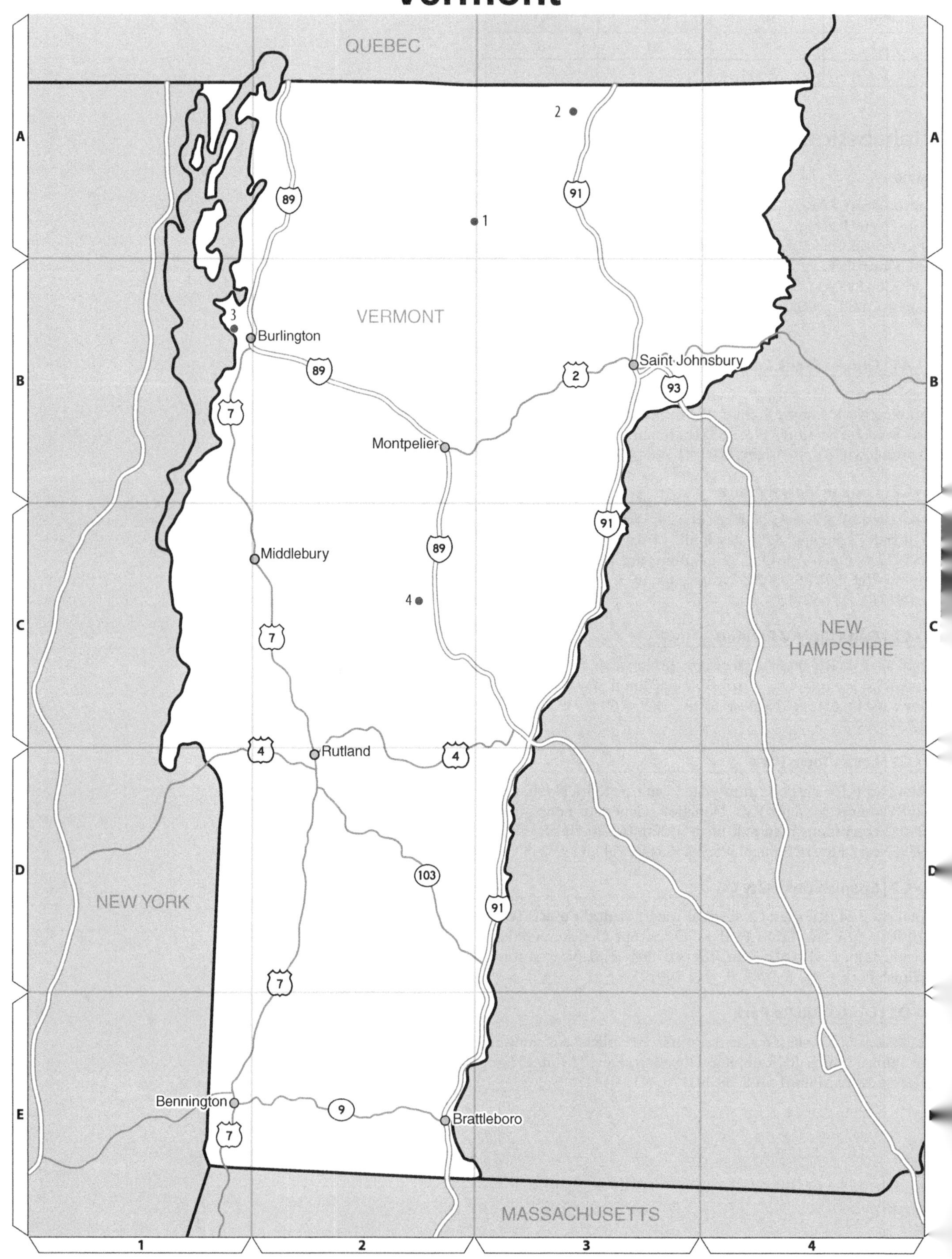
QUEBEC
VERMONT
NEW YORK
NEW HAMPSHIRE
MASSACHUSETTS
Burlington
Saint Johnsbury
Montpelier
Middlebury
Rutland
Bennington
Brattleboro
1
2
3
4
89
91
2
93
7
4
103
9
A
B
C
D
E

Map	ID	Map	ID
A2	1	B1	3
A3	2	C2	4

Alphabetical List of Camping Areas

1 • A2 | Lake Eden RA

Total sites: 25, RV sites: 17, Elec sites: 17, Central water, Flush toilet, Free showers, Tents: $25/RVs: $40, Mostly seasonal - 2 overnight RV sites available, Reservations accepted, Elev: 1252ft/382m, Tel: 802-635-7725, Nearest town: Lowell. GPS: 44.720281, -72.508787

2 • A3 | Prouty Beach City Park

Total sites: 57, RV sites: 54, Elec sites: 54, Water available, Flush toilet, Free showers, RV dump, Tents: $36/RVs: $44-75, Generator hours: 0800-2200, Open May-Oct, Reservations accepted, Elev: 686ft/209m, Tel: 802-334-7951, Nearest town: Newport. GPS: 44.948010, -72.209570

3 • B1 | North Beach City Park

Total sites: 137, RV sites: 68, Elec sites: 68, Water at site, Flush toilet, Free showers, RV dump, Tents: $37/RVs: $41-45, 29 Full hookup, Open May-Oct, Reservations accepted, Elev: 184ft/56m, Tel: 802-862-0942, Nearest town: Burlington. GPS: 44.492043, -73.233588

4 • C2 | Randolph Town Forest

Dispersed sites, No water, No toilets, Tent & RV camping: Free, No large RVs, Reservations not accepted, Elev: 857ft/261m, Nearest town: Randolph. GPS: 43.931995, -72.666865

Virginia

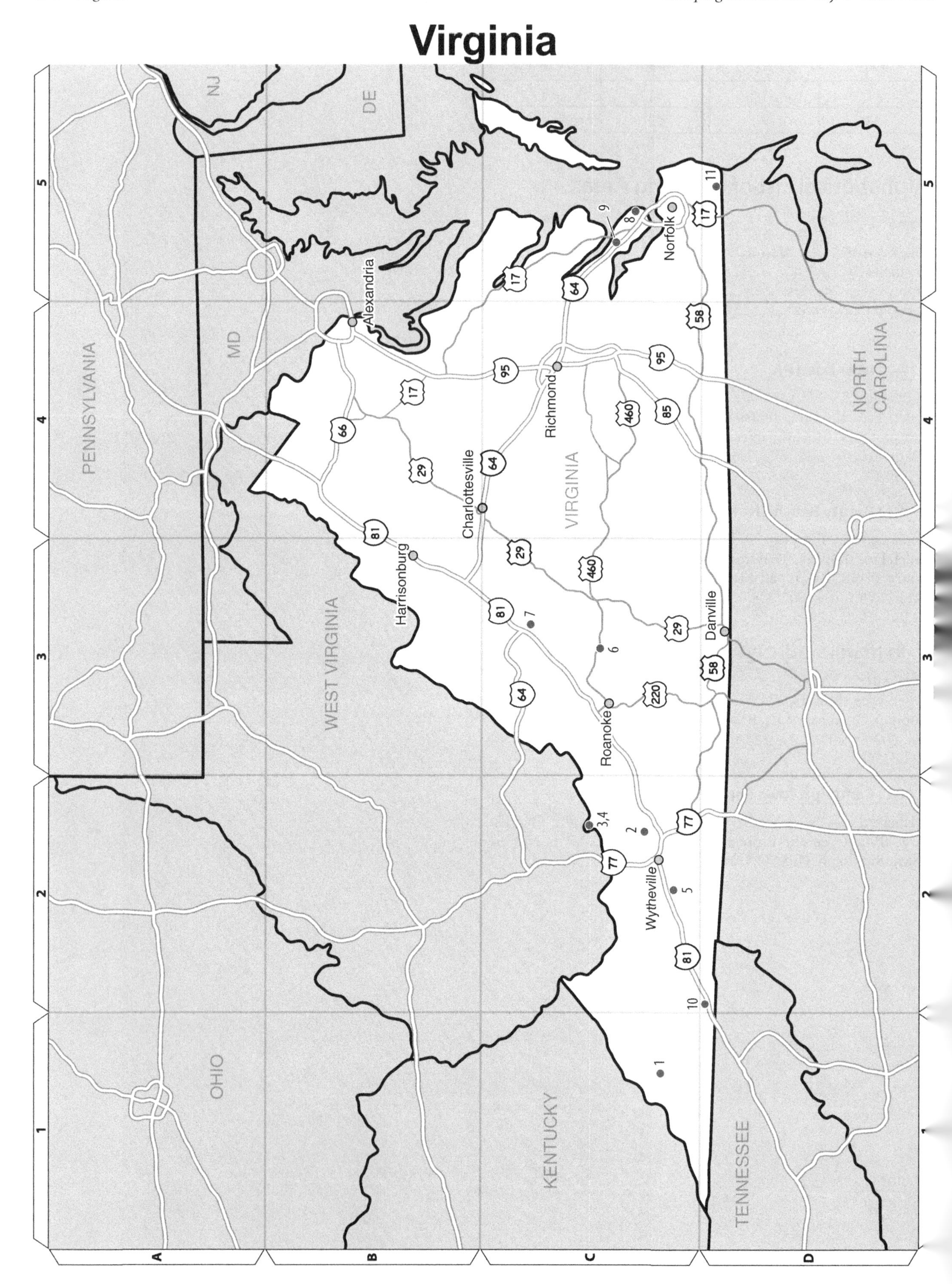
PENNSYLVANIA
NJ
DE
MD
WEST VIRGINIA
VIRGINIA
NORTH CAROLINA
OHIO
KENTUCKY
TENNESSEE
Alexandria
Richmond
Charlottesville
Harrisonburg
Norfolk
Danville
Roanoke
Wytheville
1
2
3,4
5
6
7
8
9
10
11
17
64
95
66
29
460
85
58
81
220
77
A
B
C
D
1
2
3
4
5

Map	ID	Map	ID
C1	1	C5	8-9
C2	2-5	D2	10
C3	6-7	D5	11

Alphabetical List of Camping Areas

1 • C1 | Flag Rock RA

Total sites: 18, RV sites: 18, Water at site, Flush toilet, Free showers, RV dump, Tent & RV camping: $20, 18 Full hookup, Stay limit: 14 days, Generator hours: 0600-2200, Open Apr-Oct, Elev: 3396ft/1035m, Tel: 276-679-0754, Nearest town: Norton. GPS: 36.915319, -82.629755

2 • C2 | Gatewood Lake

Total sites: 42, RV sites: 35, Elec sites: 35, Water at site, Flush toilet, Free showers, RV dump, Tents: $15-30/RVs: $35-45, Near RR, Open Apr-Oct, Reservations not accepted, Elev: 2205ft/672m, Tel: 540-980-2561, Nearest town: Pulaski. GPS: 37.043780, -80.873310

3 • C2 | Gentry's Landing

Total sites: 80, RV sites: 80, Elec sites: 80, Water at site, Flush toilet, Free showers, RV dump, Tent & RV camping: $19, Mostly seasonal, Elev: 1588ft/484m, Tel: 540-726-7509, Nearest town: Narrows. GPS: 37.374418, -80.820896

4 • C2 | Glen Lyn City Park

Total sites: 18, RV sites: 18, Elec sites: 15, Water at site, Flush toilet, Free showers, RV dump, Tents: $15/RVs: $15-20, Some Full hookup, Open May-Sep, Elev: 1555ft/474m, Tel: 540-726-7075, Nearest town: Glen Lyn. GPS: 37.372808, -80.857951

5 • C2 | Rural Retreat Lake

Total sites: 74, RV sites: 54, Elec sites: 54, Water available, Flush toilet, Free showers, RV dump, Tents: $18/RVs: $28, Open May-Sep, Reservations accepted, Elev: 2497ft/761m, Tel: 276-686-4331, Nearest town: Wytheville. GPS: 36.864607, -81.284881

6 • C3 | Bedford Welcome Center

Total sites: 3, RV sites: 3, Elec sites: 3, Water at site, Flush toilet, No showers, RV dump, No tents/RVs: $25, Full hookup sites, Open all year, Reservations not accepted, Elev: 1019ft/311m, Tel: 540-587-5681, Nearest town: Bedford. GPS: 37.324971, -79.532301

7 • C3 | Glen Maury City Park

Total sites: 52, RV sites: 52, Elec sites: 52, Water at site, Flush toilet, Free showers, RV dump, Tents: $22/RVs: $32-35, $27-$30 Sep-Apr, Passport America $20, $1 senior discount, 22 Full hookup, Open all year, Reservations not accepted, Elev: 971ft/296m, Tel: 540-261-7321, Nearest town: Buena Vista. GPS: 37.728910, -79.366310

8 • C5 | Gosnold's Hope City Park

Total sites: 16, RV sites: 16, Elec sites: 16, Water at site, Flush toilet, Free showers, RV dump, No tents/RVs: $32, Open all year, Reservations not accepted, Elev: 20ft/6m, Tel: 757-850-5116, Nearest town: Hampton. GPS: 37.072510, -76.333740

9 • C5 | Newport News City Park

Total sites: 188, RV sites: 188, Elec sites: 164, Water at site, Flush toilet, Free showers, RV dump, Tents: $32/RVs: $32-34, Youth group sites: $30-$40, Open all year, Reservations accepted, Elev: 76ft/23m, Tel: 757-888-3333, Nearest town: Newport News. GPS: 37.188939, -76.556588

10 • D2 | Sugar Hollow City Park

Total sites: 75, RV sites: 44, Elec sites: 70, Central water, Flush toilet, Free showers, RV dump, Tent & RV camping: $20, Open Apr-Oct, Reservations not accepted, Elev: 1870ft/570m, Tel: 276-645-7275, Nearest town: Bristol. GPS: 36.646112, -82.110513

11 • D5 | Northwest River City Park

Total sites: 66, RV sites: 66, Elec sites: 40, Central water, Flush toilet, Free showers, RV dump, Tents: $21/RVs: $26, Also cabins, Open Apr-Nov, Reservations accepted, Elev: 39ft/12m, Tel: 757-421-7151, Nearest town: Chesapeake. GPS: 36.584742, -76.157161

Washington

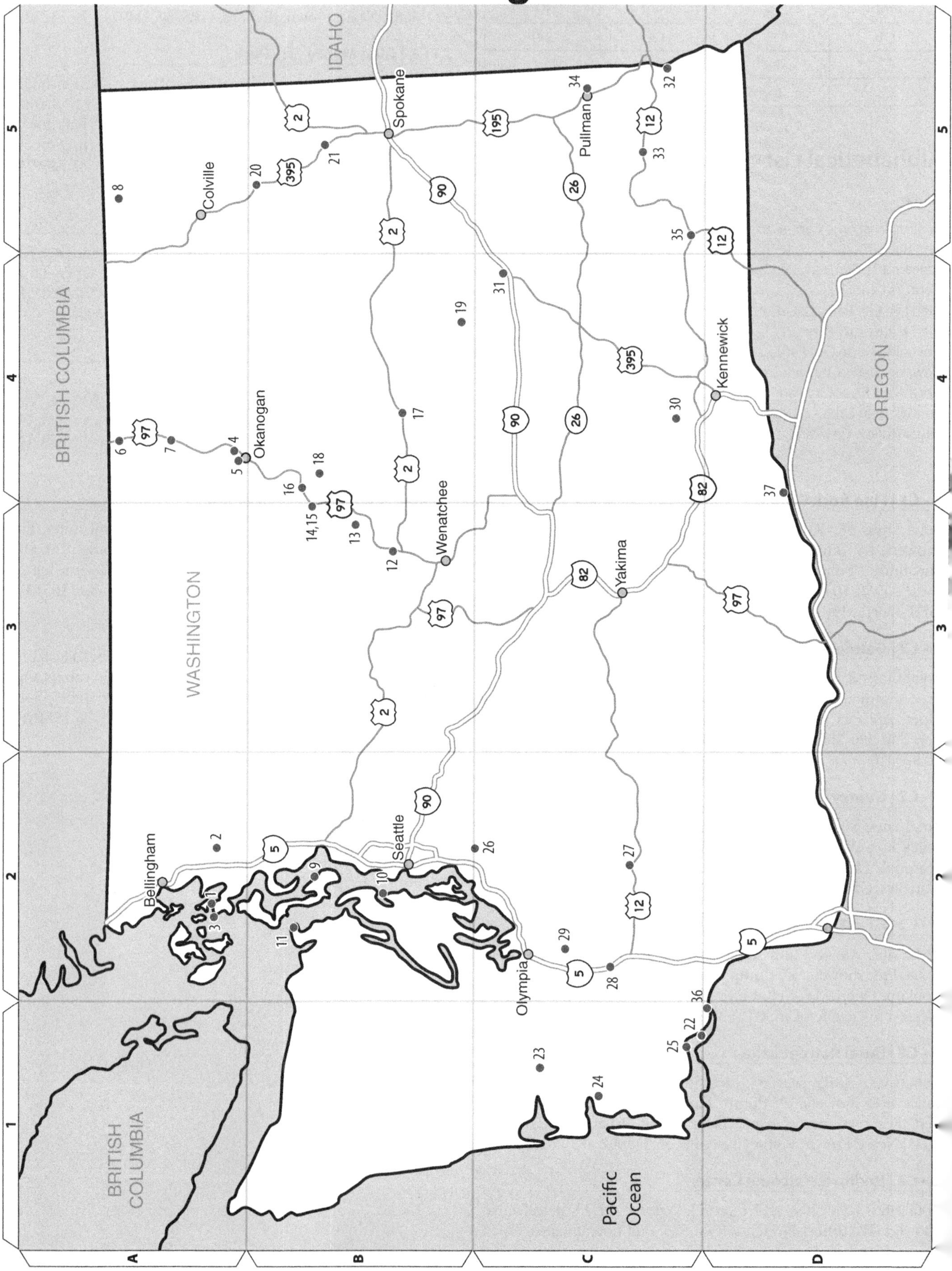
BRITISH COLUMBIA
IDAHO
WASHINGTON
OREGON
BRITISH COLUMBIA
Pacific Ocean
Spokane
Colville
Pullman
Okanogan
Kennewick
Wenatchee
Yakima
Bellingham
Seattle
Olympia
A
B
C
D
1
2
3
4
5
1
2
3
4
5
6
7
8
9
10
11
12
13
14,15
16
17
18
19
20
21
22
23
24
25
26
27
28
29
30
31
32
33
34
35
36
37
2
5
12
26
82
90
97
195
395

Map	ID	Map	ID
A2	1-3	C1	22-25
A4	4-7	C2	26-29
A5	8	C4	30-31
B2	9-11	C5	32-35
B3	12-15	D1	36
B4	16-19	D4	37
B5	20-21		

Alphabetical List of Camping Areas

1 • A2 | Cap Sante Marina

Total sites: 27, RV sites: 27, No water, Flush toilet, Pay showers, No tents/RVs: $20, Reservations not accepted, Elev: 15ft/5m, Tel: 360-293-0694, Nearest town: Anacortes. GPS: 48.516387, -122.608141

2 • A2 | Riverfront City RV Park

Total sites: 38, RV sites: 28, Elec sites: 28, Water at site, No toilets, No showers, No RV dump, Tents: $10/RVs: $25, Dump station 5 blocks, Reservations accepted, Elev: 46ft/14m, Tel: 360-855-1661, Nearest town: Sedro-Woolley. GPS: 48.491274, -122.222265

3 • A2 | Washington City Park

Total sites: 68, RV sites: 68, Elec sites: 46, Water at site, Flush toilet, Free showers, RV dump, Tents: $21/RVs: $27, City residents: $17/$21, Stay limit: 14 days, Open all year, Reservations accepted, Elev: 30ft/9m, Tel: 360-293-1918, Nearest town: Anacortes. GPS: 48.499091, -122.692114

4 • A4 | Carl Precht Memorial RV Park

Total sites: 68, RV sites: 68, Elec sites: 68, Water at site, Flush toilet, Pay showers, RV dump, Tents: $20/RVs: $33, 68 Full hookup, Winter rate: $28 w/ no water, Open all year, Reservations not accepted, Elev: 837ft/255m, Tel: 509-826-1170, Nearest town: Omak. GPS: 48.411708, -119.516397

5 • A4 | Legion RV Park

Dispersed sites, Central water, Flush toilet, Pay showers, RV dump, Tents: $6/RVs: $15, Elev: 827ft/252m, Tel: 509-422-3600, Nearest town: Okanogan. GPS: 48.376768, -119.564094

6 • A4 | Osoyoos Lake City Park

Total sites: 87, RV sites: 81, Elec sites: 18, Central water, Flush toilet, Free showers, RV dump, Tents: $16/RVs: $26-33, Stay limit: 14 days, Open Mar-Oct, Max Length: 45ft, Reservations accepted, Elev: 919ft/280m, Tel: 360-902-8844, Nearest town: Oroville. GPS: 48.948975, -119.433350

7 • A4 | Tonasket Visitors Center RV Park

Total sites: 8, RV sites: 8, Elec sites: 8, Water at site, Flush toilet, Free showers, RV dump, Tent & RV camping: $25, 8 Full hookup, Dump fee, Reservations not accepted, Elev: 902ft/275m, Tel: 509-486-4436, Nearest town: Tonasket. GPS: 48.708979, -119.439413

8 • A5 | Northport City Park

Total sites: 4, RV sites: 4, Elec sites: 4, Water at site, Flush toilet, No showers, No RV dump, No tents/RVs: $10, Max Length: 25ft, Reservations not accepted, Elev: 1319ft/402m, Nearest town: Northport. GPS: 48.921114, -117.772967

9 • B2 | Fairgrounds CG

Total sites: 50, RV sites: 30, Elec sites: 30, Water at site, Flush toilet, Free showers, RV dump, Tents: $20/RVs: $25, Limited water hook-ups Nov-Mar, Stay limit: 14 days, Open all year, Reservations not accepted, Elev: 144ft/44m, Tel: 360-221-7950, Nearest town: Langley. GPS: 48.031054, -122.402442

10 • B2 | Fay Bainbridge City Park

Total sites: 40, RV sites: 26, Water at site, Flush toilet, Pay showers, No RV dump, Tents: $20/RVs: $40, Group site $65, Stay limit: 10 days, Generator hours: 0800-2100, Open all year, Max Length: 40ft, Reservations accepted, Elev: 7ft/2m, Tel: 206-842-2306, Nearest town: Bainbridge Island. GPS: 47.702452, -122.507574

11 • B2 | Point Hudson Marina and RV Park

Total sites: 48, RV sites: 48, Elec sites: 46, Water at site, Flush toilet,

Pay showers, RV dump, No tents/RVs: $50-61, Dry camp: $31, Oct-Apr: $43-$50, Open all year, Reservations accepted, Elev: 12ft/4m, Tel: 360-385-2828, Nearest town: Port Townsend. GPS: 48.118793, -122.751646

12 • B3 | Entiat Park

Total sites: 57, RV sites: 31, Elec sites: 31, Water at site, Flush toilet, Pay showers, RV dump, Tents: $22/RVs: $28, 31 Full hookup, Open Apr-Sep, Reservations accepted, Elev: 728ft/222m, Tel: 509-784-1500, Nearest town: Entiat. GPS: 47.668871, -120.217495

13 • B3 | Lakeshore RV Park

Total sites: 163, RV sites: 163, Elec sites: 163, Water at site, Flush toilet, Pay showers, RV dump, Tents: $45/RVs: $55-65, 163 Full hookup, Wi-Fi near office, Lower off-season rates, Open all year, Max Length: 40ft, Reservations accepted, Elev: 1129ft/344m, Tel: 509-682-8024, Nearest town: Chelan. GPS: 47.846041, -120.027302

14 • B3 | Pateros City Park

Dispersed sites, Flush toilet, Free showers, Tent & RV camping: $15, Park on city street adjacent to grass along Columbia River., Reservations not accepted, Elev: 781ft/238m, Nearest town: Pateros. GPS: 48.052409, -119.900123

15 • B3 | Peninsula City Park

Dispersed sites, Tent & RV camping: Fee unk, Elev: 784ft/239m, Tel: 509-923-2571, Nearest town: Pateros. GPS: 48.048400, -119.907000

16 • B4 | Columbia Cove RV Park

Total sites: 34, RV sites: 34, Elec sites: 34, Water at site, Flush toilet, Free showers, RV dump, No tents/RVs: $35-45, 29 Full hookup, Dry camping: $15, Open all year, Max Length: 70ft, Reservations accepted, Elev: 781ft/238m, Tel: 509-733-0540, Nearest town: Brewster. GPS: 48.091241, -119.784151

17 • B4 | Coulee City Community Park

Total sites: 100, RV sites: 55, Elec sites: 55, Water at site, Flush toilet, Free showers, RV dump, Tents: $20/RVs: $35, 55 Full hookup, Open Apr-Oct, Reservations not accepted, Elev: 1578ft/481m, Tel: 509-632-5331, Nearest town: Coulee City. GPS: 47.616921, -119.290715

18 • B4 | Marina RV Park

Total sites: 22, RV sites: 22, Elec sites: 22, Water at site, Flush toilet, Free showers, RV dump, Tents: $15/RVs: $30, Full hookup sites, Nov-Mar (no water): $20, RV dump: $5, Open all year, Max Length: 60ft, Reservations accepted, Elev: 800ft/244m, Tel: 509-686-4747, Nearest town: Bridgeport. GPS: 48.013926, -119.677389

19 • B4 | Odessa City Park

Total sites: 3, RV sites: 2, Elec sites: 2, Water at site, Flush toilet, No showers, No RV dump, Tent & RV camping: $11, Free first 3 nights, Near RR, Elev: 1549ft/472m, Tel: 509-982-0093, Nearest town: Odessa. GPS: 47.333386, -118.687303

20 • B5 | Jenne Memorial City Park

Total sites: 24, RV sites: 14, Elec sites: 14, Central water, No toilets, No showers, No RV dump, Tent & RV camping: Fee unk, No water in winter, Open all year, Max Length: 50ft, Elev: 1683ft/513m, Tel: 509-935-8311, Nearest town: Chewelah. GPS: 48.279852, -117.714533

21 • B5 | Swinyard City Park

Total sites: 5, RV sites: 5, Elec sites: 5, No toilets, No tents/RVs: $10, Reservations not accepted, Elev: 2125ft/648m, Tel: 509-276-8801, Nearest town: Deer Park. GPS: 47.951901, -117.475021

22 • C1 | Elochoman Slough Marina

Total sites: 26, RV sites: 26, Elec sites: 15, Water at site, Flush toilet, Free showers, RV dump, Tents: $25/RVs: $26-35, Also cabins, Open all year, Reservations accepted, Elev: 7ft/2m, Tel: 360-795-3501, Nearest town: Cathlamet. GPS: 46.204771, -123.387601

23 • C1 | Friends Landing

Total sites: 28, RV sites: 18, Water at site, Vault/pit toilet, No showers, No RV dump, Tents: $30/RVs: $40, Open Mar-Nov, Reservations accepted, Elev: 14ft/4m, Tel: 360-861-8864, Nearest town: Montesano. GPS: 46.946891, -123.643041

24 • C1 | Helen Davis Memorial Park

Dispersed sites, No water, Vault/pit toilet, Tents: $5/RVs: $10, Elev: 14ft/4m, Nearest town: South Bend. GPS: 46.671251, -123.815592

25 • C1 | Vista Park

Total sites: 69, RV sites: 42, Elec sites: 42, Water at site, Flush toilet, Free showers, RV dump, Tents: $25/RVs: $30-40, 15 Full hookup, Oct-Apr: $5 discount, Max Length: 40ft, Reservations accepted, Elev: 121ft/37m, Tel: 360-795-8605, Nearest town: Skamokawa. GPS: 46.271290, -123.460350

26 • C2 | Game Farm Wilderness Park

Total sites: 18, RV sites: 18, Elec sites: 18, Central water, Flus toilet, No showers, RV dump, Tent & RV camping: $35, No wate Dec-Feb, Stay limit: 7 days, Generator hours: 0700-2300, Ma Length: 50ft, Reservations accepted, Elev: 163ft/50m, Tel: 253-931-3043, Nearest town: Auburn. GPS: 47.278695, -122.195828

27 • C2 | Gust Backstrom City Park

Total sites: 43, RV sites: 36, Elec sites: 29, Central water, Flus toilet, Free showers, Tents: $15/RVs: $30-32, 9 Full hookup, Sta limit: 21 days, Open all year, Reservations accepted, Elev: 922ft 281m, Tel: 360-496-6844, Nearest town: Morton. GPS: 46.559419 -122.283173

28 • C2 | Stan Hedwall Park

Total sites: 29, RV sites: 29, Elec sites: 29, Water at site, Flush toile Pay showers, RV dump, Tent & RV camping: $20, Dump fee: $ Stay limit: 7 days, Open Apr-Nov, Reservations not accepte Elev: 180ft/55m, Tel: 360-748-0271, Nearest town: Chehalis. GP 46.639759, -122.964105

29 • C2 | Tenino City Park

Dispersed sites, Flush toilet, Tents: $10/RVs: $15, Stay limit: 1 days, Elev: 282ft/86m, Tel: 360-264-2368, Nearest town: Tenin GPS: 46.854814, -122.853272

30 • C4 | Horn Rapids ORV Park

Total sites: 100, RV sites: 100, Elec sites: 100, Water at site, Flush toilet, Free showers, Tents: $10/RVs: $20-25, 100 Full hookup, Concession, Elev: 453ft/138m, Tel: 509-496-2958, Nearest town: Richland. GPS: 46.352236, -119.357723

31 • C4 | Wheat Lands Community Fairgrounds

Total sites: 55, RV sites: 55, Elec sites: 55, Water at site, Flush toilet, Free showers, No RV dump, No tents/RVs: $15-25, Elev: 1806ft/550m, Tel: 509-659-1936, Nearest town: Ritzville. GPS: 47.136915, -118.371416

32 • C5 | Asotin City Park

Total sites: 3, RV sites: 3, Elec sites: 3, Water at site, Flush toilet, No showers, No RV dump, Tents: $15/RVs: $25, Check-in at City Hall - 121 Cleveland St, Hook-ups require checking in at City Hall first, Generator hours: 0800-2100, Open all year, Reservations not accepted, Elev: 756ft/230m, Tel: 590-243-4411, Nearest town: Asotin. GPS: 46.340303, -117.056108

33 • C5 | Pataha Creek RV Park

Total sites: 20, RV sites: 20, Elec sites: 20, Water at site, Flush toilet, Free showers, RV dump, No tents/RVs: $35, 20 Full hookup, Reservations accepted, Elev: 1815ft/553m, Tel: 509-843-3740, Nearest town: Pomeroy. GPS: 46.474851, -117.613213

34 • C5 | Pullman RV Park

Total sites: 19, RV sites: 19, Elec sites: 19, Water at site, No toilets, No showers, RV dump, Tents: $10/RVs: $30, Stay limit: 10 days, Open Apr-Nov, Reservations accepted, Elev: 2356ft/718m, Tel: 509-338-3227, Nearest town: Pullman. GPS: 46.725835, -117.170725

35 • C5 | Waitsburg Fairgrounds

Total sites: 14, RV sites: 14, Elec sites: 14, Free showers, No tents/RVs: $15-25, Elev: 1289ft/393m, Tel: 509-337-6371, Nearest town: Waitsburg. GPS: 46.262161, -118.149593

36 • D1 | County Line Park

Total sites: 21, RV sites: 18, Elec sites: 18, Central water, Flush toilet, Pay showers, RV dump, Tents: $13/RVs: $23, 3 beach tent sites, Open all year, Max Length: 30ft, Reservations accepted, Elev: 282ft/86m, Tel: 360-577-3174, Nearest town: Kelso. GPS: 46.179252, -123.203686

37 • D4 | Crow Butte Park

Total sites: 50, RV sites: 50, Elec sites: 50, Water at site, Flush toilet, Free showers, RV dump, Tents: $20/RVs: $40, 50 Full hookup, Group site $80, Generator hours: 0630-2200, Open Mar-Oct, Max Length: 90ft, Reservations accepted, Elev: 295ft/90m, Tel: 509-940-7326, Nearest town: Patterson. GPS: 45.853946, -119.852603

West Virginia

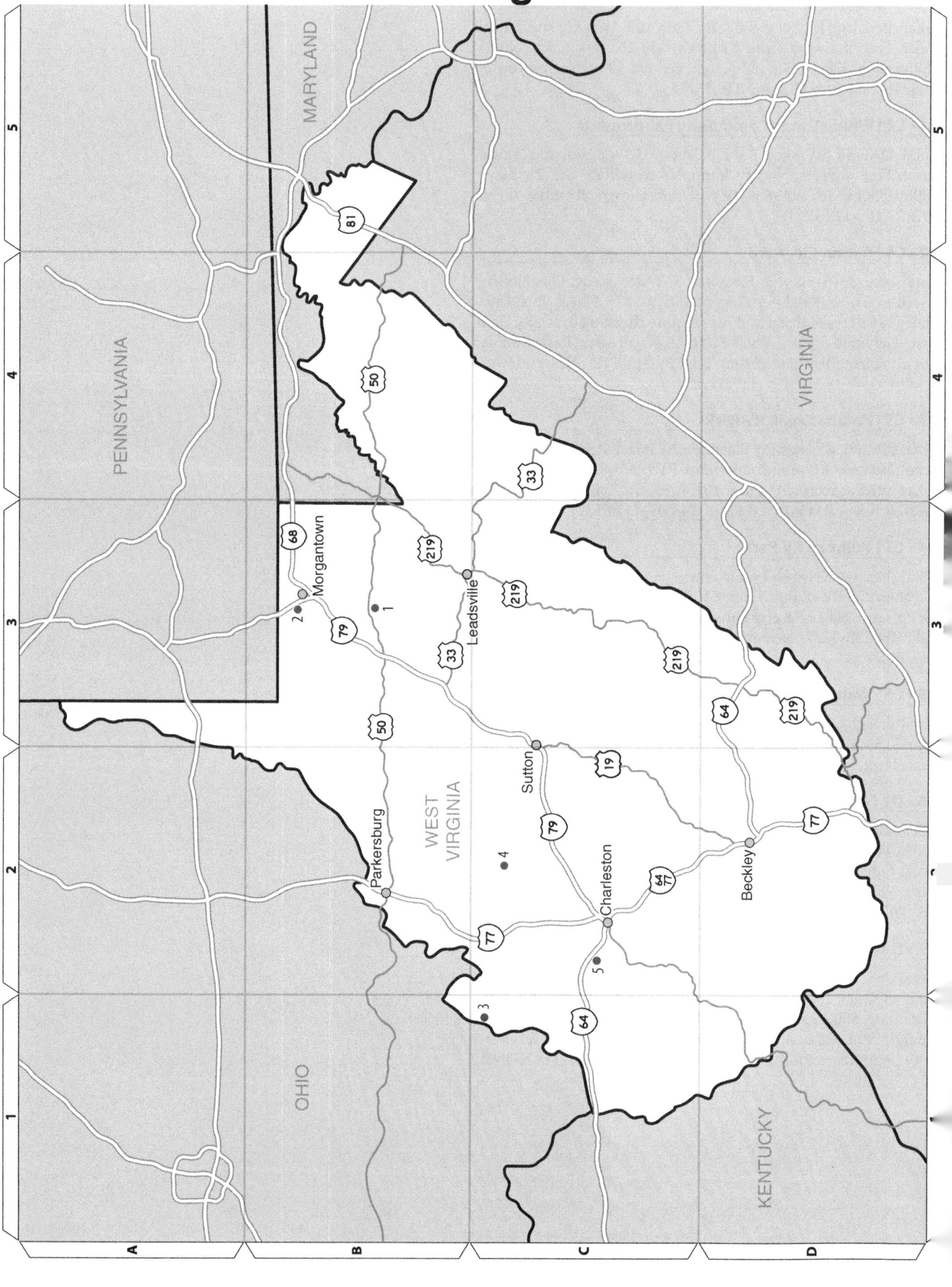

PENNSYLVANIA
MARYLAND
VIRGINIA
OHIO
KENTUCKY
WEST VIRGINIA
Morgantown
Leadsville
Sutton
Parkersburg
Charleston
Beckley
1
2
3
4
5
81
50
33
219
68
79
19
64
77
A
B
C
D

Map	ID	Map	ID
B3	1-2	C2	4-5
C1	3		

Alphabetical List of Camping Areas

1 • B3 | Grafton City Park

Total sites: 30, RV sites: 30, Elec sites: 30, Water at site, Flush toilet, Free showers, RV dump, Tent & RV camping: $40, Full hookup sites, Concessionaire, Open all year, Elev: 994ft/303m, Tel: 304-265-1412, Nearest town: Grafton. GPS: 39.317253, -80.031703

2 • B3 | Mylan Park

Total sites: 35, RV sites: 35, Elec sites: 35, Water at site, Flush toilet, RV dump, No tents/RVs: $40, 35 Full hookup, Elev: 1187ft/362m, Tel: 304-983-2383, Nearest town: Morgantown. GPS: 39.637956, -80.031813

3 • C1 | Krodel City Park

Total sites: 63, RV sites: 63, Elec sites: 63, Water at site, Flush toilet, Free showers, RV dump, Tents: $20/RVs: $25, 63 Full hookup, 14 sites open in winter, Open Apr-Oct, Reservations accepted, Elev: 597ft/182m, Tel: 304 675-1068, Nearest town: Point Pleasant. GPS: 38.839453, -82.124756

4 • C2 | Charles Fork Lake

Total sites: 10, RV sites: 5, Elec sites: 5, No water, Vault/pit toilet, No showers, No RV dump, Tents: $8/RVs: $14, Open Mar-Nov, Reservations not accepted, Elev: 744ft/227m, Tel: 304-532-7533, Nearest town: Spencer. GPS: 38.773938, -81.344389

5 • C2 | St. Albans Roadside Park

Total sites: 5, RV sites: 5, Elec sites: 5, Central water, Vault/pit toilet, No showers, RV dump, No tents/RVs: Donation, Stay limit: 2 days, Reservations not accepted, Elev: 588ft/179m, Tel: 304-722-4625, Nearest town: St. Albans. GPS: 38.388479, -81.824673

Wisconsin

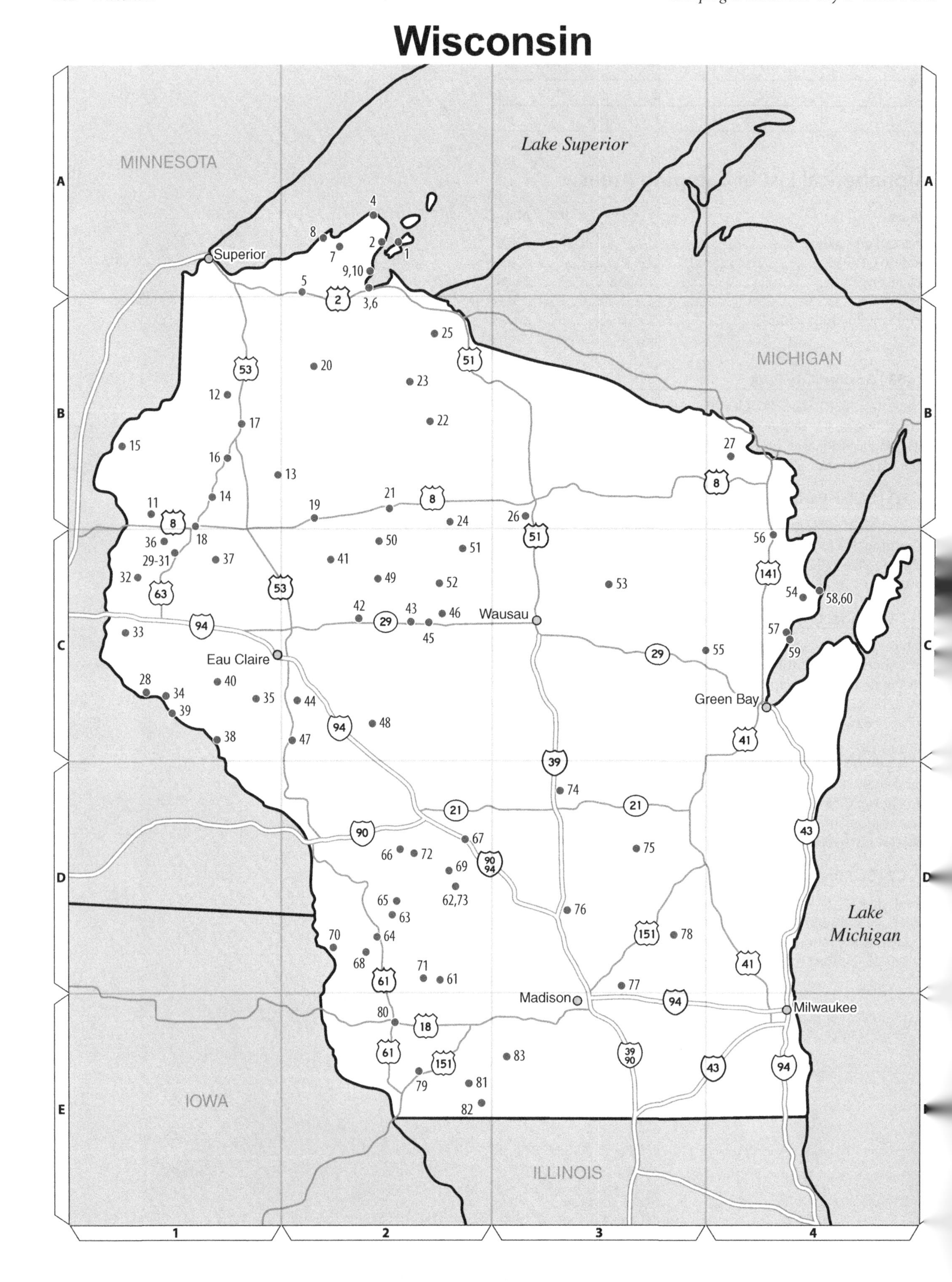
Lake Superior
MINNESOTA
MICHIGAN
IOWA
ILLINOIS
Lake Michigan
Superior
Wausau
Eau Claire
Green Bay
Madison
Milwaukee
A
B
C
D
E
1
2
3
4

Map	ID	Map	ID
A2	1-10	C3	53
B1	11-18	C4	54-60
B2	19-25	D2	61-73
B3	26	D3	74-78
B4	27	E2	79-82
C1	28-40	E3	83
C2	41-52		

Alphabetical List of Camping Areas

Name	ID	Map
Antigo Lake RV Park	53	C3
Avoca Lakeside City CG	61	D2
Badger City Park	54	C4
Bakers Field	62	D2
Balsam Lake Pine Park	11	B1
Banker City Park	63	D2
Bay City CG	28	C1
Beauford T. Anderson Park	64	D2
Big Bay Town Park	1	A2
Birch Creek City Park	41	C2
Bruce Village Park	19	B2
Cable Rec Park	20	B2
Cecil Lakeview City Park	55	C4
Chapman Park	42	C2
Chicog Town Park	12	B1
Clear Lake City Park - Main CG	29	C1
Clear Lake City Park - Maple Knoll	30	C1
Clear Lake City Park - Pine Point	31	C1
Crowley Park CG	43	C2
Crystal Lake Park	44	C2
Curtiss Village Park	45	C2
Dalrymple City CG	2	A2
Doolittle City Park	13	B1
Dorchester Rec Park	46	C2
Eagle Point Park	14	B1
Evergreen City Park	56	C4
Four Seasons City Park - Lions Club CG	47	C2
Gile Memorial Village CG	48	C2
Gilman City CG	49	C2
Hancock City CG	74	D3
Hatfield City Park	32	C1
Hattie Sherwood City Park	75	D3
Hawkins Lions Club Park	21	B2
Hines City Park	22	B2
Hoffman City Park	33	C1
Holtwood City CG	57	C4
James N McNally City CG	15	B1
Jump River Community Park	50	C2
Kreher City Park	3	A2
La Farge City Park	65	D2
Lakeview Park	51	C2
Little Sand Bay RA	4	A2
Maiden Rock Village Park	34	C1
Marian City Park	23	B2
Marinette City Park	58	C4
McKellar City Park	83	E3
Medford City Park	52	C2
Mondovi Tourist Park	35	C1
Moon Lake City Park	5	A2
Moundview Park	79	E2
North Park RV CG	36	C1
Norwalk Village Park	66	D2
Oakwood Nature Park	80	E2
Oconto City Park	59	C4
Ogema Pioneer Park	24	B2
Pecatonica River Trails Park	81	E2
Prairie Farm Pioneer Park	37	C1
Prentice City Park	6	A2
Reicks Lake Park	38	C1
River Park CG	60	C4
Riverside Park CG	67	D2
Robb City Park	68	D2
Sand Lake	27	B4
SARA Park	26	B3
Schultz City Park	69	D2
Shell Lake MunicipalPark	16	B1
Siskiwit Lake CG	7	A2
Stockholm City Park	39	C1
Sugar Creek City CG	70	D2
Tarrant City Park	40	C1
Town of Clover CG	8	A2
Trego Town Park	17	B1
Turtle Lake Village Park	18	B1
Upson Community Park	25	B2
Veteran's Memorial Field	76	D3
Victoria Riverside Park	71	D2
Village of Wilton CG	72	D2
Washburn Memorial Park	9	A2
West End Thompson City Park	10	A2
Whistle Stop CG	77	D3
Wild Goose City Park	78	D3
Wolf Creek CG	82	E2
Wonewoc Legion Park	73	D2

1 • A2 | Big Bay Town Park

Total sites: 61, RV sites: 61, Elec sites: 22, Central water, Vault/pit toilet, No showers, No RV dump, Tents: $28/RVs: $35, Ferry access, Open all year, Reservations accepted, Elev: 646ft/197m, Tel: 715-747-3031, Nearest town: La Pointe. GPS: 46.819568, -90.678073

2 • A2 | Dalrymple City CG

Total sites: 30, RV sites: 30, Elec sites: 28, Central water, Vault/pit toilet, No showers, No RV dump, Tent & RV camping: $25, Open May-Oct, Max Length: 30ft, Reservations not accepted, Elev: 696ft/212m, Tel: 715-779-5712, Nearest town: Bayfield. GPS: 46.818856, -90.807322

3 • A2 | Kreher City Park

Total sites: 33, RV sites: 33, Elec sites: 33, Water at site, Flush toilet, Free showers, RV dump, No tents/RVs: $30, Reservations only for month-long stays, Open May-Oct, Reservations accepted, Elev: 604ft/184m, Tel: 715-682-7059, Nearest town: Ashland. GPS: 46.597043, -90.880572

4 • A2 | Little Sand Bay RA

Total sites: 38, RV sites: 32, Elec sites: 32, Central water, Flush toilet, Free showers, RV dump, Tents: $20/RVs: $30, Group site:

$40, Generator hours: 0700-2230, Reservations accepted, Elev: 627ft/191m, Tel: 715-779-5233, Nearest town: Russell. GPS: 46.945789, -90.889071

5 • A2 | Moon Lake City Park

Total sites: 28, RV sites: 28, Central water, Flush toilet, Free showers, RV dump, Tents: $20/RVs: $25, Open May-Oct, Elev: 1106ft/337m, Tel: 715-372-5457, Nearest town: Iron River. GPS: 46.556482, -91.406001

6 • A2 | Prentice City Park

Total sites: 19, RV sites: 9, Elec sites: 9, Central water, Vault/pit toilet, No showers, No RV dump, Tents: $17/RVs: $30, RV dump at Kreher Park, Open May-Oct, Max Length: 18ft, Elev: 594ft/181m, Tel: 715-682-2500, Nearest town: Ashland. GPS: 46.583503, -90.921653

7 • A2 | Siskiwit Lake CG

Total sites: 9, RV sites: 9, Central water, Vault/pit toilet, No showers, No RV dump, Tent & RV camping: $15, No large RVs, Stay limit: 14 days, Reservations not accepted, Elev: 1073ft/327m, Tel: 715-742-3356, Nearest town: Cornucopia. GPS: 46.798706, -91.129643

8 • A2 | Town of Clover CG

Total sites: 40, RV sites: 13, Elec sites: 12, Water at site, Flush toilet, Free showers, RV dump, Tents: $20/RVs: $40, Generator hours: 0800-2200, Reservations not accepted, Elev: 617ft/188m, Tel: 715-774-3780, Nearest town: Herbster. GPS: 46.835898, -91.256106

9 • A2 | Washburn Memorial Park

Total sites: 51, RV sites: 51, Elec sites: 43, Central water, Flush toilet, Pay showers, RV dump, Tents: $22/RVs: $27, No large RVs, Open May-Oct, Max Length: 22ft, Reservations not accepted, Elev: 663ft/202m, Tel: 715-373-6160, Nearest town: Washburn. GPS: 46.676726, -90.880657

10 • A2 | West End Thompson City Park

Total sites: 51, RV sites: 51, Elec sites: 51, Central water, Flush toilet, Pay showers, RV dump, Tent & RV camping: $25, Open Apr-Oct, Reservations not accepted, Elev: 633ft/193m, Tel: 715-373-6160, Nearest town: Washburn. GPS: 46.666754, -90.905431

11 • B1 | Balsam Lake Pine Park

Total sites: 15, RV sites: 15, Water at site, Flush toilet, Free showers, RV dump, Tents: $30/RVs: $40, 4 Full hookup, Generator hours: 0800-2230, Reservations not accepted, Elev: 1142ft/348m, Tel: 715-485-3424, Nearest town: Balsam Lake. GPS: 45.450852, -92.457088

12 • B1 | Chicog Town Park

Dispersed sites, Tent & RV camping: Fee unk, Elev: 988ft/301m, Nearest town: Chicog. GPS: 46.052201, -91.924491

13 • B1 | Doolittle City Park

Total sites: 40, RV sites: 40, Elec sites: 40, Central water, Flush toilet, Free showers, RV dump, Tent & RV camping: $20, Open May-Sep, Elev: 1230ft/375m, Tel: 612-804-3457, Nearest town: Birchwood. GPS: 45.661865, -91.549805

14 • B1 | Eagle Point Park

Total sites: 32, RV sites: 27, Elec sites: 27, Central water, Flush toilet, Free showers, RV dump, Tents: $25/RVs: $30, Reservations accepted, Elev: 1220ft/372m, Tel: 715-419-0303, Nearest town: Cumberland. GPS: 45.546072, -92.028608

15 • B1 | James N McNally City CG

Total sites: 38, RV sites: 38, Elec sites: 38, Water at site, Flush toilet, Free showers, RV dump, Tents: $25/RVs: $30, 38 Full hookup, Open Apr-Oct, Reservations accepted, Elev: 873ft/266m, Tel: 715-463-5832, Nearest town: Grantsburg. GPS: 45.778623, -92.689252

16 • B1 | Shell Lake MunicipalPark

Total sites: 46, RV sites: 46, Elec sites: 46, Water at site, Flush toilet, Free showers, RV dump, Tent & RV camping: $30-45, 38 Full hookup, Open May-Oct, Reservations accepted, Elev: 1220ft/372m, Tel: 715-468-7846, Nearest town: Shell Lake. GPS: 45.741321, -91.923292

17 • B1 | Trego Town Park

Total sites: 50, RV sites: 50, Elec sites: 50, Water at site, Flush toilet, Free showers, Tent & RV camping: $21-26, 30 transient sites, Open May-Sep, Reservations accepted, Elev: 1066ft/325m, Tel: 715-635-6075, Nearest town: Trego. GPS: 45.910222, -91.824638

18 • B1 | Turtle Lake Village Park

Total sites: 6, RV sites: 6, Elec sites: 6, Water at site, Flush toilet, No showers, RV dump, Tents: $5/RVs: $15, Open all year, Reservations not accepted, Elev: 1260ft/384m, Tel: 715-986-2241, Nearest town: Turtle Lake. GPS: 45.398479, -92.143071

19 • B2 | Bruce Village Park

Total sites: 10, Central water, Vault/pit toilet, No showers, No RV dump, Tents only: Free, Stay limit: 3 days, Reservations not accepted, Elev: 1103ft/336m, Tel: 715-868-2185, Nearest town Bruce. GPS: 45.454617, -91.278651

20 • B2 | Cable Rec Park

Total sites: 5, RV sites: 0, Tents only: $10, Walk-to sites, Generator hours: 0700-2200, Reservations not accepted, Elev: 1383ft/422m, Tel 715-798-4440, Nearest town: Cable. GPS: 46.206079, -91.303168

21 • B2 | Hawkins Lions Club Park

Total sites: 20, RV sites: 20, Water at site, Tent & RV camping Fee unk, Elev: 1378ft/420m, Tel: 715-585-6322, Nearest town Hawkins. GPS: 45.513701, -90.724838

22 • B2 | Hines City Park

Total sites: 9, RV sites: 9, Elec sites: 9, Water at site, No toilets, No showers, No RV dump, Tents: $20/RVs: $20-25, 1 Full hookup RV dump on Case Ave - $8, Open May-Sep, Max Length: 45+f Reservations not accepted, Elev: 1503ft/458m, Tel: 715-762-243 Nearest town: Park Falls. GPS: 45.940275, -90.440738

23 • B2 | Marian City Park

Dispersed sites, Central water, No RV dump, No tents/RVs: Free Open Apr-Oct, Reservations not accepted, Elev: 1608ft/490m, Tel 715-264-4851, Nearest town: Glidden. GPS: 46.133958, -90.589864

24 • B2 | Ogema Pioneer Park

Total sites: 7, RV sites: 7, Central water, No toilets, No showers, No RV dump, Tent & RV camping: Free, No services in winter, Sta mit: 14 days, Open all year, Max Length: 45+ft, Reservations not ccepted, Elev: 1572ft/479m, Tel: 715-767-5586, Nearest town:)gema. GPS: 45.443428, -90.289615

25 • B2 | Upson Community Park

Dispersed sites, Central water, Vault/pit toilet, No showers, No RV dump, Tent & RV camping: Donation, Reservations not ccepted, Elev: 1437ft/438m, Tel: 715-561-2922, Nearest town: Upson. GPS: 46.370889, -90.412816

26 • B3 | SARA Park

Total sites: 10, RV sites: 10, Central water, Flush toilet, Free showers, No RV dump, Tent & RV camping: $20, RV dump at City Garage, Stay limit: 14 days, Generator hours: 0600-2200, Reservations accepted, Elev: 1437ft/438m, Tel: 715-453-4040, Nearest town: Tomahawk. GPS: 45.473494, -89.741434

27 • B4 | Sand Lake

Dispersed sites, No water, Tent & RV camping: Fee unk, Unconfirmed, Elev: 1311ft/400m, Nearest town: Homestead. GPS: 45.755548, -88.255201

28 • C1 | Bay City CG

Total sites: 49, RV sites: 49, Elec sites: 49, Water at site, Flush toilet, Free showers, RV dump, Tents: $20/RVs: $35, 41 Full hookup, Mostly seasonal, Open May-Oct, Reservations accepted, Elev: 679ft/207m, Tel: 715-594-3229, Nearest town: Bay City. GPS: 44.579804, -92.455732

29 • C1 | Clear Lake City Park - Main CG

Total sites: 11, RV sites: 11, Elec sites: 11, Water at site, Flush toilet, Free showers, RV dump, Tent & RV camping: $25, Reservations accepted, Elev: 1192ft/363m, Tel: 715-263-2157, Nearest town: Clear Lake. GPS: 45.258078, -92.276517

30 • C1 | Clear Lake City Park - Maple Knoll

Total sites: 6, Central water, Vault/pit toilet, No showers, No RV dump, Tents only: $10, Showers in Main CG, Reservations accepted, Elev: 1225ft/373m, Tel: 715-263-2157, Nearest town: Clear Lake. GPS: 45.257884, -92.279621

31 • C1 | Clear Lake City Park - Pine Point

Total sites: 7, RV sites: 7, Central water, Vault/pit toilet, No showers, No RV dump, Tent & RV camping: $15, RV dump and showers in Main CG, Reservations accepted, Elev: 1200ft/366m, Tel: 715-263-2157, Nearest town: Clear Lake. GPS: 45.263322, -92.278278

32 • C1 | Hatfield City Park

Total sites: 10, RV sites: 10, Elec sites: 10, Water at site, RV dump, Tent & RV camping: $25, $5 dump fee, Reservations accepted, Elev: 974ft/297m, Tel: 715-243-0440, Nearest town: New Richmond. GPS: 45.136586, -92.534632

33 • C1 | Hoffman City Park

Total sites: 15, RV sites: 15, Elec sites: 15, Central water, Flush toilet, Free showers, RV dump, Tents: $10/RVs: $20, Stay limit: 14 days, Open Apr-Oct, Reservations not accepted, Elev: 919ft/280m, Tel: 715-425-0924, Nearest town: River Falls. GPS: 44.865263, -92.609333

34 • C1 | Maiden Rock Village Park

Total sites: 12, RV sites: 12, Elec sites: 8, Central water, Tents: $15/RVs: $20, Reservations not accepted, Elev: 679ft/207m, Tel: 715-448-2205, Nearest town: Maiden Rock. GPS: 44.559393, -92.310327

35 • C1 | Mondovi Tourist Park

Total sites: 6, RV sites: 6, Elec sites: 6, Water at site, No toilets, No showers, RV dump, Tent & RV camping: $20, RV dump at the Mondovi Treatment Plant M-F 8am-3pm, Stay limit: 14 days, Reservations not accepted, Elev: 814ft/248m, Tel: 715-926-3866, Nearest town: Mondovi. GPS: 44.556623, -91.669685

36 • C1 | North Park RV CG

Total sites: 8, RV sites: 8, Elec sites: 8, Water at site, RV dump, Tent & RV camping: $30, Reservations not accepted, Elev: 1065ft/325m, Tel: 715-268-7486, Nearest town: Amery. GPS: 45.319289, -92.361341

37 • C1 | Prairie Farm Pioneer Park

Total sites: 30, RV sites: 30, Water at site, Vault/pit toilet, No showers, Tent & RV camping: $20, 2011 fee, Open May-Sep, Reservations not accepted, Elev: 1024ft/312m, Tel: 715-455-1024, Nearest town: Prairie Farm. GPS: 45.240772, -91.985341

38 • C1 | Reicks Lake Park

Total sites: 20, RV sites: 20, Elec sites: 20, Central water, Flush toilet, Free showers, No RV dump, Tent & RV camping: $20, Reservations not accepted, Elev: 666ft/203m, Tel: 608-685-3330, Nearest town: Alma. GPS: 44.355267, -91.932982

39 • C1 | Stockholm City Park

Total sites: 30, RV sites: 25, Elec sites: 25, Central water, Vault/pit toilet, No showers, No RV dump, Tents: $17/RVs: $24, Stay limit: 30 days, Open Apr-Oct, Reservations not accepted, Elev: 676ft/206m, Tel: 715-495-3226, Nearest town: Stockholm. GPS: 44.481057, -92.262959

40 • C1 | Tarrant City Park

Total sites: 24, RV sites: 10, Elec sites: 18, Water at site, Flush toilet, Free showers, RV dump, Tent & RV camping: $20, Reservations accepted, Elev: 709ft/216m, Tel: 715-672-8770, Nearest town: Durand. GPS: 44.638165, -91.947382

41 • C2 | Birch Creek City Park

Total sites: 25, RV sites: 25, Elec sites: 25, Vault/pit toilet, No showers, No RV dump, Tent & RV camping: $20, Open May-Oct, Elev: 1056ft/322m, Tel: 715-595-4127, Nearest town: Holcombe. GPS: 45.253232, -91.155552

42 • C2 | Chapman Park

Total sites: 33, RV sites: 33, Elec sites: 33, Central water, Flush toilet, Free showers, RV dump, Tents: $20/RVs: $25, Reservations not accepted, Elev: 1076ft/328m, Tel: 715-644-5758, Nearest town: Stanley. GPS: 44.966021, -90.943139

43 • C2 | Crowley Park CG

Total sites: 10, RV sites: 10, Elec sites: 10, Water at site, RV dump, Tents: $10/RVs: $15, Reservations not accepted, Elev: 1239ft/378m, Tel: 715-229-2404, Nearest town: Owen. GPS: 44.945762, -90.560808

44 • C2 | Crystal Lake Park

Total sites: 42, RV sites: 42, Elec sites: 42, Water at site, Flush toilet, Free showers, RV dump, Tent & RV camping: $27-30, 21 Full hookup, Reservations accepted, Elev: 886ft/270m, Tel: 715-533-2664, Nearest town: Strum. GPS: 44.556821, -91.381421

45 • C2 | Curtiss Village Park

Dispersed sites, Central water, Tent & RV camping: Fee unk, Unconfirmed, Elev: 1375ft/419m, Tel: 715-223-6226, Nearest town: Curtiss. GPS: 44.953127, -90.432052

46 • C2 | Dorchester Rec Park

Total sites: 30, RV sites: 26, Elec sites: 26, Water at site, Flush toilet, Free showers, RV dump, Tents: $8/RVs: $18-21, 10 Full hookup, Open May-Nov, Elev: 1414ft/431m, Tel: 715-654-5098, Nearest town: Dorchester. GPS: 44.999046, -90.326489

47 • C2 | Four Seasons City Park - Lions Club CG

Total sites: 8, RV sites: 8, Elec sites: 8, Central water, Flush toilet, Free showers, Tents: $12/RVs: $18, Reservations accepted, Elev: 768ft/234m, Tel: 715-985-3055, Nearest town: Independence. GPS: 44.357286, -91.414274

48 • C2 | Gile Memorial Village CG

Total sites: 20, RV sites: 20, Central water, No toilets, No showers, No RV dump, Tent & RV camping: $15, Generator hours: 0600-2300, Reservations not accepted, Elev: 915ft/279m, Tel: 715-333-2332, Nearest town: Merrillan. GPS: 44.447255, -90.841721

49 • C2 | Gilman City CG

Dispersed sites, Vault/pit toilet, Tents: $10/RVs: $20, $10 Deposit for key to electricity - key can be obtained at Gilman Cornerstore, Reservations not accepted, Elev: 1214ft/370m, Tel: 715-748-4729, Nearest town: Gilman. GPS: 45.162169, -90.808978

50 • C2 | Jump River Community Park

Total sites: 13, RV sites: 13, Elec sites: 13, Water available, Flush toilet, RV dump, Tent & RV camping: Fee unk, Dump fee: $10, Elev: 1184ft/361m, Tel: 715-668-5360, Nearest town: Jump River. GPS: 45.351156, -90.803158

51 • C2 | Lakeview Park

Total sites: 27, RV sites: 27, Elec sites: 27, Central water, Flush toilet, Free showers, RV dump, Tent & RV camping: $20, Open Apr-Oct, Reservations not accepted, Elev: 1608ft/490m, Tel: 715-427-5404, Nearest town: Rib Lake. GPS: 45.319245, -90.189061

52 • C2 | Medford City Park

Total sites: 9, RV sites: 9, Elec sites: 9, Water at site, Flush toilet, No showers, No RV dump, Tent & RV camping: $15, Dump facility at waste-water treatment plan, Elev: 1411ft/430m, Nearest town: Medford. GPS: 45.141151, -90.352199

53 • C3 | Antigo Lake RV Park

Total sites: 13, RV sites: 13, Elec sites: 12, Water at site, Flush toilet, Pay showers, RV dump, Tent & RV camping: $20, Max Length: 45ft, Reservations accepted, Elev: 1496ft/456m, Tel: 715-623-3633, Nearest town: Antigo. GPS: 45.142429, -89.146299

54 • C4 | Badger City Park

Total sites: 50, RV sites: 50, Elec sites: 50, Central water, Flu toilet, Free showers, No RV dump, Tents: $12/RVs: $27, Milita discount: 10%, Open May-Oct, Reservations accepted, El 636ft/194m, Tel: 715-582-4321, Nearest town: Peshtigo. GI 45.060251, -87.751652

55 • C4 | Cecil Lakeview City Park

Total sites: 40, RV sites: 40, Elec sites: 40, Water at site, Flush toil Pay showers, RV dump, Tents: $27/RVs: $32-38, Open May-S Elev: 810ft/247m, Tel: 715-853-4180, Nearest town: Shawar GPS: 44.809862, -88.453741

56 • C4 | Evergreen City Park

Total sites: 38, RV sites: 38, Elec sites: 38, Central water, No toile No showers, RV dump, Tent & RV camping: $25-30, Open Ma Oct, Reservations accepted, Elev: 748ft/228m, Tel: 715-856-53 Nearest town: Wausaukee. GPS: 45.380578, -87.950465

57 • C4 | Holtwood City CG

Total sites: 45, RV sites: 45, Elec sites: 45, Water at site, Flush toil Free showers, RV dump, Tents: $19-20/RVs: $28-30, Open Ma Oct, Reservations accepted, Elev: 591ft/180m, Tel: 920-834-77 Nearest town: Oconto. GPS: 44.889395, -87.885314

58 • C4 | Marinette City Park

Total sites: 17, RV sites: 9, Elec sites: 9, Water at site, No RV dum Tents: $10/RVs: $20, Reservations accepted, Elev: 612ft/187 Tel: 715-732-2006, Nearest town: Marinette. GPS: 45.091549 87.638892

59 • C4 | Oconto City Park

Total sites: 9, RV sites: 9, Vault/pit toilet, Tent & RV camping: $ Open May-Oct, Reservations not accepted, Elev: 600ft/183 Tel: 920-834-7706, Nearest town: Oconto. GPS: 44.858798, 87.856799

60 • C4 | River Park CG

Total sites: 58, RV sites: 58, Elec sites: 58, Water at site, Flush toil Free showers, RV dump, Tents: $20/RVs: $25-35, 54 Full hooku Generator hours: 0700-2230, Open May-Oct, Reservatio accepted, Elev: 588ft/179m, Tel: 906-863-1737, Nearest tow Menominee. GPS: 45.104644, -87.621959

61 • D2 | Avoca Lakeside City CG

Total sites: 75, RV sites: 75, Elec sites: 75, Central water, Flu toilet, Free showers, RV dump, Tent & RV camping: $30, Op Apr-Nov, Elev: 696ft/212m, Tel: 608-532-6188, Nearest tow Avoca. GPS: 43.189730, -90.319640

62 • D2 | Bakers Field

Dispersed sites, Central water, Flush toilet, Tents only: Free, Alo 400 State Bike Trail, Elev: 925ft/282m, Tel: 608-464-3114, Near town: Wonewoc. GPS: 43.652355, -90.223898

63 • D2 | Banker City Park

Total sites: 12, RV sites: 12, Central water, Flush toilet, Fr showers, RV dump, Tent & RV camping: Fee unk, Reservatio not accepted, Elev: 764ft/233m, Tel: 608-627-1831, Nearest tow Viola. GPS: 43.505838, -90.672684

64 • D2 | Beauford T. Anderson Park

Total sites: 30, RV sites: 30, Elec sites: 30, Water at site, No toilets, No showers, Tent & RV camping: $15, Reservations not accepted, Elev: 732ft/223m, Tel: 608-624-3264, Nearest town: Soldiers Grove. GPS: 43.395332, -90.775115

65 • D2 | La Farge City Park

Total sites: 12, RV sites: 12, Elec sites: 12, Central water, Flush toilet, Free showers, RV dump, Tents: $10/RVs: $20, Elev: 882ft/269m, Tel: 608-625-4422, Nearest town: La Farge. GPS: 43.580006, -90.638216

66 • D2 | Norwalk Village Park

Total sites: 10, RV sites: 10, Elec sites: 10, Central water, Flush toilet, Pay showers, Tents: Free/RVs: $20-25, Reservations accepted, Elev: 1023ft/312m, Tel: 608-823-7760, Nearest town: Norwalk. GPS: 43.831827, -90.618878

67 • D2 | Riverside Park CG

Total sites: 74, RV sites: 74, Elec sites: 50, Water at site, Flush toilet, Pay showers, RV dump, Tents: $15/RVs: $25, Some Full hookup sites, Open May-Oct, Elev: 882ft/269m, Tel: 608-562-3534, Nearest town: New Lisbon. GPS: 43.882249, -90.158926

68 • D2 | Robb City Park

Total sites: 12, RV sites: 12, Elec sites: 12, Central water, Flush toilet, No showers, RV dump, Tent & RV camping: $15, Elev: 702ft/214m, Tel: 608-735-4341, Nearest town: Gays Mills. GPS: 43.320139, -90.850192

69 • D2 | Schultz City Park

Total sites: 25, RV sites: 8, Elec sites: 8, Water at site, Flush toilet, Free showers, RV dump, Tents: $12-18/RVs: $28, 8 Full hookup, Reservations accepted, Elev: 948ft/289m, Tel: 608-462-2400, Nearest town: Elroy. GPS: 43.728509, -90.267663

70 • D2 | Sugar Creek City CG

Total sites: 12, RV sites: 8, Elec sites: 8, Central water, No toilets, No showers, No RV dump, Tent & RV camping: $10, Use of A/C prohibited, Reservations not accepted, Elev: 631ft/192m, Tel: 608-734-9077, Nearest town: Ferryville. GPS: 43.340107, -91.082589

71 • D2 | Victoria Riverside Park

Total sites: 40, RV sites: 32, Elec sites: 32, Central water, Flush toilet, Pay showers, RV dump, Tents: $10/RVs: $25, Open May-Oct, Reservations accepted, Elev: 682ft/208m, Tel: 608-739-3182, Nearest town: Muscoda. GPS: 43.196555, -90.439102

72 • D2 | Village of Wilton CG

Total sites: 30, RV sites: 15, Elec sites: 15, Central water, Flush toilet, Pay showers, RV dump, Tents: $7/RVs: $10, $7 per person per night, Open May-Oct, Reservations not accepted, Elev: 973ft/297m, Tel: 608-435-6666, Nearest town: Wilton. GPS: 43.811932, -90.525485

73 • D2 | Wonewoc Legion Park

Total sites: 25, RV sites: 5, Elec sites: 5, Central water, Flush toilet, Free showers, Tents: $10/RVs: $25, Bath facilities at nearby pool, Reservations accepted, Elev: 1037ft/316m, Tel: 608-464-3114, Nearest town: Wonewon. GPS: 43.658823, -90.219748

74 • D3 | Hancock City CG

Total sites: 71, RV sites: 56, Elec sites: 56, Central water, Flush toilet, Free showers, RV dump, Tents: $15/RVs: $22-25, Open May-Oct, Reservations accepted, Elev: 1092ft/333m, Tel: 715-249-5496, Nearest town: Hancock. GPS: 44.127984, -89.498327

75 • D3 | Hattie Sherwood City Park

Total sites: 38, RV sites: 27, Elec sites: 38, Central water, Flush toilet, Free showers, RV dump, Tent & RV camping: $28, Stay limit: 14 days, Generator hours: 0830-2200, Open May-Oct, Elev: 817ft/249m, Tel: 920-294-6380, Nearest town: Green Lake. GPS: 43.842041, -88.966309

76 • D3 | Veteran's Memorial Field

Dispersed sites, Tent & RV camping: $15, Permission required, Elev: 785ft/239m, Tel: 608-742-2178, Nearest town: Portage. GPS: 43.538055, -89.448157

77 • D3 | Whistle Stop CG

Total sites: 50, RV sites: 50, Elec sites: 50, Water at site, Flush toilet, Free showers, RV dump, Tents: $45-50/RVs: $50-60, 46 Full hookup, All sites $25 early spring and fall, Concessionaire, Open Apr-Oct, Reservations accepted, Elev: 890ft/271m, Tel: 608-655-3080, Nearest town: Marshall. GPS: 43.159973, -89.068453

78 • D3 | Wild Goose City Park

Dispersed sites, Central water, Flush toilet, Free showers, Tent & RV camping: $10, Max Length: 18ft, Reservations not accepted, Elev: 909ft/277m, Tel: 920-386-4800, Nearest town: Juneau. GPS: 43.412817, -88.696037

79 • E2 | Moundview Park

Total sites: 8, RV sites: 8, Elec sites: 8, Water at site, Flush toilet, Free showers, Tents: $15/RVs: $20, Reservations not accepted, Elev: 1001ft/305m, Tel: 608-348-9741, Nearest town: Platteville. GPS: 42.740881, -90.460174

80 • E2 | Oakwood Nature Park

Total sites: 5, RV sites: 5, Elec sites: 5, Central water, Flush toilet, No showers, No RV dump, No tents/RVs: $10, RV dump at wastewater treatment plant on Hwy 61 South, Max Length: 36ft, Reservations accepted, Elev: 1122ft/342m, Tel: 608-822-6119, Nearest town: Fennimore. GPS: 42.980742, -90.635502

81 • E2 | Pecatonica River Trails Park

Total sites: 32, RV sites: 32, Elec sites: 30, Central water, Flush toilet, Free showers, RV dump, Tents: $15/RVs: $20, Stay limit: 14 days, Reservations not accepted, Elev: 824ft/251m, Tel: 608-776-4970, Nearest town: Darlington. GPS: 42.680376, -90.121677

82 • E2 | Wolf Creek CG

Total sites: 34, RV sites: 34, Elec sites: 24, Water at site, Flush toilet, Free showers, RV dump, Tents: $10/RVs: $15, Open Apr-Sep, Reservations not accepted, Elev: 794ft/242m, Tel: 608-922-6617, Nearest town: Gratiot. GPS: 42.581391, -90.024023

83 • E3 | McKellar City Park

Total sites: 15, RV sites: 6, Elec sites: 6, Water at site, No toilets, No showers, RV dump, Tents: $10/RVs: $20, Pay box at City Hall, Reservations not accepted, Elev: 814ft/248m, Nearest town: Blanchardville. GPS: 42.810321, -89.859259

Wyoming

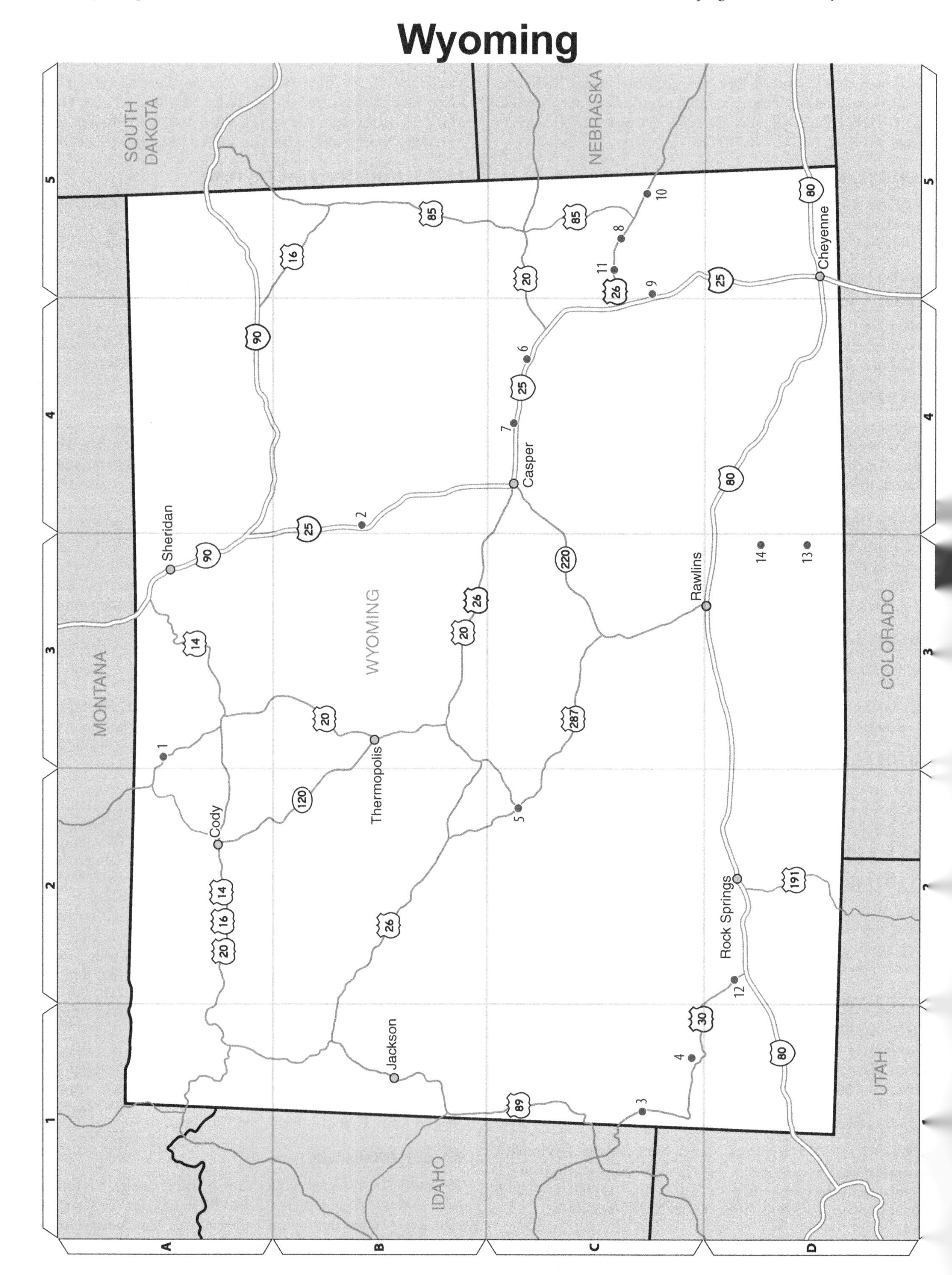
SOUTH DAKOTA
NEBRASKA
MONTANA
WYOMING
COLORADO
IDAHO
UTAH
Sheridan
Casper
Cheyenne
Rawlins
Thermopolis
Cody
Jackson
Rock Springs
1
2
3
4
5
6
7
8
9
10
11
12
13
14
90
16
85
20
25
26
80
220
287
120
14
89
30
191
A
B
C
D
1
2
3
4
5

Map	ID	Map	ID
A3	1	C4	6-7
B4	2	C5	8-11
C1	3-4	D2	12
C2	5	D3	13-14

Alphabetical List of Camping Areas

1 • A3 | Lovell Camper Park

Total sites: 15, RV sites: 15, Central water, Flush toilet, Free showers, RV dump, Tent & RV camping: Free, 3-day limit, Max Length: 32ft, Reservations not accepted, Elev: 3819ft/1164m, Tel: 307-548-6551, Nearest town: Lovell. GPS: 44.841517, -108.383533

2 • B4 | Kaycee Town Park

Total sites: 10, RV sites: 3, Central water, No toilets, No showers, No RV dump, Tent & RV camping: Free, Max Length: 30ft, Reservations not accepted, Elev: 4695ft/1431m, Tel: 307-738-2301, Nearest town: Kaycee. GPS: 43.713383, -106.630616

3 • C1 | Cokeville City Park

Dispersed sites, No water, No toilets, No tents/RVs: Free, Town square, Beside RR, Elev: 6199ft/1889m, Tel: 307-279-3227, Nearest town: Cokeville. GPS: 42.085258, -110.959562

4 • C1 | Kemmerer Tent Park

Total sites: 5, RV sites: 0, No water, Vault/pit toilet, No showers, No RV dump, Tents only: Fee unk, Tents-only, water at City Hall during business hours, Reservations not accepted, Elev: 6946ft/2117m, Tel: 307-828-2360, Nearest town: Frontier. GPS: 41.816013, -110.534412

5 • C2 | Lander City Park

Total sites: 25, RV sites: 7, Central water, Flush toilet, No showers, RV dump, Tent & RV camping: Free, Stay limit: 3 days, Elev: 5411ft/1649m, Tel: 307-332-4647, Nearest town: Lander. GPS: 42.821589, -108.737037

6 • C4 | Riverside City Park

Total sites: 20, RV sites: 20, Central water, Flush toilet, Free showers, RV dump, Tent & RV camping: Free, Stay limit: 2 days, Reservations not accepted, Elev: 4805ft/1465m, Tel: 307-358-9750, Nearest town: Douglas. GPS: 42.762937, -105.391996

7 • C4 | South Recreation Complex

Total sites: 4, RV sites: 4, Flush toilet, RV dump, Tent & RV camping: Free, Elev: 5033ft/1534m, Tel: 307-436-9294, Nearest town: Glenrock. GPS: 42.835782, -105.873727

8 • C5 | Fort Laramie Municipal Park Grounds

Total sites: 8, RV sites: 8, Elec sites: 8, Water at site, No toilets, No showers, No RV dump, Tent & RV camping: $3, Near RR, Open all year, Elev: 4232ft/1290m, Nearest town: Fort Laramie. GPS: 42.210845, -104.518588

9 • C5 | Lewis Park

Total sites: 15, RV sites: 10, Elec sites: 10, Central water, Flush toilet, Pay showers, RV dump, Tent & RV camping: Donation, 3-days free, Reservations not accepted, Elev: 4760ft/1451m, Tel: 307-322-2962, Nearest town: Wheatland. GPS: 42.048131, -104.954783

10 • C5 | Pioneer Park

Total sites: 12, RV sites: 12, Water at site, Flush toilet, No showers, RV dump, Tent & RV camping: $15, No services incl elec in winter, Near RR, Stay limit: 10 days, Open all year, Reservations not accepted, Elev: 4091ft/1247m, Tel: 307-532-5666, Nearest town: Torrington. GPS: 42.057878, -104.191337

11 • C5 | Trail Ruts Golf and Camp

Total sites: 16, RV sites: 16, Elec sites: 16, Water at site, Flush toilet, Free showers, No RV dump, Tents: $14/RVs: $20, Open Apr-Oct, Elev: 4311ft/1314m, Tel: 307-836-2255, Nearest town: Guernesy. GPS: 42.257925, -104.742384

12 • D2 | Granger City Park

Dispersed sites, Central water, Flush toilet, No tents/RVs: Fee unk, Unconfirmed, Near RR, Elev: 6277ft/1913m, Nearest town: Granger. GPS: 41.594125, -109.966825

13 • D3 | Encampment City Park

Total sites: 9, RV sites: 9, Elec sites: 8, Water at site, Flush toilet, No showers, RV dump, Tent & RV camping: Donation, 3 Full hookup, 3-day limit, Stay limit: 3 days, Max Length: 50ft, Reservations not accepted, Elev: 7274ft/2217m, Tel: 307 327-5501, Nearest town: Encampment. GPS: 41.211165, -106.792195

14 • D3 | Saratoga Lake CG

Total sites: 74, RV sites: 74, Elec sites: 50, Central water, Vault/pit toilet, No showers, No RV dump, Tents: $10/RVs: $15, Showers at Hobo Pool, Reservations not accepted, Elev: 6782ft/2067m, Tel: 307-326-8338, Nearest town: Saratoga. GPS: 41.468483, -106.786643

Made in the USA
Las Vegas, NV
29 October 2023